SCIENTIFIC TYPES

Science in Modern Society
The Social Relations of Science

Francis Bacon: The First Statesman of Science
Founders of British Science
Scientists of the Industrial Revolution
British Scientists of the Nineteenth Century
British Scientists of the Twentieth Century
Statesmen of Science

Famous American Men of Science
Soviet Science
Discoveries and Inventions of the Twentieth Century
A Short History of Science
Science Unfolds the Future
The Sciences of Energy
Nuclear Energy in Industry
Radioastronomy and Radar
Science in Liberated Europe
Industry and Education in Soviet Russia
Science in Soviet Russia
An Outline of the Universe
The Progress of Science
The Science of Petroleum
The Young Man's Guide to Civil Engineering
Electricity
The A.B.C. of Chemistry
The Story of Agriculture
Six Great Scientists
Six Great Inventors
Six Great Engineers
Six Great Doctors
Six Great Astronomers
Osiris and the Atom
Short Stories in Science
Science for You
Science and Life

J. G. CROWTHER

SCIENTIFIC TYPES

Individual Investigators
Charles Thomson Rees Wilson
John William Strutt, Lord Rayleigh
Thomas Young

Teachers
Thomas Henry Huxley
John Tyndall
Augustus de Morgan

Scientist Inventors
James Dewar
Osborne Reynolds
Charles Babbage

Organizers
Walter Morley Fletcher
Arthur Schuster
George Biddell Airy

DUFOUR EDITIONS INC.

Printed in Great Britain

'Scientists are often enumerated, divided into categories, constructed into tables, illustrated by graphs, and pronounced upon in bulk. But it is sometimes forgotten that they are human beings . . .'

—*Lord Florey*
The Development of Modern Science:
First David Rivett Memorial Lecture,
Melbourne, 1963

CONTENTS

SCIENTIST INVENTORS

1*

INTRODUCTION

SCIENCE is becoming increasingly important in human affairs and in the actual working of daily life. Researches are being made on how it can be better organized so as to become more fruitful, and serve the needs of humanity more efficiently. The organization of science is often approached, however, as if it were merely a problem in quantitative management. Estimates of the resources and scientists necessary to achieve various objects, such as certain standards of industrial production, education and health, and viability of national defence, are worked out. In these, scientists are usually treated impersonally. For example, it may be held that an effective scientific institution should have a staff containing certain proportions of first, second and third class men, together with so many technicians and assistants. Investigations of this kind are necessary and valuable, but they have their limitations. As Lord Florey has remarked, it is sometimes forgotten that scientists are human beings. Nevertheless, analysis is necessary in order to understand scientists better, so that the different kinds can be placed in positions in which they can do their best.

A treatment that is neither too general nor too analytical, and pays more attention to the intellectual and human qualities of scientists, is needed by the public, and by many who have to make immediate practical decisions about how scientists should be supported, and their abilities utilized.

The general notion of 'scientist' leaves out differences between actual scientists; it treats them as if they were all alike. For some things they may be: they may all eat approximately the same quantity of food, and need approximately the same income to bring up a family. These quantitative similarities have their importance, but they are much easier to understand and deal with than the profound qualitative differences between scientists. These are the most difficult things to be dealt with in the organization of scientists and science.

This book is intended to direct attention to some of these qualitative differences by describing a selection of scientists in which they are strikingly prominent.

As the public is now the chief supporter of scientists, it is of the first importance that it should have as good an understanding of them as is practically possible. In Britain it provides, through the medium of government, the major part of the £1,000 million now spent annually on research and development.

Between the public and the scientists are statesmen, administrators and employers. It is essential that these should have as much insight as possible into the nature and types of scientists.

'Scientist' is a general term for describing persons who engage in science. It is drawn from the characteristics of those who do scientific work. There is no such thing as an 'archetype', of which actual scientists are more or less perfect materializations. Actual scientists are very varied, and any particular scientist may depart widely from the general notion of 'scientist'. Thus assertions about 'scientists' may or may not apply to him.

Until recently, this did not matter very much, because scientists were few and inexpensive, and their work rarely had any large immediate impact on ordinary life. They operated as individuals, extending their own researches, often at their own expense, and enjoying the freedom that arises from lack of immediate importance. Only small sections of the public were interested in them, and what they were doing. Consequently, scientists as such were little studied. But with their increasing immediate importance they began to attract attention.

In the second half of the nineteenth century Francis Galton investigated their mental traits, and the statistical distribution of these traits among them. His researches have been extended by others, including recent investigators such as Anne Roe and Bernice T. Eiduson. But the results of this kind of investigation, though interesting, seem to be difficult to act upon in practice. For example, these investigators have looked into the question whether fathers or mothers have the greater influence in their children becoming scientists. Galton made enquiries among 300 British scientists, and found that 'In many respects the character of scientific men is strongly anti-feminine; . . . They have little sympathy with female ways of thought. It is a curious proof of this, that in the very numerous answers which have reference to parental influence, that of the father is quoted three times as often as that of the mother . . .' Galton wrote in the 1870's. Bernice Eiduson reported in the 1960's on her investigation of the psychology of 40 American scientists that 19 did not know their father very well. Their achievement was more identified with their mother. She thought that the adoption of science was in some cases a form of anti-paternal demonstration; the son took up science because his father could not understand it. Anne Roe found in the 1950's that most physicists got on well with their fathers, while social scientists did not. Physicists were more masculine.

It seems that until this kind of research is much more advanced, it may not present agreed findings on which practical action can be taken. At present, qualitative descriptions appear to be of more immediate use. The description of scientists in the round, with emphasis on qualities clearly bearing on organizational problems, is, therefore, the approach which has been adopted in this book.

The biography of scientists has not yet emerged as a special literary form. It has often been conceived as merely an account of the subject's contribution to science, everything else except the barest personal details being considered irrelevant, and ignored. In this sort of biography it is often said that the chief guide to a scientist is his works. A better sort of biography consisted of a full account of the facts of the subject's life and the main points of his works, from which the reader could draw his own conclusions. This is valuable up to a point, but it leaves out the interpretation of the subject's relations to his contemporaries and predecessors, and the relations between his work and his personality, and of both to the historical and social background of the times. It does not give much help to those who are learning about scientists in order to form opinions as to how they should be supported, assisted, or governed.

The requirement now is for biographies in which all these factors are kept in mind, and at the same time attention is focused on qualities of organizational significance.

When scientists are looked at more closely, they are found to fall into many different types. Four of these, which appear to be reasonably recognizable, may be described as *Individual Investigators, Teachers, Scientist Inventors* and *Organizers*. All scientists belong in some degree to all of these types, but in most cases more to one than the others.

Four groups of three scientists have been selected as examples. Those chosen for the first type of *Individual Investigators* are C. T. R. Wilson, Rayleigh and Thomas Young. Few probably will quarrel with this classification, even though Wilson also had much influence as a teacher, and Rayleigh accomplished a good deal as an organizer. Young was an almost pure example of the type; his individual efforts were prodigious, while his contribution as a teacher was small, and as an organizer possibly negative;

as the latter he may well have done more harm than good. Nevertheless, Young had the honour of being a scientific hero to Helmholtz, Clerk Maxwell and Rayleigh. The latest demonstration of his extraordinary genius is the award of a Nobel prize in 1967 to three investigators whose work includes the final proof of the three-colour theory of colour vision, which Young proposed more than a century and a half ago.

The three scientists chosen as *Teachers* are Thomas Henry Huxley, John Tyndall and Augustus de Morgan. Huxley and Tyndall were such masters of the spoken and written word that much of what they did has become part of modern culture. Many of their ideas seem now mere common sense, if not conventional; in fact, this is a tribute to the great effect of their efforts as teachers of the public. If they had had radio and television at their command, their influence might have been still greater, and they might have disintegrated more of the obstinate opposition of their time to science and technology, which has in the end left Britain a so much weakened country. Augustus de Morgan appears a much more significant figure today than he has done for most of the last hundred years. His influence on mathematical teaching through his own efforts and those of his pupils such as E. J. Routh and Isaac Todhunter, not to mention his influence in other directions through Walter Bagehot and W. S. Jevons, was immense. He inspired Boole to invent Boolean algebra, the natural language of computers, and he inspired the foundation of the London Mathematical Society, which has been the focus of British mathematics for a century. He foresaw the threat to science from the rise of professionalism, and his writings on the history of science are still among the most stimulating in the English language. He accomplished a vast work in popular education, and he combined scientific and literary ability in an extraordinary degree. Such a talent would be of very great value in today's situation.

De Morgan's best-known book *A Budget of Paradoxes* serves as an introduction to the understanding of the third type, *Scientist Inventors*. He was particularly concerned with the modes of thought in scientific innovation, which often first appears in the form of paradox, that is, a new explanation of phenomena, which seems at first to be contrary to common sense, but turns out to be correct. He gave the Copernican theory as a classical example.

The three who have been chosen as exemplars of the scientist inventor are Dewar, Osborne Reynolds and Babbage. They all exhibited paradoxical thinking, and difficulties of psychology associated with it. They had the contrary modes of mind often associated with their sort of genius. They illustrate how dependent their type is on an understanding and supporting environment. The notion that innovating genius should be left to find its own way, and be personally responsible for the exploitation of its discoveries is simply a disastrous social fallacy, shown most dramatically in the life and work of Babbage, who now appears as one of the greatest figures in British history. Besides inventing the computer, Babbage pointed out its implications, and he applied mathematics to the improvement of manufacturing operations, in a form of operational research. It is of interest that the present President of the Royal Society, Professor P. M. S. Blackett, who automatized the Wilson cloud chamber and was a leader in the modern development of operational research, is distantly connected with Babbage.

The examples of *Organizer* scientists are Walter Morley Fletcher, Arthur Schuster and George Biddell Airy. Morley Fletcher was one of the first and most brilliant of the scientist-administrators in government service. His personality, scientific work and social background throw light on one of the combinations of qualities needed in this new profession. Arthur Schuster is another whose work appears more important today than it did to most of his own generation, though not to Rutherford, who appreciated him magnificently. As an organizer of academic and international science few have equalled him. His life and work are of growing significance, as an illustration of the qualities required in guiding the organization of academic science and international research. George Biddell Airy possessed unusual organizational gifts, but failed to find the most suitable medium for their exercise. His contributions to science were large, but he is chiefly remembered for his failure to appreciate J. C. Adams's discovery of *Neptune*. It appears that Airy was not cast by society in the role most appropriate to his talents. Society must bear the blame for the *Neptune* affair, as much as Airy himself. If a proper use had been made of his gifts, he might have carried British scientific technology considerably beyond the stage it reached in his day, and brought it into a better condition to face the twentieth century.

By seeing where scientists of various types succeeded, and where they failed, it becomes easier to make correct judgments and decisions on how the reservoir of scientific talent can best be utilized, to the benefit of mankind and the felicity of the scientists themselves.

ACKNOWLEDGMENTS

The main sources which have been drawn upon are given in the references at the end of the book.

Miss J. I. M. Wilson and Dr James Paton kindly provided me with a valuable collection of information about C. T. R. Wilson. I am deeply indebted to Sir Lawrence Bragg for his recollections of him, and of his influence on his own thinking when he was founding the science of X-ray crystal analysis. Professor P. I. Dee has given me the benefit of conversation on his experiences in working with Wilson. Dr John N. Howard, Chief Scientist of the US Air Force Cambridge Research Laboratories, Bedford, Massachusetts, most helpfully sent me an account of the proceedings at the dedication of the Rayleigh Archives at the AFCRL on 30 March 1966. Professor Jack Allen provided useful references on Osborne Reynolds. Dr R. A. Lyttleton gave me the opportunity of reading his unique play: *A Matter of Gravity*, on the circumstances of the discovery of the planet *Neptune*. I cannot recollect any other instance of an authority on planetary theory writing a play about one of the most famous incidents in his subject, nor indeed of a comparable effort in any other branch of science.

I am most grateful to Miss J. I. M. Wilson for permission to reproduce the portrait of C. T. R. Wilson; to the Hon. C. R. Strutt for the portrait of his grandfather, Lord Rayleigh; to Dr Norah H. Nicholls for the portrait of her father, Sir Arthur Schuster; to Lady Morley Fletcher, Dr Charles Fletcher and the Cambridge University Pitt Club for the portrait of Sir Walter Morley Fletcher; to the Wellcome Historical Medical Museum for the portrait of Thomas Young; to the University of Manchester and Professor J. Diamond for the portrait of Osborne Reynolds; to the Royal Society for the portrait of Charles Babbage; and to the Royal Institution for the portraits of James Dewar and George Biddell Airy.

I am much indebted to the Librarian of the Royal Institution, and to Mr S. T. Thompson, Librarian of the Bridlington Public Library, who secured the loan of many books and papers for me.

J. G. CROWTHER

LIST OF PLATES

SCIENTIFIC TYPES

INDIVIDUAL INVESTIGATORS

CHARLES THOMSON REES WILSON
1869-1959

I

SENSE OF BEAUTY AND SEARCH FOR UNDERSTANDING

C. T. R. WILSON, affectionately known to his generation as 'C.T.R.', was the inventor of the most extraordinary of all scientific apparatuses, his cloud chamber, by which the tracks of atomic particles were made visible, through condensing trails of cloud along them, like the vapour trails left by aircraft high in the sky. Atomic and sub-atomic particles are almost unimaginably small, and may travel at speeds approaching that of light, that is, up to 186,000 miles a second. It seemed inconceivable that the paths of such minute particles travelling at such immense speeds should ever be made visible, until it was done.

Wilson's cloud chamber proved to be an instrument of discovery as powerful as it was simple, elegant, ingenious, and uniquely original. Ever since he introduced it in 1911 it has been one of the major instruments in the creation of modern atomic physics.

Wilson showed in this invention a combination of artistic sense and scientific penetration comparable with that of Leonardo da Vinci. Like him he was a very individual worker, and had remarkably few personal pupils. He thought and worked everything out with his own mind and hands, with almost infinite patience and persistence. The very first photographs of the cloud-tracks of atoms, which he took in 1911, have up to the present day never been surpassed in quality. While Wilson obtained exquisite results, he never used apparatus and arrangements which were better than were needed for the purpose, but he took infinite pains to make the essential parts as perfect as possible. He got extraordinary results by using simple things with extreme intelligence and insight, in order to answer important questions.

Wilson's individuality was, however, quite unlike that of Leonardo da Vinci and Henry Cavendish, who also worked by themselves. He was alone not through detachment from mankind, but through modesty and shyness. He had a particularly strong family life which, being Scottish, extended to distant as

25

well as close relatives. As Appleton remarked, visitors felt they were admitted not merely to his house, but to his home.

Wilson made it clear that his scientific work was inspired by crucial aesthetic experiences in his youth, when he first became aware of the beauty of the world, through sights of the hills in Arran. His supreme cloud-chamber invention arose out of his desire to reproduce in the laboratory, and investigate, the marvellous coloured haloes, or 'Brocken spectres', which he first saw on the summit of Ben Nevis, around his own shadow thrown by the sun on the top of the cloud below. Besides being gifted with the aesthetic sense to respond so powerfully to these sights, he had the invention and manual skill, exercised with equal aesthetic sense, to devise and make the apparatus for their reproduction and investigation. What Leonardo was with the pencil, Wilson was with the scientific apparatus.

He was extremely observant, and alert to anything new in the phenomena under investigation, but he was more fortunate than Leonardo in living at a time when the significance of the new things he observed could be recognized and utilized immediately.

Wilson's extraordinary gifts were not obvious. If one had met him in a railway carriage without knowing him, one would have thought him a quiet, typical, cautious, modest, wiry Scotsman. After a while, one might have become conscious of his very observant eyes, an agreeable humour, and a modesty bordering on diffidence. One might have travelled with him for a considerable time before discovering that he was a scientist.

His wiriness and health were remarkable. He lived until he was ninety, and six days before he died, of the only serious illness in his life, he wrote a letter with his own hand, in his perfect style, containing a classical example of his characteristically felicitous expressions. At the age of eighty-seven he published a long and important paper, on the theory of the generation of electricity in thunderclouds, in the Proceedings of the Royal Society, when he had already for four years been the Society's oldest Fellow; no other example of the oldest Fellow publishing such a paper could be recalled since the first days of the Society three hundred years before.

The aesthetic fineness of Wilson's perceptions were of a kind not usually associated with such toughness of mind and physique. He inherited the latter from his ancestors, who had been for generations sheep-farmers in the Scottish hills. His modes of thought and social habits were rooted in Scottish civilization. His father had been a progressive sheep-farmer, who published papers on farming experiments in Scottish agricultural journals. His mother was descended from Glasgow merchants who had become cotton and muslin manufacturers in the Industrial Revolution of the eighteenth century.

When his father died, Wilson was four years old. The family moved to Manchester, where he was educated in one of the best periods of the city's intellectual and scientific life. The family was helped especially by his his elder stepbrother William, who provided financial support and encouraged him to secure a university education. William had entered commerce and gone to India at the age of twenty. He prospered in Calcutta, and died at the age of thirty-five on the journey home from India, three months too soon to hear that his young stepbrother had justified his confidence by gaining a scholarship at Cambridge.

Thus Wilson's inherent abilities were nurtured by the health and feudal family solidarity of Scottish hill sheep-farmers, the tradition of inventiveness and modern education stimulated by the Industrial Revolution, and the profits of Imperial commerce. Something assuredly does not arise from nothing, and Wilson's rare achievement had various and deep roots.

His creative scientific life spread over the space of sixty-two years. Yet in all that time, he had only about six personal research pupils, though many benefited from his lectures and conversations. He was a very kind and amiable man, and yet very few worked for long under his direction. One of the causes of this was his search for perfection. He would repeat and repeat and repeat the making of a piece of apparatus, until he was fully satisfied with it. Rutherford used to recount how, before he left on a visit to Australia, he saw Wilson grinding a piece of glass apparatus. When he returned months later, Wilson was still grinding the same piece of glass; it was still not perfect.

His care and deliberation in the search for perfection prevented him from accomplishing several fundamental advances that he had long had in mind. He had noted the recoil of electrons from X-rays, and pondered on them much, but before he had any conclusion for publication, A. H. Compton interpreted their significance in terms of his 'Compton effect'. No one in Cambridge proceeded to apply the magnetic field to a cloud chamber, which permits the charge and energy of the particles photographed to be measured, because it was believed that Wilson intended in due course to do so himself. Skobeltzyn in Leningrad consequently took the lead in this direction.

The investigators in America and in the Soviet Union had in

these instances the advantage of not being in Cambridge, and were free from the mental attitudes uppermost there at that time.

Wilson was a highly individual worker, though not at all an individualist. He thought and worked like an artist in a studio producing a masterpiece. When Sir Lawrence Bragg was assembling historic apparatus for the museum in the Cavendish Laboratory, he asked Wilson whether the cloud chamber for photographing atomic tracks, which he presented, was the original, Wilson replied in his Scottish accent: 'Therr was neverr but the one'. He had made only one, but the photographs obtained with it were the Leonardos of experimental physics. Like himself, his apparatuses were highly individual. They were also extremely inexpensive; he never spent more than £5 on one.

Evidently, so individual, deliberate, precise and artistic a type as Wilson required very careful management within the scope of modern scientific organization. What conditions should be provided to enable such a genius to be fruitful?

Wilson himself said: 'The whole of my scientific work undoubtedly developed from the experiments I was led to make by what I saw during my fortnight on Ben Nevis in September 1894. It is hardly necessary for me to say that these experiments might have had little result had it not been that they were made in the Cavendish Laboratory at the beginning of the wonderful years of the discovery of the electron, X-rays and radioactivity.'

Wilson was in charge of the teaching of advanced practical physics in the Cavendish Laboratory from 1900 until 1919. He therefore participated in a most important way in the organization of the Cavendish Laboratory. Yet he entered only peripherally into the nascent organization of scientific research, which was beginning to emerge. He was most influential as a very gifted, highly individual investigator. As Cockcroft has remarked, Wilson was not the only highly individual worker in the Cavendish. G. I. Taylor and F. W. Aston were other examples. Their presence, like Wilson's, was always a stimulus, even if they did not participate in the organization of the research of others. Their conversation, and what they stood for, was a source of inspiration. When Cockcroft organized the huge institution at Harwell for atomic research, he took care to provide scope for two or three men with highly individual qualities.

The coming together of many qualities and many conditions are needed to produce a C. T. R. Wilson. By taking thought, it may be possible to foster more such scientists, and provide the conditions in which their extraordinary talents can become fruit-

ful. At least, it is necessary to identify these qualities and conditions, so that the emergence of such genius is, as far as possible,
not left to chance.

II

A SCOTTISH FARMER'S SON

Charles Thomson Rees Wilson was born on 14 February 1869,
at Crosshouse farm at the foot of Castlelaw, in the parish of
Glencorse in Midlothian, the Scottish county immediately south
of Edinburgh. His father John Wilson was a sheep-farmer whose
forebears had lived in this pastoral countryside for generations.
Besides being deeply rooted in the society and the soil, his father
belonged to the Scottish tradition of agricultural experiment and
improvement which had produced not a few scientists in the
past, such as James Hutton, one of the founders of modern geology. John Wilson published papers on farming in the *Journal
of the Highland and Agricultural Society*. His first wife died early
and left him an elder son William, and several other children.
He married again, this time a second cousin, Annie Clark Harper,
descended from a family of muslin and thread makers who had
become prosperous in Glasgow during the eighteenth century.

Several Harpers had been educated at Glasgow University,
and C. T. R. Wilson's second cousin, George Harper, became
Professor of English Literature at Princeton, and an author of
note. Charles was the youngest of John Wilson's second family,
and of all his eight children.

The farmer hoped that his youngest son would become the
farmer in the family, but John Wilson died at the age of fifty-
three, when Charles was only four years old. If this had not
happened, Wilson would very probably have ultimately become
a sheep-farmer.

Mrs Wilson was faced with the problem of looking after three
young children of her own and four stepchildren. She moved to
Manchester to be near her parents, who had settled there after
the decline of the old family business of muslin manufacture in
Glasgow. Mrs Wilson ardently desired that her own two young
boys should ultimately go to the university, but what was more
remarkable, her eldest stepson, William, and his brother, equally
ardently desired that their two young stepbrothers should receive the higher education which they had desired, but had been
denied by circumstance.

William had entered commerce, and in 1877, when he was

about twenty years old, and his youngest stepbrother was eight, he took a post in a firm in Calcutta. He prospered, and was able to send financial support to the family at home. Within fifteen years, by the age of thirty-five, when he died prematurely, he had become a partner in his firm, a town councillor and a member of the Calcutta Chamber of Commerce. Wilson said that his half-brother's encouragement and faith in him, and his desire not to disappoint him, had been among the strongest influences of his life.

Mrs Wilson was interested in philosophy, literature and art, and though shy and retiring, she started a working man's club in one of the dreariest parts of Manchester, which became very succ sful.

Charles was sent to the private Greenhayes Collegiate School from the age of nine to fifteen. No science was taught. He went on a holiday to North High Corrie in Arran. He 'there became strongly impressed with the beauty of the world'. He spent all his spare time in Manchester looking for, and studying, beetles and pond-life, which he 'also learned to love'.

When he was thirteen a friend of the family had given him and his brother a microscope, with the injunction to pass it on when he had finished with it. Seventy-seven years later Wilson wrote that 'that time never came', for he subsequently used it as part of his apparatus for recording the electric fields of thunderclouds.

Charles and his own brother made a microtome, a machine for cutting thin slices of substances, and became skilled in preparing botanical and zoological specimens. Stepbrother William in Calcutta was delighted with the news of the signs of scientific interest and ability. He contributed means for realizing the desire of his stepmother and himself that the two young boys should go to the university. It was decided that Charles and his brother should go to Owens College in Manchester, with the intention of qualifying in medicine. Wilson entered Owens at the age of fifteen, and registered as a medical student. He began by reading physics, chemistry, botany, zoology and geology.

When he entered Owens, the college was still young and small, and retained its remarkable group of professors, including Balfour Stewart in physics and Roscoe in chemistry. Balfour Stewart was a very mild man who had difficulty in keeping his students quiet. Wilson attended one of his lectures, when he asked his elderly and bearded laboratory assistant, Mr Binyon, to recite verses from the *Ancient Mariner*, to demonstrate the reactions of a sensitive flame to sibilant noises. Deafening applause followed the request, and Balfour Stewart was reduced to the strongest reproach of which he was capable, to quell the applause. He announced that 'the experiment will cease'.

Wilson remembered one of the lecturers referring to a recent discovery by Joseph Thomson, adding that he had been a member of the class eleven years before.

He graduated with a first-class in zoology at the age of eighteen. His mother and William were delighted with his success and urged him, like other able Manchester students such as J. J. Thomson, to compete for an entrance scholarship at Cambridge, and continue his scientific education there. He spent a fourth year at Manchester studying philosophy, Latin and Greek, which he would require for entrance to Cambridge, and in 1888 sat for a scholarship, being awarded one at Sidney Sussex College. William was filled with joy at the news, and wrote that he was confident that Charles would one day be president of the British Association. Unfortunately, he did not live to see him achieve yet higher honours. Wilson shared the Nobel Prize for Physics with A. H. Compton in 1927, and was awarded the Copley medal of the Royal Society in 1935.

When Wilson sat for the college scholarship, he had never done any practical work in physics and chemistry. His first entry into a Cambridge laboratory was to take an examination in practical science, in which he had never been instructed. The examiner in charge was the chemist F. H. Neville. Wilson went up to him and explained the situation. Neville was understanding and sympathetic, and encouraged him to do as well as he could under the circumstances. Wilson found himself awarded a scholarship in Neville's college, Sidney Sussex, and with Neville as his tutor.

Before going to Cambridge in 1888, Wilson had made up his mind that he wanted to study physics rather than medicine. He took physics, chemistry, geology and botany in his first examination. He would have liked to have taken some mathematics, too, but at that time students could take only the whole mathematics course or nothing. He felt worried because his science course did not appear to be qualifying him for a job through which he could contribute to the support of the family, as there were very few jobs for physicists in those days. He felt he might be of use as an explorer, as he had some knowledge of a wide range of sciences, and his powers of endurance had been tested on the Scottish hills.

Neville reassured him, and encouraged him to settle down and work hard. He studied practical physics under H. F. Newall, who was 'assisted by G. F. C. Searle'. He thoroughly enjoyed it. He studied chemistry under S. Ruhemann, who had arrived in Cambridge three years before from Berlin. Dewar, the professor of chemistry, had become hampered by the lack of teaching in organic chemistry, and had asked A. W. Hofmann in Berlin to recommend an organic chemist who could come to Cambridge and start a course. Hofmann had sent his pupil Ruhemann, who found that the university had no laboratory for organic chemistry. He was provided with no apparatus, and a small dark room which could accommodate only a few students, for his lectures and demonstrations. Ruhemann was twenty-nine when Wilson attended his course. He had already quarrelled with, and parted from, the difficult Dewar; he taught in the laboratory of Caius College. He lectured at great speed in fluent but peculiar English, and packed in a great deal of detail about such substances as sugars. Wilson could not memorize it all, and Neville was disappointed when he failed to recollect everything. Ruhemann insisted on very thorough chemical analyses and preparations of chemical compounds. When Wilson was successful he said: 'You are a duke, Wilson'; but if things went wrong he said: 'You are a crock.' As Wilson noted, Ruhemann's English had a character of its own. In his first lecture in the University Laboratory, he had begun with the words: 'Gentlemen, I hope you will excuse the bad language I shall use.'

Wilson attended the physics lectures by Glazebrook and Napier Shaw. Glazebrook always lectured in detail about definite experiments, while Napier Shaw, who arrived at the lecture room in morning coat and silk hat, was inclined to look on all sides of a question, and avoid committing himself to a conclusion.

Wilson took his degree in 1882. He was the only student in Cambridge in that year to graduate with physics as his main subject, a striking illustration of the difference between his times and ours. His stepbrother William's health had declined, and on the voyage home from India he died of tuberculosis, three months before Charles's graduation, so he was denied the joy of witnessing the successful beginning of his Cambridge life.

As for Wilson himself, the tragic event made him feel all the more keenly the duty to help his family, which had now lost William's support. His mother and the family returned to Scotland, and settled near their old home, in a house belonging to the Clerks of Penicuik, the family to which the father of James Clerk

CHARLES THOMSON REES WILSON

Maxwell had belonged. No connection could be more appropriate than one between these two great Scotsmen, whose combination of imagination and skill were supreme examples of the Celtic genius.

Wilson obtained some work as a demonstrator in the science laboratories at Cambridge, and was much relieved to find that with this, and fees from the coaching of private pupils, he received what he felt was a quite reasonable income. But it absorbed a great deal of time and energy, of which he had little left for research. He was trying to investigate how the behaviour of a substance in solution in a liquid compared with that of a gas, by studying the distribution of the substance in a quantity of liquid hot at the top and cold below. This he attempted by means of an optical method.

Wilson's characteristic choice of problem and method, the behaviour of fluids investigated by optical means, was already to be seen in his early research.

He pursued his laborious course, but his research proceeded slowly. He felt his position in Cambridge was becoming increasingly precarious, so he accepted a position as an assistant science master at Bradford Grammar Schoool. The head of the science side at that time was a noted master, Arthur Thornton, later headmaster of Bridlington School. His choice of Wilson was a credit to his judgment as a scientist, but Wilson was not happy in the position. He said he enjoyed teaching boys, especially introducing them to geology, but he again found he had no time for research. It is in fact not easy to visualize him as an effective teacher of average boys. He was a marvellous artist-investigator, who deeply influenced those able to follow him, but he always left a good deal to the intelligence of his hearers. He was not cut out to teach those who did not want to learn.

He said he soon realized that he had made a mistake. He would never be able to get any research done as a school science master, and he ought not to give up any hope of pursuing research at Cambridge, even if his situation there might, for a time, be very insecure.

He felt the presence of two moral imperatives: to help his family, and to investigate nature. He therefore embarked on the 'desperate venture' of returning to Cambridge without any definite employment, hoping, without seeing clearly how, he would succeed in obeying his imperatives. As in other classic instances, such as that of Faraday, the settling of moral problems was accompanied by the illuminations of genius.

2

Wilson arrived back at Cambridge with brilliant scientific inspirations, which he was impatiently waiting to test. He settled in the cheapest and dreariest lodgings. But now man, as well as nature, was kind to him. The university had decided to expand the teaching of physics to medical students. This was energetically organized by T. C. Fitzpatrick, who engaged Wilson to assist in the supervision of the students' practical work in the physics laboratory.

He found himself with just enough to live on, with ideas which he burned to try, and the time to try them.

III

THE ASCENT OF THE MOUNTAIN

Moses ascended the mountain and heard the voice of God. Wilson ascended Ben Nevis, and saw a manifestation of Nature that held his mind for ever. He had first recognized 'the beauty of the world' at Corrie in the hills of Arran. He spent his holidays, when he could, in the Scottish hills, to which he became profoundly attached. He and his own brother, who subsequently became a medical doctor and practised in Peebles, frequently visited Corrie.

On the summit of Ben Nevis, the highest mountain in Britain, an observatory had been founded in 1883. It was conducted by the Scottish Meteorological Society. When members of the permanent staff took their fortnight's summer vacation, their places were offered to volunteers. In 1894 Wilson offered himself, and acted as a temporary observer for a fortnight in the September of that year.

When Wilson arrived at the summit, large patches of the previous winter's snow still lay around. many feet deep. Water for all purposes was obtained from it by melting in a large pot, which was always kept on the top of the kitchen stove. There was no luxury; indeed, conditions were rough. The cook had served in the stern conditions of sailing ships for a lifetime, yet even he appeared to prefer the sea. The Observatory was cut off for weeks during the winter. In the summer the Observatory horse ascended the mountain daily, to bring stores and lay in stocks for the winter months.

Visitors who were climbing to the summit of the mountain used to call, and ask for jocular messages to be sent to their friends below, such as 'Nearer to Heaven than you will ever be', through the Observatory's telegraph connection. The climate at the summit was severe and varied. Atlantic gales blew on it, virtually direct from the ocean. Quantities of insects blown from distant places were deposited on the snow, and these, besides the physical effects, attracted Wilson's interest. There were fogs, mists, rain, snow, and violent thunderstorms. Sometimes the atmosphere was so clear that the Outer Isles could be seen, nearly a hundred miles away.

Wilson began his observations at 5 a.m. The most memorable days were those when the early morning clouds were below the summit and the sky overhead was clear. The optical effects were breath-taking. 'The most striking of all were seen from the edge of the precipice overlooking the great corrie when the observer's shadow (the Brocken spectre) was formed on a thin sheet or wisp of cloud only a few feet below.' A photograph of the Brocken spectre, taken from the place where C. T. R. stood, by J. E. Tinkler, was reproduced in *Weather* in October, 1954.

In his Nobel Prize address in 1927, Wilson said that 'The wonderful optical phenomena shown when the sun shone on the clouds surrounding the hill-top and especially the coloured rings surrounding the sun (coronas) or surrounding the shadow cast by the hill-top or observer on mist or cloud (glories) greatly excited my interest and made me wish to imitate them in the laboratory.' Besides the haloes and glories he saw rainbows, aurorae, zodiacal light, St Elmo's fire and other phenomena in the sky.

He said that the whole of his scientific work undoubtedly developed from the experiments he was led to make by what he saw during his fortnight on the mountain in September 1894.

Wilson was at the base of the mountain on 19 June in the following year, and saw the terrific thunderstorm on the summit, in which the Observatory was struck. He learned next morning that a flash of lightning had fused one of the steel keys of the telegraph instrument. While St Elmo's fire was active, his colleague Bruce collected insects conspicuous on the snow.

His two lifelong interests, in clouds and in atmospheric electricity, had been aroused. The Observatory was closed in 1904, after only twenty-one years of operation. But in that period it had provided a major inspiration.

Wilson returned to Cambridge in the autumn of 1894, intent on reproducing in the laboratory effects he had witnesssed on the mountain. At the beginning of 1895 he made artificial clouds by the expansion of moist air by the method invented by Coulier and the Scottish meteorologist John Aitken. The latter was born

at Falkirk, and became an engineer. His health broke down, and
this led him to spend much time in the fresh air. He began to
study the clouds, and then used his engineering skill to imitate
them with home-made apparatus. Aitken discovered that water
vapour in the atmosphere will not condense to form clouds unless
dust is present, upon which condensation can begin. When he
removed the dust from the air which he used in his expansion
apparatus, he was unable to produce cloud by expansion. He
used the drops condensed by expansion on dust particles in
ordinary air to count the number of dust particles in the known
quantity of air in his apparatus.

Adapting Aitken's apparatus, Wilson was able to reproduce in
the laboratory the beautiful optical phenomena of the Brocken
spectres, glories and coronas that he had seen on the mountain
top. Almost immediately, his alert mind observed something new,
which promised to be even more interesting than the optical
phenomena. He discovered that moist air which was free from
dust did give cloud, if it was expanded beyond a certain limit.

He now designed and made a new expansion apparatus, in
which the degree of expansion necessary to produce cloud in
clean moist air could be exactly measured. He found that an
expansion to more than 1.252 of the original volume, corresponding to a four-fold supersaturation of the air, was necessary
to produce drops in dust-free air. As Blackett has remarked,
the precision of this figure was typical of Wilson's experimental perfection. If the expansion was larger than this, a
shower of drops occurred. He found that each time the expansion was repeated, the number of drops produced did not
decrease. This showed that some kind of nuclei on which the
water vapour could condense, other than dust, were continually
being regenerated in the air. Wilson published this discovery in
the spring of 1895.

He was now down from the mountain, and launched from
aesthetic experiences of nature into the different and equally
wonderful world of intellectual and manual aesthetics.

IV

AN ARTIST IN EXPERIMENTAL INVESTIGATION

On the mountain his aesthetic sense has been exercised through
his eyes, in the laboratory through his mind and hands. He
invented and constructed several ingenious types of cloud expansion apparatus, which Blackett described as a major experimental

innovation. They 'allowed repeated and very accurately controlled fast expansions of the gas in a glass vessel under conditions of great chemical cleanliness'.

Wilson described his second innovation as 'somewhat more elaborate' than the first. All were outstanding. They were ingenious and effective, and inexpensive in materials, but made heavy demands on skill and time. They involved difficult glass-blowing, and very accurate grinding of glass parts to fit. Often certain of the glass parts broke to bits the first time they were used in an experiment, and had then to be made all over again, with extraordinary patience and care. Wilson said he believed that this had inspired various stories which arose regarding his almost innumerably repeated grindings of glass apparatus.

With his second apparatus he discovered that there was a second critical degree of expansion. If this was to more than 1·37 of the original volume, or an eight-fold supersaturation, there was a rapid increase in the number of drops, and beyond that, a thick fog.

He observed that if the clouds so formed were illuminated, the coloured rings due to diffraction of the light by the drops were blue for an expansion of 1·408 and changed to red for 1·42. Below expansions of 1·38 the drops were too small to produce colours, and above 1·44 they were too large. In the intervening range the colour phenomena were very beautiful, owing to the small and uniform size of the drops.

Condensation within the two critical limits of expansion remained small, like a shower of rain. It was much the same in pure gases as in air, though the critical limits of expansion were different. The dense clouds formed when the expansion was beyond the second limit consisted of drops condensed on molecules of vapour or gas.

The clouds like showers of rain, which occurred between the two critical expansions, excited his interest from the first. The very fact that their number was so small and they were always regenerated, and the fact that 'the supersaturation required indicated a magnitude not greatly exceeding molecular dimensions, at once suggested that we had a means of making visible and counting certain individual molecules or atoms which were at the moment in some exceptional condition. Could they be electrically charged atoms or ions?'

A few months later, in the autumn of 1895, came the news of Röntgen's discovery of X-rays. Wilson borrowed a primitive X-ray tube which J. J. Thomson's assistant Ebenezer Everett had made, to see whether the X-rays, which were already known to electrify air, might affect the phenomena in the air in his expansion apparatus. 'I can well recall my delight when I found at the first trial that no drops were formed on expansion of the cloud chamber when exposed to X-rays if the expansion was less than 1·25, a fog which took many minutes to fall was produced when the expansion lay between the rain-like and cloud-like limits; X-rays thus produced in very large numbers nuclei of the same kind as were always being produced in very small numbers in the air within the cloud chamber.'

During the next two years he studied the nuclei produced by X-rays, uranium rays, ultra-violet light, point electrical discharges and other agents. The nuclei produced in these different ways all required the same expansion in order to lead to the formation of cloud. He concluded that they must be ions, because no cloud was formed when they were swept from the air by the action of an electric field.

He now investigated the behaviour of negatively and positively charged ions. He found that while the lower critical expansion, corresponding to a four-fold supersaturation, produced clouds from negative ions, a larger expansion, corresponding to six-fold supersaturation, was necessary to obtain cloud from positively charged ions.

Wilson saw that 'it was now possible to make visible the individual ions as condensation nuclei, and distinguish between the positive and negative'.

These discoveries were of great tactical importance in fundamental physics. J. J. Thomson and his colleagues immediately applied them to determine accurately the size of the electric charge carried by an ion. Thereby the fundamental electrical constant of nature, the charge on the electron, was determined. Shortly afterwards, H. A. Wilson applied it to determine the value of e to within one per cent, by calculating the degree of expansion required to cause negative ions to grow into visible drops.

Wilson now suspected that air might always contain the same kind of nuclei as those on which rain drops could condense. He made experiments to find whether there was a measurable conduction of electricity through air in a closed vessel containing dust-free air. 'These led at once to positive results, and proved that the air in a closed vessel is always ionized.'

Geitel in Germany published a similar result shortly before Wilson. Geitel and his colleague Elster, who became distinguished in fields of research similar to those of Wilson, were schoolmasters, but as such their careers were very different from his. Under the German system of secondary education, masters might have little routine teaching, leaving them with time and energy for research; very different from the conditions in which Wilson worked when he was a schoolmaster. The restricted opportunity for research in the English school system is one of its worst defects.

Wilson pursued his research on the conductivity of air in closed vessels. It led 'to the detection of radioactive matter carried down by rain and snow', which is now of fundamental importance in connection with the atomic fall-out from atomic explosions, and it led 'to the direct measurement of the current between the atmosphere and the earth, and to the study of atmospheric electricity generally'.

Wilson noted in 1900 that the ionization which occurred within closed vessels might be due to radiations penetrating the walls, and even coming from outside the earth. This was the first suggestion of the existence of the cosmic rays.

Wilson showed that the most perfectly insulated electrically charged object gradually lost its charge. He devised exquisitely simple and elegant instruments for demonstrating the phenomenon. He showed that the sensitivity of the gold-leaf electroscope, one of the oldest of electrical instruments, could be enormously increased by tilting at a particular angle.

When Wilson began his splendid investigations in the autumn of 1894, the Cavendish Laboratory was a quiet place. Research was done by senior people in such time as they could spare from other duties. They rarely spent long hours in the laboratory, so no regulations had been made limiting the freedom of those who wanted to work on their own. Wilson took advantage of this, working there whenever he wanted. During the summer vacation of 1895 he spent every day there, and was generally the only person in the whole laboratory.

There were no students whose whole duty was research. These were not instituted until October 1895, when the first three arrived. They were Townsend, Rutherford and McClelland. Wilson 'immediately felt the pleasure and stimulus of their companionship'. They created the cheerful, friendly atmosphere which became so characteristic of Cavendish research. Rutherford started a daily tea-break, which gave everybody, including J. J. Thomson who had been Cavendish professor for eleven years, and had reached the ripe age of thirty-nine, opportunity to relax.

It was this atmosphere which encouraged Wilson's persistence in difficult glass-blowing, followed by many hours of accurate glass-grinding, done in the knowledge that the whole apparatus was almost certain to fall to pieces at the first trial. He had only three successes out of many attempts. In the successful experiments, the wonderful coloured phenomena produced in the apparatus made it look 'as if it were filled with a beautifully coloured liquid'. The colours changed in perfectly regular ways as the increase in the number of droplets caused a decrease in their size.

Wilson was elected to the Clerk Maxwell Studentship in 1896. This gave him three years in which he could devote himself entirely to research. He was very proud of holding this award, both as a scientist and a Scotsman.

J. J. Thomson's powers were then at their height. His mind was so full of new ideas, and Wilson acutely observed them reflected in the expression of his face. 'It was in Great St Mary's church during the University Sermon that I remember on more than one occasion being able to study his countenance while we were both unusually free from distraction. His alert and eager expression seemed to indicate a mind that had already reached the solution of some great and fundamental problem and was now tremendously active in following out the many consequences of this solution.' Wilson's recollection indeed raises the question of exactly what these two great men were doing in church. Neither seems to have been following any conventional religious exercise.

Wilson said that J.J.'s extreme powers of concentration did not hinder him from being always available for discussing others' problems, but they did seem to prevent him from realizing sometimes how much he owed to the suggestions of other people. He had a remarkable instinct for knowing which problems were most worth while, and the best way of investigating them. Unlike his predecessor, Rayleigh, he was not interested in designing experiments elegant for their own sake, but only in those which were effective, elegant or not. He did not try to influence Wilson in the design of his experiments, but Wilson could judge from the amiability of his manner whether he thought he was spending too much time on perfecting his methods.

J. J. Thomson, for his part, later wrote of Wilson's work on the cloud chamber that those who were not in the Cavendish Laboratory at the time could hardly realize the amount of work it entailed. 'For many years he did all the glass-blowing himself, and only those who have tried it know how exasperating glass-blowing can be, and how often when the apparatus is all but finished it breaks and the work has to be begun again. This never seemed to disconcert Wilson; he would take up a fresh piece of glass, perhaps say "Dear, dear," but never anything stronger, and begin again.'

Old research students on revisiting the laboratories were apt to remark that many things had changed, but C.T.R. was still glass-blowing. His beautiful photographs required years of un-remitting work before he had brought them up to his required standard, but when they were at last obtained, they remained unsurpassed.

The general stimulation caused by the arrival of the first re-search students in the Cavendish in 1895 was followed by the starting of fortnightly physics meetings. Stokes, who was then Secretary of the Royal Society, used to come to them. He rarely spoke, but Wilson recorded that occasionally 'his rather stern and solemn face lighted up with a most wonderful smile'. Stokes's comments were always illuminating. Wilson said that he had 'seen exactly the same transformation on the face of Niels Bohr, and no one who has seen Bohr lecturing can have failed to notice his sudden change from solemnity to humour'.

Stokes and Kelvin came to look at Wilson's expansion appara-tus, and 'showed obvious delight in the beauty of the colour changes produced by large expansions'. Wilson's keen visual observation and subtle understanding were finely exemplified in these recollections.

He said that the early Cavendish research students had un-usual physical energy, especially Langevin and Rutherford. 'Langevin had the most extraordinary vitality which even seemed to be proclaimed by the intense blue-black colour of his hair.' Rutherford does not seem to have made his full impression on him until after he had gone to Montreal where he and Soddy worked out the theory of radioactive disintegration. Seeing him after this time, Wilson noticed also the extraordinary 'brightness of his eyes and the alertness of his expression'.

As his Clerk Maxwell Studentship drew to an end in 1899, Wilson was strenuously wandering in the Scottish hills. One day, coming back for lunch at Coyburn Bridge in the Cairngorms, a boy brought him a telegram, summoning him to a meeting of the Meteorological Society in London, to discuss what research should be conducted on atmospheric electricity. He considered his research on ions as an obvious starting point for research on that subject, so he carried on with this, now with the Society's support.

Wilson's mother had come to live with him in Cambridge soon after 1895. In 1900 his position became fully established. He was elected a fellow of his college, and appointed University Lecturer in Physics, with a salary of £100, and Demonstrator at £50 a year. In this year, too, Wilson was elected a Fellow of the Royal Society. He 'lost no time in hurrying' to tell his mother of 'this wonderful news'.

V

AS TEACHER

In his vacations Wilson made researches on atmospheric electricity near Peebles, where his brother had set up in medical practice and which presently became the family home. When in Cambridge he also pursued aspects of the subject. Ultimately these researches led to the fulfilment of his 'dream of isolating a portion of the earth's surface and measuring the charge on it and the current flowing into it from the atmosphere'.

They also had an unforeseen bearing on cosmic rays and the measurement of radioactivity in rain.

Wilson found the preparation of his Cambridge lectures very hard work. They were on Light, and he thought the whole subject out afresh from first principles. He said that perhaps the work he put into getting his own ideas clear was a help to the members of the class. These lectures were highly original, and stimulated very significant research by others. Unfortunately, he never wrote them up and published them; the effort would have been too agonizingly severe.

In his recollections, Sir Lawrence Bragg has given an historic example of their influence on research: 'For two years I was in his Part II Practical Class at the Cavendish. C. T. R. Wilson had organized a series of experiments for this class. There were not many of them, perhaps some 15 or 20, but they covered the whole of physics. There was one set of gear for each experiment and we took them on in turn (there were about 15 in my class). What I well remember is C.T.R.'s curbing of our impatience to finish an experiment and count it as "done". He forced us to regard it as a small research and look for strange unexplained effects. In his very hesitant gentle way he was quite firm in not letting us give up an experiment until we got everything out of it we possibly could.

'His lab boy was Crowe, then in his teens. I well remember that Crowe, when our finals approached, made out a list of the classes which we would all get and to the best of my recollection he was almost 100 per cent right. There was really no need for the external examiners.

'C. T. R. Wilson lectured on optics. The lectures were the best, and the delivery was the worst, of any lectures to which I have ever been. He mumbled facing the board, he was very hesitant and jerky in his delivery, and yet the way he presented the subject was quite brilliant. I think his lectures on optics set the standard for similar lectures all over this country when later his pupils got chairs.

'I remember so well the start of the cloud chamber. He came down to the laboratory to tell me about the first photographs of α-rays and I remember his saying about the tracks that "they are as fine as little 'heers'". He had expected to see broad and woolly clouds and was astonished that the tracks were so narrow. He chose me, a great honour, to go with him to the Royal Society Soirée and demonstrate the cloud chamber for the first time. A highlight of this occasion was my explaining an electron to Larmor; in my gauche student way I had not realized who he was.

'Later when Hilger asked me to organize a series of stereoscopic pictures of crystal structures, I showed the Hilger letter to Wilson. I have a vivid recollection of his saying "Oh yes, about a year ago Hilger wrote to me about stereoscopic pictures of cloud tracks. I 'reely' must reply to that letter."

'I remember too after the war his telling me that he was puzzling over short tracks which appeared when X-rays shot through a gas, as he put it "like little fish swimming in the direction of the X-ray beam". These were the Compton recoil electrons. I think that Wilson regretted that, with his usual slowness and caution in making sure of every step, he had not published his results on these recoil electrons before the "Compton effect" was published. He had been thinking about them for a very long time.

'I loved him dearly, he was one of the kindest, most considerate and modest of people. I think he had a somewhat kind regard for me because he usually confided in me about his work sometimes at quite an early stage.

'On one occasion a suggestion from him was wonderfully fruitful. I had worked out theoretically that one could consider X-ray diffraction as due to the reflection of the X-rays in the crystal plane. It was Wilson who suggested I should try specular reflection from cleavage sheets of mica. The experiment came off and I published it in *Nature* and this caused quite a furore of similar experiments . . . It was C.T.R.'s treatment of a grating diffracting white light, which he had given us in his lectures, which set me thinking on the right lines when I gave a simpler treatment in November 1912 of Laue's diffraction experiments. You will see how much I owe to him.'

Thus Wilson's inspiration contributed to the foundation of the great new science of X-ray analysis, which has led to the development of molecular biology, and transformed knowledge of the structure of living as well as non-living materials.

Wilson made laboratory notes and records throughout his scientific life, which contained accounts of his ideas as they arose and developed, besides the results of his original observations. These notebooks, which Wilson made freely available to his pupils, were a source of a great deal of inspiration, which in some cases started men on a lifetime of investigation. As Dee and Wormell have remarked, they illustrate 'in a fascinating manner the processes of individual discovery and the gradual evolution of scientific generalizations by the combination of experimental practice with imaginative ideas'.

A remarkable feature of them are arguments and counter-arguments, in which Wilson soliloquized over summaries and conclusions which he had drawn from his experiments and observations. Dee and Wormell suggested that he thought out and wrote down these soliloquies because his extreme modesty and shyness inhibited discussion of his problems with other workers. However, it seemed to be a difficulty of communication, for he could speak vigorously at College meetings, and he chatted incessantly with Dee when they were collaborating.

Wilson wrote in an extremely clear yet sensitive and varied style. Every word cost him pains. He never wrote a book; his nearest approach to one was his long article on *Atmospheric Electricity* in the *Dictionary of Applied Physics*. His writings were works of art in classic taste, besides being scientifically profound and stimulating. With the pen, as with the eye and the instrument, he was an artist.

Wilson was in charge of the teaching of advanced practical physics in the Cavendish for nineteen years, from 1900 to 1919. He made a profound contribution to the Cavendish style and method in experimental physics through his teaching as well as his research.

In 1919, when Rutherford succeeded J. J. Thomson as professor, and director of the Cavendish Laboratory, Wilson moved his experimental work to the Astronomical Observatory, some way from the Cavendish Laboratory. This may have been to escape Rutherford, who always wanted results, whereas Wilson was more interested in the process of discovery. Like that other eminent Scotsman, Robert Louis Stevenson, he was more interested in the journey than in arriving.

As a teacher of practical physics he believed in leaving students scope to plan their work. He was opposed to his colleague Searle's method, which was to have the description of each experiment written out very fully, so that the student could immediately find the solution of all his difficulties. Searle's system tempted students to write out the answers without actually doing the experiments.

Wilson liked to work out problems in the simplest way from first principles. Dee once walked home with him from the Observatory at 2.30 a.m., on a morning when the aspect of the moon suddenly caught Wilson's attention. It was not immediately obvious how it could appear in that position. Wilson stopped, and for the next ten minutes worked out its position with the aid of his fingers, while Dee stood around in the cool early morning air.

Wilson would lay his hand on anything that he thought might help an investigation forward. Dee has described how, after listening to Chadwick's first description of the discovery of the neutron, at a meeting of the Kapitza Club at Cambridge in 1932, the idea for an important experiment occurred to him. He was working at the time with C. T. R. Wilson at the Observatory. He saw that Wilson's expansion chamber at the Observatory might be used to look for the recoil of electrons struck by neutrons. Chadwick lent Dee the radioactive source which he was using during the day in the Cavendish Laboratory, so that Dee could use it at the Observatory at night. Wilson was at first somewhat sorry that the experiments in which he and Dee had been collaborating were interrupted, but he soon became intensely interested in Dee's new experiments. These were being disturbed by gamma radiations. Lead shields were usually used for keeping these radiations out, but gold would be even better. Wilson turned up with all his gold medals, including the one that went with his Nobel Prize, and suggested they should be used. He helped Dee with the apparatus in making the experiments. He was not particularly skilful in the ordinary operative sense. For instance, when taking photographs, he was quite liable to forget to change the plate or film. He was not at all an absolutely sure-fingered artisan.

The next major addition to Wilson's cloud-chamber method of visually investigating atoms was made by one of his small band of personal pupils, C. F. Powell, who developed the method of tracing atomic paths in solid pieces of photographic emulsion. This enabled the track to be examined and re-examined at leisure, and gave other advantages. The method has been of immense importance in the study of cosmic rays and the fast particles by giant accelerators.

Powell was not only a Cambridge man, he was also a member of Wilson's college, Sidney Sussex. It is hard not to believe that Wilson's special qualities as an experimenter had a formative influence on Powell. The particular research Powell carried out as a student under Wilson's direction had a bearing on the properties of steam, and proved to be of importance in engineering, which had been quite unforeseen.

From the conventional point of view, as Sir Lawrence Bragg remarked, Wilson was not a good lecturer. He dropped his voice, especially when he came to important points, which he whispered to the blackboard. He juggled with pieces of chalk, and had other mannerisms. But his material and personality were fascinating for good students, though not always for others. Wilson recollected that when he was asked to give a Friday Evening Discourse at the Royal Institution, Sir James Dewar, then the Director, came to him at the end of the lecture and told him he had 'made every mistake that it was possible for a lecturer to make'. Wilson's lecturing might be compared with that of Niels Bohr, which was also almost inaudible and unintelligible, yet in its effect very inspiring. Like Wilson, Bohr had an extraordinary power of conveying to his hearers that they were in the presence of profound insight, and in direct contact with the inner workings of nature, whether or not they could follow his argument.

At the luncheon given in honour of Wilson and his wife, at the Allan Ramsay Hotel at Carlops, to celebrate his ninetieth birthday, by Appleton, Cockcroft, Occhialini, Powell and others, Appleton described how Wilson lectured on light with both hands, writing on the blackboard with one, and wiping off with the other a few seconds later what he had written. His hearers had to be pretty intent to follow what was going on, which they were most anxious to do, knowing that what was being said was of unique quality. The class used to speculate why material was removed so rapidly from the board, and they thought that possibly

as a cautious Scot he was careful not to leave anything there for
fear it might be wrong. However, they came to the conclusion that
this would not be in keeping with his personality. Ultimately
they concluded that he didn't want Searle, another of the great
personalities of the Cavendish, to acquire his material for one of
his textbooks. Searle used to contend that J. J. Thomson, Rutherford and others sacrificed teaching for research, and battled
for what he regarded as the undergraduates' and the teachers'
rights. He had resented Rutherford's tendency as a research
student in his early days to raid the small stock of teaching
apparatus in order to turn it to research purposes. As so many
were worshipping the idol of research, Searle, who was a vege-
tarian and held contrary views on many topics, devoted himself
to the idol of teaching. Not that he was not good at research; he
had done excellent work on electromagnetic theory, and was the
only scientist who preserved friendship with that isolated genius
Oliver Heaviside, whose contrariness he was so well qualified to
understand.

If Rutherford raided apparatus for research, Searle was justified in raiding material for teaching. Wilson's student audience
conceived the theory that he must have been trying to conceal
his material from Searle. Wilson described his lectures as on
Light, while Searle described his as on Optics. It was noted that
Wilson used to leave on the board what he wrote on Atmospheric
Electricity, in which Searle was not interested, and the class
claimed this as a proof of the correctness of their surmise.

Wilson said he liked the informal teaching in the laboratory,
but this, and his lecturing, left him with little time for research.
'For years I used to think and dream of what the cloud method
could be made to reveal. Would it be possible to avoid displacement of the droplets condensed on ions and photograph them?
Would one in this way make visible the tracks of ionizing particles? It was not until 1911 that I saw and photographed the
first tracks in an apparatus I had designed and which had been
made in the workshop at the Cavendish. They revealed more
than I had dreamed would be possible.'

VI

THE MOUNTAIN SPEAKS AGAIN

Wilson's experiences on Ben Nevis in 1894 led to the invention,
in 1911, of his third design of cloud chamber, the most extraordinary of all physical apparatuses. Its breath-taking capacity

for accomplishing the apparently impossible, of revealing single atomic particles travelling with speeds comparable with that of light, by the simplest and most inexpensive means, of the highest ingenuity and aesthetic elegance, is classic. Rutherford described the cloud chamber as 'the most original apparatus in the whole history of physics'. For thirty years the cloud chamber led the visible revelation of the behaviour and properties of atoms, cosmic rays and sub-atomic particles.

Ben Nevis had given the original inspiration, but what was still more extraordinary, it reinforced its original inspiration, leading not merely to one scientific miracle, but to two.

On the afternoon of 26 June 1895, Wilson wandered from Ben Nevis to the summit of the neighbouring mountain, Carn Mor Dearg. 'The sky had become overcast', he wrote, 'as I climbed up from Allt a'Mhuilinn, and mist hid the top of Ben Nevis; there was a faint muttering of distant thunder. Suddenly, I felt my hair stand up; I did not await any further developments but started to run down the long scree slope leading to the bottom of the corrie. The storm broke overhead with a bright flash, and loud thunder just after I had left the summit. This experience drew my attention very forcibly to the magnitude of the electric field of a thunderstorm and its sudden changes.'

Again Wilson began to see in his imagination how nature works. He conceived thunderstorms, and the whole earth itself, as gigantic electrical machines. He began to seek for precise information on how the earth as a whole is electrified, and how lightning flashes are generated in thunderstorms. He visualized the earth and thunderstorms as giant natural machines beside which the biggest man-made machine would be puny.

He investigated the phenomena experimentally. He designed special electrometers, Wilson plates and Wilson spheres, to measure the earth's electric field, and the charges produced in it by thunderstorms.

The earth is known to be negatively electrified. It is found to be negatively charged at the equator and at the poles, at land and at sea. Wilson suggested that this negative electrification is due to an excess of negatively charged particles, shot down into the earth during thunderstorms.

He devised the experimental methods and made the first observations which gave reliable measurements of the size of the electric charges, and the voltage differences, involved in lightning flashes and discharges. He was the first to realize the magnitude of the electric current carried by the point discharges below thunderstorms, and he made the first reliable estimate of the vertical electric current maintained by a storm between the ground and the upper atmosphere.

He estimated that at any moment about 1,000 thunderstorms are in operation on the earth's surface, and that these would be sufficient to give the earth the kind and degree of electrification which it was observed to possess.

He pointed out that voltages of 1,000,000,000 occurred between thunderclouds and the earth, and that these could accelerate electrons to enormous speeds. When Skobeltzyn obtained the first photograph of a cosmic ray track in 1927 with a Wilson cloud chamber, he suggested that the track might have been made by one of Wilson's very fast electrons, named 'runaway' electrons by Eddington. Thus, besides making the original suggestion that the rays, now known as cosmic, came from outside the earth, Wilson also suggested a conceivable mechanism by which they might be generated on the earth, through the acceleration of particles in thunderstorms.

He worked out theories of the origin of the huge electrical charges produced by thunderstorms. He attributed them to natural operations in the thundercloud, which included an intensification of an existing vertical electric field by processes of the same kind as those utilized in electrical influence machines.

While the processes described by Wilson may have a major role, the problem of how thunderstorms work is still not fully settled. A striking feature of this last contribution was that Wilson published it in 1956, when he was eighty-seven years old.

Wilson's researches on thunderstorms and the electrical condition of the atmosphere were one of the sources of inspiration to the work of Appleton on the electrical condition of the upper atmosphere, and of Watson-Watt on thunderstorms. These researches, in turn, led to the invention of radar, and this contributed to the development of radioastronomy.

Wilson was appointed observer in Meteorological Physics at the Solar Physics Observatory in 1913. Much of his research on thunderstorm electricity, and on cloud chambers for tracing atomic tracks, was done there. As it was some way from the Cavendish Laboratory, his presence in the latter was less frequent, and his influence on Cavendish workers more occasional. He was appointed Reader in Electrical Meteorology in 1918, and in 1925 Jacksonian professor of natural philosophy.

Wilson's absences through his research on atmospheric electricity at the family home in Peebles, and his working at the

Solar Physics Observatory, were among the causes of his having so few personal research colleagues and pupils. Neverthelesss, these included C. F. Powell, P. I. Dee, and J. G. Wilson in cloud-chamber research, and T. W. Wormell in atmospheric electricity.

Appleton recalled that in the 1920's Wilson had allowed him to use his special aerial and hut on elevated ground on the Madingley Road in Cambridge, which he had erected to study the changes in the electric field during thunderstorms. Wilson once asked him whether he had ever felt nervous when a thundercloud approached a station. Appleton replied that he had been too busy making observations to worry about possible danger. Wilson remarked that when he had felt a little apprehensive in the hut, he used to comfort himself with the reflection that it had never yet been struck.

Appleton had attended Wilson's lectures as a student, and worked on thunderstorm research under his guidance. He succeeded him as Jacksonian professor in 1936. This was after a year's interregnum, which, Appleton suspected, was one of Wilson's brilliant ideas, and a Scottish one, too. Appleton found that when he came to the chair, a year's professorial salary had been saved, which could be used for research. This more than paid for the little radio laboratory on the Madingley Road, which J. A. Ratcliffe subsequently put to such good use in investigating the ionosphere.

Later on, Ratcliffe helped to provide the base from which Martin Ryle was to carry out his great creative work in radio-astronomy.

VII

REVEALING THE ATOM

After ten years of thinking and dreaming about the possibilities of the cloud chamber, Wilson began, towards 1910, to design a third cloud chamber, to measure the electric charge on an electrified atom by making such atoms visible by condensing drops on them, and then photographing and counting the drops.

While he was at work on this, R. A. Millikan achieved the same end by a different method, so that his attempt to measure the ionic charge became unnecessary. But he had also had in view 'the possibility that the track of an ionizing particle might be made visible and photographed by condensing water on the ions which it liberated'.

He completed a rough apparatus in 1911. He ionized the air

in the chamber by X-rays and made an expansion, 'with little expectation of success', but was 'delighted to see the cloud chamber filled with little wisps and threads of clouds'. These were the tracks of the electrons ejected by the action of the X-rays. A radium-tipped metal tongue was then placed inside the cloud chamber, and 'the very beautiful sight of the clouds condensed along the tracks of the α-particles was seen for the first time . . .'

The cloud chamber which Wilson used was constructed in the workshop of the Cavendish Laboratory. Sixteen years later, on the occasion of his Nobel Prize address in 1927, Wilson said that it was 'the one which I have had in use up to the present time'.

Wilson said that the first results were to confirm conclusions already drawn. 'I remember showing W. H. Bragg one of the first good pictures of α-ray tracks very shortly after it had been obtained. He at once showed me a diagram he had just published showing examples of what he considered likely forms of the paths of α-rays. The similarity between the actual photograph and Bragg's ideal picture was astonishing.' His pictures revealed examples of single and compound scattering of impinging particles, the existence of which Rutherford had deduced indirectly.

In 1913 he introduced stereoscopic photography of the cloud chamber, so that the tracks could be seen in three dimensions. He observed the recoil of electrons from collisions with quanta of radiation, which Compton used to prove the quantum theory of radiation.

When the First World War started in 1914, he laid this research aside, and did not advance it again until 1921. Then he showed the separation of positively and negatively charged particles by an electric field.

His stereoscopic pictures provided five different kinds of information. They revealed the point of origin of the tracks, their direction, range, form of track, and amount of ionization produced. He found that a particle with an electron energy of 21,000 volts had a range of 1 cm in air.

In 1923 he secured pictures of a quality and beauty never surpassed. He showed electrons recoiling from individual quanta, which specifically confirmed A. H. Compton's quantum theory of the scattering of X-rays.

His technique was adopted by Blackett, who obtained with it the first photograph of the disintegration of an atom, and equally important detailed information about the trails made by different kinds of particles. Consequently, when a trail was observed, the kind of particle that had made it could be inferred from its appearance. This made it possible to identify the products of atomic disintegration, and thus elucidate the mechanism of the atomic reactions.

Irène Curie, Lise Meitner, P. I. Dee, Bothe, Auger and others made further basic discoveries by means of the technique. D. Skobeltzyn deflected the tracks with a magnetic field. From the character of the track, the strength of the field and the amount of the deflection, the energy of the particle could be calculated.

Later on, C. D. Anderson discovered the positron and the meson with a Wilson chamber, and Blackett's colleagues G. D. Rochester and C. C. Butler discovered the first of the new order of sub-atomic particles, the 'strange particles'. These appear when particles which make up the nuclei of atoms themselves disintegrate, and they are governed by a new kind of force, different from that which holds the constituent particles of atomic nuclei together.

Thus the cloud chamber, among all its other achievements, has led to the discovery of a new fundamental force in nature.

VIII

RETURN TO THE SOURCE

Wilson married in 1908 Jessie Fraser Dick, the daughter of a Scottish minister. In due course, they had three children. In the year after he retired from his Cambridge chair in 1935 he moved to Edinburgh, and then, in 1949, after his eightieth birthday, he settled in a delightful cottage at Carlops, near his birthplace at Glencorse. He continued his researches on atmospheric electricity and thunderstorms, slowly pondering and turning over in his mind these very complex phenomena. He wandered continually in his beloved hills, and retained an extraordinary physical and mental vigour. At the age of eighty-two he led his friend James Paton up the gully on Caisteal Abhail to the Witch's Step, in Arran. Sitting on the ridge, he whispered to Paton apologetically, as if he might be construed to be boasting: 'It's 64 years since I first sat here.'

Wilson unconcernedly skipped round precipices, while his former pupils, now middle-aged and substantial men, followed him gingerly. He use to travel by bus once a week to lunch with a group of friends, most of whom were half his age, and who described themselves as the Alcovians, because they used to lunch together in an alcove in a busy Edinburgh restaurant. He eagerly discussed news of researches in his field, and entertained his friends with pawky reminiscences of Kelvin, Marie Curie, J. J. Thomson, Rutherford, and colleagues at the Cavendish Laboratory at the turn of the century.

He delighted to welcome old friends and students into the intimacy of his family circle at Carlops. There he would exchange reminiscences, and take up scientific discussions at the point where they might have been interrupted a generation earlier. As Wormell put it: 'There, at the hands of the young man of ninety, one recaptured something of the passionate enthusiasm and excitement of scientific enquiry.'

At the age of eighty-six he first began to fly, in joining Edinburgh University students of meteorology in the Royal Air Force's observation flights with *Anson* aircraft. He soon flew regularly over the Western Isles, and derived enormous pleasure in observing and identifying the mountains he had explored on foot. He watched from above the clouds he had used to study from below. Paton described how on one of these flights, when he was eighty-eight, the aircraft on the return flight from Benbecula had to call at Fermanagh in Northern Ireland to pick up an officer. The machine was not in good order, and after some alarming incidents, it was pronounced unserviceable. It appeared that the party might be stranded in Ireland, but it was discovered that it was still possible to catch the night boat from Belfast. When they arrived at the boat, it was very full and no sleeping berth could be found for him. Wilson dozed on the settee in the smoking room, and was up very early to see the coast and hills of his beloved Arran.

After the ship had been moored to the wharf in Glasgow, he clambered off it, together with the cattle. He got onto a train to the railway station, to catch the train for Edinburgh. As he stepped into the train he remarked: 'Now, if we had bicycles, we could say that we had used every form of mechanical transport within twenty-four hours.'

He safely found his way home, and when rung up later to ask whether he was all right, he replied: 'But why should I be tired? It was a wonderful experience.' The aircraft had flown through a thunderstorm with a faulty engine, and while others had been alarmed, he had been completely absorbed in studying the meteorological phenomena.

He accepted an invitation to attend the inauguration of the nuclear reactor *Dido* at Harwell in 1956, when he was eighty-seven. Feather was his travelling companion on that day. Wilson

rose at 5.30 a.m. and was in Edinburgh by 7. They made the
return journey in one day, and he did not arrive home again until
about 11 p.m. They flew to London by B.E.A. *Viscount*. At
Harwell, he saw everything that was to be seen. He climbed all
the ladders, and looked through all the observation holes. Only
one thing detracted from complete joy: he found the *Viscount*
passenger aircraft unattractive compared with the rigours of the
ancient *Anson* used on the weather flights.

He wrote a masterly account of his *Reminiscences* of his early
years for the *Notes and Records* of the Royal Society, which he
completed ten days before he died. It was expressed in his
quiet and perfectly chosen language, which reflected his 'enthusiasm, integrity, humility and gentleness'.

In answering a query about the article, he wrote to Sir Harold
Hartley that it had arrived when he was just developing a rather
sudden attack of pneumonia. This was 'a new and interesting
experience'. He had delayed answering his letter until his doctor
had assured him that the pneumonia had responded to the penicillin treatment. But he was 'getting on with the reminiscences';
thinking about old days had given him a good deal of pleasure.

Six days before he died he wrote a magnificent final letter to
Sir Harold Hartley, in a hand by then unsteady, but perfectly
expressed, giving final instructions about scientific and other
illustrations for his *Reminiscences*. He apologized for being 'so
slow in getting things done. My doctor has been keeping me in
bed this week. We have all been much distressed by the unexpected illness of our much loved Highland pony, and the need
to have to decide to have her put down.'

Six days later, Wilson himself died, surrounded by all his
family, with his mind alert to the end.

As Wormell said, admiration was lost in a warm and lasting
affection for Wilson. He became a legend in his lifetime, absolutely himself, and yet unusually admired and loved.

Wilson had fine qualities in a very high degree, and in a rare
combination. Besides being modest, shy, aesthetically sensitive
and scientifically acute, he was exceptionally persistent and
physically wiry.

The quality which put most strain on his colleagues was his
deliberation. One of the lessons of his life and career is that it is
not possible to have too much patience in fostering this type of
scientist. Another is that the most delicate qualities may be
associated with exceptional toughness, and may draw much sustenance from a deep family life and social tradition.

This raises the question whether it is a good thing for scientists of Wilson's type to depart from their original environment, for example by emigrating to another country. Is it possible for his kind of genius to be successfully transplanted from its original soil?

The recognition of Wilson's talent does not appear to have been difficult. From the beginning he was a successful student. But the successful emergence of his genius seems to have depended a great deal on luck.

By studying the type and its needs it is possible that more of this rare and unobtrusive kind of genius will be uncovered, and encouraged to unfold.

JOHN WILLIAM STRUTT
THIRD LORD RAYLEIGH
1842-1919

I

AN EXEMPLAR OF RESEARCH METHOD

DURING the second half of the nineteenth century William Thomson, Lord Kelvin, became the most famous of contemporary British physicists. His achievements were immense in importance, range and bulk, and published in no fewer than 661 scientific papers. Few were aware that in spite of this huge effort his genius was less than Clerk Maxwell's, who unfortunately died in 1879 at the age of forty-eight, before his electromagnetic theory of light had been widely accepted, and sufficient time had elapsed for the depth of his numerous scientific intuitions to become generally evident.

By the beginning of the twentieth century it had become clear that Clerk Maxwell was more significant than Kelvin for the future of physics. In the second half of the twentieth century, however, a third figure, that of Rayleigh, is threatening to displace Kelvin from even the second place among the British physicists of his own period.

Rayleigh's works, like Kelvin's, were very extensive; he published 446 papers. For a long time his collected papers have been found more relevant to contemporary science than Kelvin's, and are more frequently consulted. J. J. Thomson said that he thought them the best examples of research method. 'The physical ideas direct the mathematical analysis into the shortest and most appropriate channels, while the mathematics gives precision and point to the physics.' Yet he continues to be a much less well-known figure.

Rayleigh and Kelvin were personally very friendly, and it is said that Rayleigh suggested that Kelvin should be made a peer. Their attitudes towards the exploitation of science were, however, in sharp contrast. Kelvin had many patents, and sometimes went to the Patents Office even before he had finished writing his original paper on a new idea. Rayleigh never patented any of his work.

What kind of a scientist was he? Has this any bearing on his being less well known? How far was this due to the nature of his researches, his personality, his social situation and interests? What light does Rayleigh's career throw on the kind of conditions which best foster his sort of genius?

Rayleigh particularly admired Thomas Young. In recognition of this, the tablet in Westminster Abbey to his memory was placed opposite to that of Young. They were of a similar scientific type. They were both very individual in their modes of research. They worked much by themselves, and they tended to choose deep problems and attack them directly.

Rayleigh's sister-in-law, Mrs Henry Sidgwick, who was a sister of the statesman A. J. Balfour, assisted him in research in the Cavendish Laboratory for five years. As a collaborator and a relative, she was well placed to see his mind at work. She said that when he started on any problem he always 'began at the big end'. He made patient and profound efforts to form a physical conception of a phenomenon before he carried out much calculation about it. He said that 'a good instinct and a little mathematics is often better than a lot of calculations'. Consequently, his work has been exceptionally fruitful in providing starting-points for the researches of others. He enjoyed reducing a confused scientific problem to intellectual order, and was less interested in the comprehensive development of an opening after it had been cleared in principle.

For nearly a century now, scientists have repeatedly turned to his works for insight on how to attack complex new problems which were as yet loosely defined. These defy facile calculators who can quickly derive conclusions from precise premises, but are unable to obtain useful results from basic data which are not narrowly defined.

Rayleigh's approach has been especially valuable in fields such as the flow of liquids and gases, and the development of aerodynamics. After a life-time of contributions he published, in 1910, at the age of sixty-eight, a universal formula for calculating the force which an air stream exerts on a body. His approach has enabled the properties of engineering materials to be handled scientifically, and latterly it has been of fundamental value in the development of modern wave-mechanics. Rayleigh was himself too old to take to quantum theory, but his methods have been invaluable in its mathematical development. Professor A. F. Huxley has recently given a remarkable example from biology and optics of Rayleigh's special power of choosing significant problems. Dr Land discovered that the sea scallop has eyes which operate with mirrors instead of lenses. The part which had hitherto been thought to be an image-forming lens proved to be a plate for correcting spherical aberration arising from reflection from a mirror at the back of the eye. In fact, the scallop sees by telescopes which work on the principle introduced by Schmidt. However, it appears that nature had invented the Schmidt telescope two hundred million years ago. The mirrors at the back of the scallop eye consist of layers of transparent material, which nevertheless function as excellent reflectors. Rayleigh in one of his last papers, published in 1919, when he was seventy-seven, had already given the theory of reflection from multi-layer structures of this kind. The best reflectors are now made commercially on the same principle, a stack of thin transparent layers being built up by deposition, through evaporation in a vacuum.

Rayleigh commented on types of scientists: 'one class of investigators relies mainly on reiterated appeals to experiment to resolve the questions which appear still to be open, while another prefers, with Thomas Young, to base its decisions as far as possible upon deductions from experiments already made by others'. As Rayleigh had a particular regard for Young, this no doubt reflected his own taste for critical analysis, but in his own case it was combined with a most determined devotion to experiment.

Rayleigh himself gave the best description of the kind of scientist he was. When the Order of Merit was instituted in 1902, while his brother-in-law was prime minister, he was made one of the twelve original recipients. At a dinner in their honour he said that 'the only merit of which he was personally conscious was that of having pleased himself by his studies, and any results that may have been due to his researches were owing to the fact that it had been a pleasure to him to become a physicist'.

While Rayleigh was very independent, he did not despise reputation. He wrote of Stokes that 'no one could be more free than he was from anything like an unworthy jealousy of his comrades. Perhaps he would have been the better for a little more wholesome desire for reputation. As happened in the case of Cavendish, too great an indifference in this respect, especially if combined with a morbid dread of mistakes, may easily lead to the withholding of valuable ideas and even to the suppression of elaborate experimental work, which it is often a labour to prepare for publication.'

The background which contributed to these attitudes will now

be examined, before moving on to the consideration of several of
the more important essays of his pioneering mind.

II

INHERITANCE AND ENVIRONMENT

There was virtually no sign of scientific talent among Rayleigh's
paternal ancestors, the Strutt family in Essex. Significantly,
records of the Strutts first appeared about 1660, at the time of the
Restoration, after the Commonwealth had changed the character
of the English social order. The Commonwealth cleared the way
for tradesmen, financiers and industrialists, who drew a large part
of the capital for their enterprises from a profitable agriculture.

The Strutts were corn-millers who steadily prospered in these
conditions after 1660. They acquired many of the water-driven
mills in the neighbourhood of Maldon, obtaining a monopoly
of mechanical power in the region, when this still depended on
water. They invested part of their profits in neighbouring lands,
and built up a modest family estate. Consequently, when steam
superseded water, they were no longer dependent on the milling
of corn by water-power, for they could live on their income from
the rents of their tenant farmers. They were transformed from
tradesmen into country gentlemen. Later Strutts pulled down
water-mills, but remains of one were incorporated in the Strutt
country mansion. The local stream, the Ter, which ran through
the garden had formerly been dammed. The pond was converted
into an ornamental lake. Rayleigh drew upon the water-power
from this former mill-pond in his early researches on hydrodynamics and wave-motion. Thus one of his most characteristic
scientific interests was related to the technical interests of his
earlier ancestors in the long period when they were tradesmen
and craftsmen, making their way up the social scale.

The first Strutt to acquire a position as a country gentleman
was Rayleigh's great-grandfather, John Strutt. He had a house
in Terling, which is pronounced Tarling, in Essex. He bought
the Manor of Terling Place in 1761. His son J. H. Strutt built
the existing mansion in 1820. He constructed a steep flight of
steps to reach the kitchen garden. Rayleigh subsequently used
the musical echo from the echelon of steps to illustrate the action
of a diffraction grating. He used pin-hole photographs of the
steps in his studies on the resolving power of optical instruments,
which were of fundamental importance for the design of the
great modern telescopes at Mount Wilson and elsewhere.

J. H. Strutt sat in Parliament as member for Maldon for forty
years, as a Tory. He married Lady Charlotte Fitzgerald, a
daughter of the Duke of Leinster, and a descendant of a brother
of Robert Boyle. Her own brother, Lord Edward Fitzgerald,
was hanged for his part in the Irish Rebellion of 1798. J. H.
Strutt was quite out of sympathy with Lord Edward. In contrast,
he was offered a peerage by George IV, but requested that it
should be conferred on his wife, which was duly done. Consequently, when his wife died, his son J. J. Strutt inherited the
title though he was still alive. J. J. Strutt became thereby
the second Baron Rayleigh, the title being derived from the
neighbouring Essex market town of that name.

The second Lord Rayleigh devoted himself to an evangelical
form of religion and to the management of his estates, aided by a
formidable bailiff called Charles Richardson. He was an early
user of nitrate as a manure, but Richardson remained uncon-
verted, holding that artificial manures were as harmful to the
land as drugs like morphia to man, and forecast that the advantages they brought in the present would have to be paid for
in the future.

At the age of forty-six, early in 1842, the second Rayleigh
married Clara Elizabeth La Touche Vicars, the seventeen-year-
old daughter of the widow of an engineer officer, several ancestors
of whom had attained distinction as military engineers. It oc-
casioned surprise, for it had been assumed that the widow was the
object of his attentions.

On 12 November in the same year, Lady Rayleigh, at the
age of eighteen, gave birth to her first child, John William Strutt,
who was to become the great scientist. His ancestry through its
Boyles and its Vicars was not without scientific connections, but
these were remote. Like Isaac Newton, John was a seven months'
child, and delicate throughout his infancy and childhood. This
may have strengthened a tendency to solitary interests. He was
observant, but he did not learn to speak until he was three. A
year later he became noticeably enquiring. He showed no early
aptitude for reading, but learned by heart. He could recite the
119th Psalm, and a long poem on the distances of the stars from
the earth.

At the age of ten he went to a technical exhibition and was
much interested in the processes. During the same London visit
he was taken to the House of Lords, where, as the eldest son of a
peer, he was permitted to stand on the steps of the throne. His
mother was mortified to observe from the gallery that when the

Duke of Wellington happened to come in, and seeing the small boy made as if to speak to him, John turned away in shyness.

Rayleigh himself recollected that at the age of three he was much puzzled by what made people laugh. In his mature years he compiled a collection of jokes which he had come across in reading or conversation. They were by no means stunning, and illustrate a facet of his personality. He included several jokes of the class of the American lynchers who found they had killed the wrong man, and felt that some apology was due to the widow. They accordingly sent a deputation to her, whose spokesman said that they must own that this time she had the laugh on them.

Then there was the Southerner who married a Boston girl who died prematurely. Thereafter, whenever he heard the scratch of a slate pencil, he wept. He attributed to Pepper the remark, in lecturing before Queen Victoria that 'the oxygen and hydrogen will now have the honour of combining before your Majesty'. He noted Herbert Spencer's remark to him in the Athenaeum, at the beginning of the Home Rule movement, that he could only congratulate himself on leaving no descendants. He recorded Lord Fisher's remark that it was a mistake not to be on speaking terms with people, because it removed opportunities for saying nasty things.

Rayleigh commented on the lack of sense of humour in others, but his own was somewhat blunt. He was a gentle and kind man, but inclined to be unconscious of how his actions and remarks might affect his hearers. When his gifted son gave his first lecture at the Royal Institution, Rayleigh sat in the middle of the front row, and whenever the lecturer showed signs of faltering, spontaneously helped him out, in his desire that the discourse should be a success. He thereby added considerably to the lecturer's anxiety.

The Strutt household during Rayleigh's infancy was quite uninterested in science. He received no early stimulation in it. He heard, however, a popular science lecture by the local clergyman, in which he was much struck by the experimental demonstration that an egg would sink in ordinary water, but float in salt water.

Owing to his early slowness in learning to speak, and his delicate health, he was given only spasmodic instruction and was not sent to school until he was ten. He seems also to have been prone to accidents. On occasions in his infancy he was nearly killed by falling downstairs, or into the sea.

His father felt that he should receive a classical education, and sought for a preparatory school for Harrow. He laid the problem before the Almighty in his meditations, but the Lord did not make it plain to him how this could best be done, so he decided 'with much prayer and anxiety and too little faith' to send him to Eton, where provision was made for little boys.

John was delighted at the prospect of school, but he stayed at Eton only half a year, and spent part of it in the sanatorium recovering from an attack of smallpox. After he came home he caught whooping cough, so it was decided that he should be withdrawn from Eton, and given a tutor.

A few months later he was sent to a school on Wimbledon Common, where he received what he subsequently regarded as a satisfactory grounding in algebra, trigonometry and statics. His master recorded that teaching him was unusually easy and pleasant. At the age of thirteen he refused to join the school debating society for history, but enthusiastically joined in one for science. In the same letter to his father he mentioned that his Latin master had had knowledge of the notorious poisoner Palmer, when he had been lodging in Rugeley. He had told him that Palmer had named one of his horses 'Goldfinder' and the other 'Strichnine', which seemed to imply that strychnine was his goldfinder.

The Palmer poisoning case attracted considerable scientific attention. The eminent scientist and lawyer, W. R. Grove, the inventor of the fuel cell, was retained to defend him, though without success.

John made pocket money by keeping pigs, which his father thought might interest him in agriculture. He was able to buy scientific apparatus and chemicals with the proceeds, and burnt himself badly with phosphorus.

At fourteen he was sent to Harrow, which, it was thought, might suit his health better. There he found himself compelled to do algebra papers for half his house. He assumed he was being bullied, and it did not occur to him until long afterwards that the others really could not do the algebra. He never quite lost his feeling against those who had bullied him at school.

He did not remain at Harrow much longer than at Eton. He was not strong enough to play football, and was sympathetically excused by the captain of the house, George Trevelyan, who subsequently became an eminent historian. He suffered from his chest, and fears were felt for his life.

At fifteen he was sent to a school at Torquay, which was much more congenial than the others. There he won a set of drawing

instruments on a bet with the future Field-Marshal Lord Gren-
fell. Another fellow-pupil was H. M. Hyndman, who became
the noted socialist propagandist and acquaintance of Karl Marx.
Hyndman remembered Rayleigh as a very popular boy, physically delicate, tall, slender and studious, and not strong enough
to participate in many of the others' activities. Hyndman, who
was specially studying mathematics, said that Rayleigh was already showing high mathematical promise. Rayleigh later said
repeatedly that at that time Hyndman was a better mathematician
than himself.

Many years later, Hyndman attended a fashionable house in
the evening of the day when he had been acquitted of causing a
riot, and the sacking of shops in Piccadilly. The upper classes
were looking at him askance, but when Rayleigh came in, he
went up to Hyndman as soon as he saw him, and congratulated
him on his acquittal. Hyndman treasured his friendliness, for
Rayleigh was conservative, and ultimately 'die-hard', in politics.

John competed for a minor scholarship at Trinity College in
1860, but was unsuccessful. His delicate health and intermittent
schooling had delayed his intellectual training, and he was not
precocious. He later described himself as having been an average
boy, and having wasted much time and energy on studying
classics, from which he had not gained much, never knowing
Greek well enough to appreciate the language and literature.

At about the age of fifteen he became interested in photography.
This interest continued throughout his life; he became a master
in both the art and the science of it. He made superb photographs by the difficult early processes such as wet collodion,
which provided him with considerable training in experimental
manipulation. He began to apply photography to research, and in
1860, when he was seventeen, planned to photograph the eclipse
of the sun in that year. Photography was one of the stimuli of
his researches in optics and wave motion.

He did not neglect outdoor sports altogether, becoming a very
good croquet player and rifle shot. For the latter he used a
muzzle-loader. Many years later, when his son went out shooting
he was expected to use the old muzzle-loader. The young man
complained of the tediousness of loading it, but Rayleigh was
quite out of sympathy with this. He always believed in making
things do, and disliked buying new things. It became a characteristic mark of his scientific work. After he had become famous
he had many scientific visitors, who were astonished at the rough-
ness and provisional character of the apparatus with which he

had made fundamental discoveries, such as that of the rare gas argon. This economy of means marked his intellectual as well as his manual operations, obtaining theoretical results of the first importance by simple but profoundly directed calculations.

His tendency to economy caused him to collect large used envelopes and other lumber in his laboratory. He insisted on burning old wooden apparatus on his study fire, because he had no confidence that anyone else would burn it. He was neat and clean, but wore his clothes until they were threadbare. He horrified people by travelling in a frock coat and brown shoes. On returning from a day's work in London in his later years, he dined with satisfaction at Liverpool Street Station for sixpence, on a bun and a glass of milk. He hated to see food wasted, and insisted that his children should finish their helpings and leave clean plates.

This passion for economy had nothing to do with meanness; he was generous on a grand scale. When he received the Nobel Prize for Physics in 1904, he gave the whole of it to the Cavendish Laboratory for an extension. It was a fundamental characteristic of his mode of thought..

John entered Trinity College in 1861 as a fellow-commoner, the rank accorded to the eldest sons of peers and the wealthy. As such, he dined with the dons, and not with the other undergraduates. The system was subsequently abolished, but he appreciated the social intercourse with the dons and thought it a valuable institution.

His father did not give him an allowance, but paid all bills himself. John Strutt spent very little, and when his younger brothers followed him to Trinity, they found that he had established an embarrassing tradition of economy with their father.

During the summer before he went up to Trinity he was given some special coaching in mathematics, and recommended to place himself under the great teacher E. J. Routh. At Trinity he did not devote all his time to mathematics, for during the long vacations he joined with friends in climbing on the roofs of the college.

It was not immediately evident that Strutt would achieve high distinction as a student. His powers were unfolded through the later and more advanced parts of Routh's instruction. He first found Routh hard to keep up with, or, as he described it, *rough*.

That formidable teacher, who trained twenty-eight Senior Wranglers, was a notoriously exacting critic. Lord Fletcher Moulton, the most successful of all Wranglers, who more than

JOHN WILLIAM STRUTT (LORD RAYLEIGH)
In 1870, aged 28, photographed by himself with a wet collodion plate

doubled the marks of the next man, no less a person than G. H. Darwin, was one of his pupils. He has described how, being nettled by Routh's lack of congratulation on his excellent exercises, he determined to turn in one that was perfect. When Routh handed it back, Moulton read it through eagerly, but the only comment he could find was: 'Fold neatly'.

Rayleigh did not smoke, drank little except tea, which he found stimulating, and worked only seven hours a day, a good deal less than most of the leading men.

Later, when President of the Royal Society, he had to refer to Routh's death. He said that he was indebted to him for instruction and stimulus, and vividly remembered the extent and precision of his knowledge, and the speed with which he dealt with problems put to him. He thought that the earlier editions of Routh's famous book on *Rigid Dynamics* suffered from the then Cambridge vice of regarding mathematics as an end in itself rather than an instrument for the solution of scientific problems. However, he considered the later editions improved and made a first-rate work. Rayleigh said he never had cause to regret any of the time he spent on mathematics at Cambridge, and he believed Routh's scientific merits were underrated.

Besides reading his mathematical texts, such as the books of Todhunter and Routh, he read the current philosophic books on mathematics and science by Boole, Babbage, Whewell and John Herschel; Tyndall on *Mountaineering* and several of Mill's works. Trollope became his favourite novelist.

He began to attend Stokes's lectures on optics in his third year. It was his first close contact with a leading physical scientist. He was excited by Stokes's optical experiments, which had not yet been published.

Strutt sat for his degree examination in 1865. As the year approached he emerged as one of the best students. He began to study the past examination papers and the idiosyncrasies of the examiners. He guessed what some of the questions would be, and worked out improved answers to them. He heard subsequently that one of the examiners had remarked that his proofs were better than those found in the books. He also attended to the swift answering of questions. As his name began with S, he succeeded in answering one more question while the papers of candidates whose names began with earlier letters in the alphabet were being collected.

He was Senior Wrangler, and Alfred Marshall, later the eminent economist, was Second. Rayleigh followed this by winning

3

the First Smith's Prize. He attributed his success to his ability to perceive the essential points in a problem, and attack them immediately.

His son, the fourth Lord Rayleigh, also an eminent physicist, believed that his father's early successes at Cambridge gave him more pleasure than any of his subsequent achievements. These must have seemed beyond reach in his delicate boyhood. His strength grew gradually, and his success consequently gave him more satisfaction.

Rayleigh later became very friendly with William Thomson, Lord Kelvin. They liked to talk over old Cambridge days, and his son recorded that his father once commented on Challis, the unfortunate professor of astronomy who failed to discover *Neptune* after J. C. Adams had provided him with the data, that he had a curious knack of getting hold of the wrong end of the stick. Rayleigh asked Kelvin whether he had ever come across Challis's fallacious law in hydrodynamics. Kelvin replied that Challis had set it in his own examination for the Smith's Prize. Kelvin saw that it was erroneous and did not answer the question. His rival Parkinson, the Senior Wrangler who had defeated him in the tripos, correctly reproduced Challis's erroneous law. Nevertheless Kelvin won the prize.

III

BECOMING A SCIENTIST

After his examination successes, Strutt set about trying to become a scientist, and found it difficult. There were virtually no facilities at Cambridge for experimental work through which systematic training in experimental investigation could be acquired. Stokes was kind and civil, but did not invite him to assist in his experiments, or tell him where appropriate apparatus could be obtained. Strutt had never learned the orthodox methods of using tools. When he showed some of his early self-made apparatus to his scientific son, trained in a later generation, the latter remarked that it would have been no more trouble to have made it properly, to which his father replied that that was no doubt true, but he did not know how to make it what was now called 'properly'.

He competed for a fellowship at Trinity in 1866. The competition was not very severe in that year, and he was elected in spite of his poor knowledge of classics. His father was dubious of the social propriety of his competing, as the eldest son of a peer, for such a thing. After all, the Duke of Devonshire and Lord Lyttleton had not condescended to it.

Among the friends whom he made at this time was Arthur James Balfour, like himself a fellow-commoner at Trinity. Balfour found him sociably disposed, never in a hurry, and always with time at his disposal. They were both players of the game of real tennis.

In 1867–68 he was twice sounded on standing for Parliament, but he was too much under the influence of J. S. Mill to make a conventional Conservative. He indicated that he would stand if he saw strong reason for it, but not otherwise. In later years he was strongly against Home Rule for Ireland. He favoured a passive role for the House of Lords after he had entered it, because, his son thought, it would enable him to give to science the time he would otherwise have to devote to politics. In 1882 he spoke strongly in favour of private capitalist enterprise in the development of the new electrical industry, and against measures which would enable it to be taken over by local authorities.

Returning to his earlier years, he read Clerk Maxwell's great papers on electromagnetism, and on colour vision. He found them very inspiring. He started to correspond with Maxwell in 1870, and sought to cultivate him as much as he could. He met him at British Association meetings, and when he was examining at Cambridge.

He extended Maxwell's observations with the colour top, showing that it was possible to make closer matches than Maxwell had done; and he succeeded in producing a compound yellow from a mixture of red and green. He also developed Maxwell's analogy between the self-induction of electric currents and the inertia of matter in motion.

In December 1870 he received one of Maxwell's wonderful letters, in which the nature of the Second Law of Thermodynamics was discussed. Maxwell propounded in it his famous 'finite being', who could sort out fast from slow molecules of gas, and thus raise or depress the temperature of a gas without doing any work. The being was 'very intelligent and exceedingly quick, with microscopic eyes'. He was like a pointsman on a railway shunting the express along one line and goods along another. He did 'not see why even intelligence might not be dispensed with and the thing made self-acting'. In fact, 'The Second Law of Thermodynamics has the same degree of truth as the statement that if you throw a tumblerful of water into the sea, you cannot get the same tumblerful of water out again.'

Maxwell subsequently published his famous conception of the 'sorting demon' in his *Theory of Heat.*

He also thanked Strutt for suggestions with which he had improved the book he was writing, the classic *Treatise on Electricity and Magnetism.* These improvements had to do with the correction of a sign in an equation, terms in kinetic energy involving products of currents and velocities, and magnetization and its effects in galvanometry.

The remarkable absence of provision for experimental physics at Cambridge, so notably illustrated in Strutt's own early experience, had been painfully clear for a considerable time, and men such as Maxwell had prepared the way for improvement by introducing questions into the mathematical examination, which could not be answered without a knowledge of experimental physics. The movement had led to the Duke of Devonshire, who in his day had been Second Wrangler, First Smith's Prizeman and Eighth Classic, providing funds for the construction of a laboratory. The University founded a chair of experimental physics, bearing the name of the donor's family of Cavendish, to plan and direct the new laboratory. In 1871, the first appointment to the chair was to be made. Strutt wrote to Maxwell, expressing his hope that he would accept it, which, fortunately, he did. Strutt wrote to his father that this would almost certainly happen, and he was relieved to hear it, because some people had suggested that he should be a candidate if Maxwell refused the chair.

Maxwell thanked Strutt for his good wishes, and expressed the hope that he would help in the effort to make Experimental Physics 'bite into our university system which is so continuous and complete without it'. Maxwell commented that it was very trying at first to have to wrench the mind from symbols, and even from experiments on paper to concrete apparatus. It was also possible to become fascinated in making observations without any scientific point. They might be in danger of corrupting the youth in this way, and turn them into Senior Ops instead of Wranglers, that is, into second instead of first class graduates. Maxwell subsequently expressed some of these views in his inaugural lecture.

The limitation of Cambridge men's reading was illustrated by the circumstances through which Rayleigh entered into the study of sound. When examining for a prize at Eton, his fellow examiner told him he ought to learn to read German. Rayleigh asked for a suitable German book to start on, and was recommended Helmholtz's *Lehre von der Tonempfindung.*

His reading of Tyndall's experiments on the imitation of the blueness of the sky, and his own experiments with the Maxwell colour top led him to one of his best-known researches, on the explanation of the blueness of the sky. He had noticed that the matches made with the top were affected by the degree of blueness of the sky at the time. He began to study this blueness directly. He showed that Tyndall's theoretical explanation of his results was in conflict with the wave theory of light, and by a simple application of the method of dimensions, he showed that the intensity of the scattered light was inversely proportional to the fourth power of the wavelength of the incident light. Consequently, the blue light of short wavelength was scattered much more intensely than the light of longer wavelength, so the sky appeared intensely blue. Rayleigh did not determine the nature of the particles causing the scattering in this first research.

Maxwell suggested to him that the scattering might be due to molecules, and that the effect might be utilized to find out more about molecules. Rayleigh returned to the problem twenty-six years later. He extended his analysis very elegantly, and did indeed find that molecules could scatter light sufficiently to produce much of the blueness observed.

Strutt did not allow his early research to disrupt his social life. In 1869 Lord Eustace Cecil, who was M.P. for West Essex, and had been his father's guest at Terling, invited him to dine at his house in London. There he met Evelyn and Eleanor Balfour, the sisters of his Cambridge friend, A. J. Balfour.

Shortly afterwards he was invited by Lord Salisbury to stay at Hatfield, where he found Balfour and his sisters members of the party. After this, he was invited to the Balfour home at Whittingehame in East Lothian, where he went riding, played croquet and participated in picnics. Evelyn Balfour was interested in music, so he lent her Helmholtz's book on sound.

Strutt and Balfour attended the British Association Meeting at Liverpool in 1870. In those days, when science was little organized and men like Maxwell and Strutt were working in their country houses far from universities and scientific institutions, the annual meetings of the Association were an important opportunity for the exchange of ideas. Several of Rayleigh's researches, for example on colour vision and on the determination of electrical constants, were inspired or stimulated by British Association discussions.

In 1875 he was called home from the Meeting of that year to

learn that his wife had borne a son and heir, Robert John Strutt, who also became an eminent scientist. It presently became clear that Rayleigh's son and heir had inherited a generous share of his father's solid scientific genius, with the subtlety and whimsical humour of the Balfours.

The statesman Lord Salisbury, who was an amateur of science and was to give a notable Presidential Address to the British Association in 1894, showed him his laboratory at Hatfield in 1870. Salisbury experimented on magnetism and had obtained puzzling results, and sought Strutt's advice on how they were to be explained. Strutt thought Salisbury too awkward to be a good experimenter.

Then he was invited to stay with the Gladstones. He was impressed by the power of Gladstone's personality, and its striking contrast with his incapacity for scientific thinking. Gladstone was convinced that snow had a peculiar power of penetrating boots, and Strutt could not convince him that it was water from thawed snow, not the snow itself, which penetrated the boots. Gladstone also exhibited his incapacity for seeing various kinds of jokes, and expressed the opinion that Dante, Charlemagne, Innocent III and St Thomas Aquinas were the greatest men of Christian times. Strutt enjoyed quoting this to Nonconformist admirers of Gladstone.

In 1871 Strutt saw more of Balfour and his sisters in London. They used to go to the Royal Institution together, to listen to Tyndall's lectures. He usually sat next to Evelyn Balfour, who by this time had no doubt digested Helmholtz's book. They became engaged in May, and were married in July 1871, Lord Salisbury lending them Hatfield for their honeymoon. Strutt's marriage involved the important consequence that he had to give up his fellowship at Trinity.

He and his wife attended the British Association Meeting at Edinburgh, where Strutt made the acquaintance of William Thomson, who was President for that year.

Early in 1872 Strutt suffered a severe attack of rheumatic fever; it appeared doubtful whether he would survive. Intense medical efforts were made to save him, which gradually succeeded, but both his lungs and joints were affected. When he was able to get up, he was seen to be a physically changed man. He had previously had a very slight, youthful figure, now he appeared middle-aged, and for the remainder of his life suffered from shortness of breath.

The Strutts intended to settle in a house near Terling, and

Strutt asked Maxwell how to set up a laboratory in it. Maxwell gave him characteristically sensible advice. The laboratory had two adjoining rooms, one light and the other dark, for optical experiments. Strutt used it for research on the photographic reproduction of diffraction gratings.

However, he went on a voyage to Egypt, in order to recover his strength after his serious illness. While sailing up the Nile he began his famous treatise on the *Theory of Sound*. He spent the mornings on it in his cabin, and he was able to write the earlier part of it without many references. On the way home, he and his wife were joined by A. J. Balfour and Spencer Lyttleton. The party then went on to tour Greece.

After returning to London, the Strutts stayed with the Balfours at 4 Carlton Gardens. This they continued to do, whenever they were in London, for the rest of their lives, and consequently they never had a London House.

Strutt's father died in the summer of 1873, and Strutt then became the third Lord Rayleigh. He was distressed by his bereavement, and also by the prospect of having to manage the family estates, which he feared would distract him from scientific work. He moved into the family seat at Terling, and provided the house with its own gas works, to supply gas for lighting, and also for Bunsen burners in the laboratory which he again set up. The gas works was stoked by one of the under-gardeners. He never installed an electric plant, largely owing to his distaste for expenditure. He could not bear spending time on making decisions whether to buy this or that.

The laboratory consisted of a converted stable loft, divided into two rooms. One was blackened for optical experiments. This was done with a mixture of lamp-black and beer, invented by the estate's bricklayer. One of the drawbacks of the blackened room was that it was difficult to find things against the dark background.

Electric current was obtained from a battery of Grove cells. Current from five of these was used by Rayleigh in the first isolation of the rare gas argon from atmospheric air.

He had a small workshop with a foot-lathe and a bench with vice. He used the lathe himself before he secured an assistant in 1879.

His laboratory was separated by a thick brick wall from the bedroom where he and his wife slept. In the laboratory on the other side of this wall, he fired pistols and rifles to increase the abruptness of the break in the primary circuit of an induction coil. This was to see whether the lengthening of sparks obtained with the aid of a condenser was due to the increased abruptness which it caused in the break of the circuit.

When he was engaged in his investigation of how the origin of a sound is located by the hearer's pair of ears, a hole was made in the wall, so that the listening could be done through tubes carried into the bedroom, which was free from stray sounds. This research became of military importance in the First World War, when methods were developed for locating submarines by listening to their noises.

Rayleigh was elected a Fellow of the Royal Society in 1873. He continued to live at Terling from 1874 until 1879. Also in 1874, he became interested in spiritualism, through his acquaintance with, and admiration for the work of, Sir William Crookes. Henry Sidgwick, F. W. H. Myers and other friends at Trinity, like many able people in the middle of the nineteenth century, were also interested in it. Rayleigh never became a convinced believer, but he held that it ought to be seriously investigated, for if its claims proved to be true, these would be far more important than accepted science. He held this view until the end of his life. He delivered the Presidential Address to the Society for Psychical Research in 1919, in the month before he died, which he concluded by saying that while some members of the Society had outstripped him in conviction, he had never felt any doubt as to the importance of the work the Society had carried out over many years.

Attempts were made in 1875 by Rayleigh's Conservative friends to induce him to enter politics, by seconding an Address in the House of Lords. He did this, but without enthusiasm. In the following year he spoke with more interest on the regulation of physiological experiments on animals, at the suggestion of his gifted brother-in-law F. M. Balfour, whose researches notably advanced embryology. He was unfortunately killed in 1882, in a climbing accident in the Alps.

In 1872, at the age of twenty-nine, Rayleigh had already served on a Royal Commission of the type very fashionable nearly a century later, on the financial resources of the universities and colleges of Oxford and Cambridge. He became one of the commissioners appointed in 1877 to make new statutes for them.

During this period Rayleigh met Beauchamp Tower, while on a visit to an Essex country house. Tower was an engineer who had been trained by William Froude, the eminent naval architect and investigator of fluid motion, who was a younger brother of the historian J. A. Froude. Rayleigh invited Tower to become his assistant at Terling. They were soon busy constructing a hydraulic laboratory in the grounds, using the water-power from the converted old mill-pond for experiments on a considerable scale. One of these was to confirm a calculation by Rayleigh that the pressure in the middle of the plane of a slit-shaped aperture would be 0·58 of the head of water producing the jet. Tower was followed as an assistant by Arnulph Mallock, who was a relative of William Froude and also had been trained by him. But Rayleigh found that Tower and Mallock were not the kind of assistants he needed; a mechanic was what he really required. After they left he worked without an assistant, which he subsequently regretted.

In 1876 he was invited to be an examiner for the Cambridge Mathematical Tripos, probably on the suggestion of Clerk Maxwell. He invited the other examiners to Terling to discuss the questions. This academic duty prevented him from being at Hatfield on the occasion of the political reconciliation between Lord Salisbury and Disraeli.

As an examiner Rayleigh set questions which involved points of principle. They were generally not difficult, but in giving marks he insisted that they should be properly answered.

Between 1871 and 1879 Rayleigh devoted much effort to his research on the making of diffraction gratings by micro-photography. A large model grating was photographed on a much reduced scale. In the course of this, he anticipated by four years Soret's invention of zone plates, but did not publish it. He succeeded in copying glass gratings by contact printing with the aid of the very fine-grained photographic emulsions then in use. He gave copies to his friends, one of whom was H. C. Sorby, who used his in making classical studies of the absorption spectra of natural colouring matters. Rayleigh observed that the first spectra in some of his copies were brighter than the central image, and deduced from this a principle which Michelson developed in his echelon grating.

The most important effect of these researches was, however, theoretical. They directed his attention to the theory of the resolving power of spectroscopes, a matter of major importance, as spectroscopic analysis and measurement are fundamental for many branches of science. The performance of modern astronomical spectroscopy, in which the displacement of spectral lines is used to measure the speed of movement of astronomical bodies, and in particular very distant nebulae, rests on Rayleigh's work.

3*

When Rayleigh inherited his estates, agriculture was prosperous, owing to the contemporary trade boom. Consumption had risen, and rents were high. The immediate prospect before him was that of a well-to-do country gentleman. He had visions of creating a considerable private scientific research institution at Terling, with a staff of several assistants. However, the situation began to change almost immediately, with the world recession in trade which started in 1874. The purchasing power of the British industrial population fell, and in the United States the recession drove urban workers into the virgin lands, stimulating the production of cheap wheat. The agricultural situation in Essex was made still worse by a succession of bad seasons.

Rayleigh found himself hard up. Tenants could not pay their rents and left. New tenants did not come forward, so Rayleigh was compelled to begin cultivating the untenanted farms with his own capital. When he inherited the estate he had grudged the time he had had to take from science in order to attend to it. He did not at first sympathize with his tenants' difficulties, though he presently learned to understand them better, gradually accumulating a considerable knowledge of agriculture. His younger brother, after leaving Cambridge, was trained in farm management, and after 1876 undertook the management of the estate.

Meanwhile, in the worsening economic conditions, Rayleigh continued with his treatise on *The Theory of Sound*. Maxwell encouraged him with the observation that there was only one good book on the subject, and that was by Helmholtz, 'who is sound not because he is German but because he is Helmholtz'.

Rayleigh wrote the manuscript on the backs of Cambridge examination papers, a kind of economy very characteristic of him, and also of Charles Darwin, who wrote his books on the backs of old manuscripts. The book was published in 1877 and reviewed in *Nature* by Helmholtz, who compared it with Thomson and Tait's *Treatise on Natural Philosophy*.

Then came the disastrous illness and premature death of Maxwell in 1879. Cambridge was again looking for a Cavendish professor of experimental physics, and the chair was again refused by Sir William Thomson. Rayleigh was now the obvious candidate. His brother-in-law, the embryologist F. M. Balfour, told him his acceptance was necessary to the welfare of the university. Cambridge men expressed the hope that he would take it.

Rayleigh informed his mother that neither he nor his wife much liked the prospect of living in Cambridge, but a few years there might see them through the agricultural depression. He was no doubt also influenced by the prospect of more scientific equipment and assistance for research, which he was not able to buy for himself.

So Rayleigh in 1879 became the second Cavendish professor of experimental physics, and retained the chair until 1884, when his personal resources had improved, and suitable candidates to succeed him had appeared.

Economic pressure appears to have been the chief force in causing him to accept this scientific post which has since become so famous. The effect of the opening-up of the wheat lands in the American Middle West was a factor in this pressure, and thus had its part in causing Rayleigh to cease being an amateur and become, for a period, a professional scientist.

IV

CAVENDISH PROFESSOR

Rayleigh found the Cavendish Laboratory very ill-equipped with apparatus. It had been supposed that the Duke of Devonshire, besides providing the building, had also provided all necessary apparatus. Maxwell had felt that there was a limit to the number of bills that could be sent to the Duke, so after a time no more were sent. The existing equipment became out of date, and inadequate for new experiments conceived long after it had been bought.

Rayleigh immediately created a fund for apparatus, which he started with £500 of his own money, though he was not well off at the time. The Duke gave a further £500, and another £500 was raised from other donors. Rayleigh also gave the fees paid by the students to the professor to the equipment fund.

He intended to start classes in experimental physics, for which he required numbers of simple instruments. These had not yet become articles of commerce, and could not be bought in the market. The professor of engineering helped to make some of them.

Nor was there any technical assistance. Maxwell had had only one assistant, who was not well, and soon died. Rayleigh advertised for a new assistant, and chose George Gordon, a Liverpool shipwright, for the post. Gordon was a rough but effective mechanic, which suited Rayleigh, who had no use for 'finish', and only wanted apparatus that would work. When Gordon began in the Cavendish, he adopted what he considered to be a superior accent. Rayleigh wore this down by personally speaking slang to him. Gordon became Rayleigh's lifelong assistant.

Rayleigh found the experimental teaching inadequate, and far behind that provided by Helmholtz for his students in Germany. Maxwell had been too occupied and too ill to devote much time to it himself. There had been no system of instruction. Students came and went as they wished. Rayleigh secured the appointment of R. T. Glazebrook and W. N. Shaw as demonstrators, and promoted a systematic course of experimental instruction which they worked out.

Mrs Henry Sidgwick said that his success in inspiring others to work, both for themselves and for him, was due to his gentleness and sympathetic interest. He rarely expressed annoyance, and he never pushed himself forward or exhibited personal ambition. She thought him an excellent teacher and lecturer, who did a great deal to develop the Cavendish as a university laboratory. He was particularly impressive in his early reflections on a new problem; his hearers could then see how his mind tended to pierce at once to its essence.

Though Rayleigh was generally Conservative in his social attitude, he initiated the opening of the classes of the Cavendish Laboratory to women, on equal terms with men. This was at the comparatively early date of 1882. His sister-in-law and collaborator, Mrs Sidgwick, was an ardent feminist and pioneer of higher education for women. She was associated with both of the women's colleges in Cambridge, having a part in the founding of Girton, and becoming Principal of Newnham. Rayleigh only partially agreed with these developments, but he respected her opinions.

Besides systematic teaching, Rayleigh also sought to identify the Laboratory with an extensive research, in which a number of men could be brought to co-operate with a common object. He chose the redetermination of the electrical standards for this purpose. The advance of electrical science, and the beginning of electrical engineering required that units of electrical measurement such as the ohm, volt and ampere should be known to a high degree of accuracy. This was necessary for research and for economic reasons. When electrical energy became an article of commerce, and was to be sold in large quantities, buyers and sellers must know exactly how much they are dealing with in their transactions. The values for the electrical units which were obtained in the Cavendish under Rayleigh were far more accurate than those previously known.

Among the individual researches proceeding in the Cavendish in Rayleigh's time were comparisons of electrical resistances by J. A. Fleming. Glazebrook worked on optics, Shaw on meteorology, and Horace and George Darwin attempted to detect the disturbance of gravity by the moon.

Rayleigh usually had a lecture audience of about sixteen. J. J. Thomson was one of his students. J. J. measured the ratio of the electrostatic and electromagnetic units, a research arising naturally out of the general research on electrical units. Rayleigh had designed the apparatus and had intended to use it, but on putting it into the hands of this student, he found that no further intervention by himself was necessary.

At Cambridge Raleigh lived in a comparatively small house in Station Road. He worked at home in the mornings, and in the afternoon his wife drove him to the laboratory in an open carriage drawn by a pair of ponies. Tea was taken in his room, and others working in the laboratory sometimes came in. A teapot with a broken spout was used; Lady Rayleigh suggested that it should be replaced, but it was not.

The Rayleighs, the Sidgwicks and Frank and Gerald Balfour used to dine together once a week. At that time, the Sidgwicks and the Balfours were inclined to be Radicals, whereas Rayleigh was always politically on the Right.

In 1882–83 he had a recurrence of rheumatic illness. He feared that he would become a cripple. Ultimately, he took the waters at Bath. After this, the illness disappeared, and never returned.

Later in 1884 he presided at the Meeting of the British Association at Montreal, the first to be held outside the United Kingdom. He was only forty-two. Arthur Balfour wrote to him that his responsibilities were appalling, for he represented 'not only Science but England and the Peerage!'.

In his Presidential Address he spoke on the rise of the new electrical industry, and he reviewed the progress of physics. He expressed himself strongly in favour of the teaching of modern languages. He was not opposed to Latin and Greek for those who could learn them well, but he believed that the majority could learn modern languages more easily, and would find them far more useful.

After he returned to England he resigned from the Cavendish chair. During the five years of his professorship he published sixty papers, besides developing the Laboratory and the teaching of experimental physics. He did not feel that he could continue to work at this rate, and there were now several possible successors on the horizon. The electors in 1884 chose as the third Cavendish professor J. J. Thomson, who was then twenty-eight years of age.

V

ESCAPE FROM PROFESSIONALISM

When Rayleigh returned to the family seat at Terling in 1884, he and his wife received a feudal welcome. A deputation of the villagers at the gates expressed their joy at their resumption of residence. The church bells were rung, and the houses decorated with illuminations. A large crowd assembled at the house to do, as it were, homage.

Such was the apparent social background during the next ten years, in which one of the most significant achievements of modern science was brought to fruition, the discovery of argon and the inert gases. This was the first of the breaks with classical science which inaugurated the modern era.

Argon was a concrete substance of a new type, a new element apparently without chemical properties. It was a material fact, the significance of which did not depend on interpretation, like the Michelson-Morley experiment. Its discovery was swiftly followed by that of X-rays, radioactivity, the quantum theory and relativity.

The discovery of argon undermined the old physical certainties and beliefs, and prepared the scientific world to look at the properties of matter with a radically open mind.

The feudality of the celebrations at Terling was, of course, only superficial. One of the reasons for the return of the Rayleighs was that their estates promised to become more profitable. However, improvement was slow, and in 1886 Rayleigh thought of becoming a candidate for a new chair of physics at the Royal College of Science in London. He told William Thomson that it was doubtful whether he would be able to stay at Terling unless farming improved.

He and his brother jointly developed the farming, on the basis that he provided the capital and his brother the skill. In 1879 they had farmed only 1,000 of their acres; by 1892 the area had risen to 6,000. About 1885 the low price of wheat, the main East Anglian crop, had directed their attention to dairy farming. Terling was near London, which would be a convenient market for milk. They started with about a dozen cows. The herd was gradually increased, until in 1919 there were 800, with 60 milkers.

They opened their own shops, 'Lord Rayleigh's Dairies', the first of which was in Great Russell Street, London, near the British Museum. The aim was to cut out the middlemen. They opened seven more in different parts of London.

By the end of the century the income from the estate was comfortable, and during the First World War the Rayleighs became prosperous. Rayleigh attended to the formulation of policy for the estates, but once this had been properly laid down, he was glad to leave the practical conduct to other members of the family, and concentrated on science.

He kept his hand in in the professional world of science, without engaging himself deeply, by accepting the professorship of natural philosophy at the Royal Institution in 1887, after the retirement of Tyndall. The duties involved giving only seven lectures a year, and laboratory facilities for research were available. Rayleigh stayed with A. J. Balfour when he came up to London to prepare and deliver the lectures.

At home Rayleigh concentrated on those problems and studies which interested him most. Maxwell had said in his introductory lecture at Cambridge in 1871 that 'the history of science shows that even during the phase of her progress in which she devotes herself to improving the accuracy of the numerical measurement of quantities with which she has long been familiar, she is preparing the materials for the subjugation of the new regions, which would have remained unknown if she had been contented with the rough methods of her early pioneers. I might bring forward instances gathered from every branch of science, shewing how the labour of careful measurement has been rewarded by the discovery of new fields of research, and by the development of new scientific ideas.'

Rayleigh probably had Maxwell's comment in mind when he mentioned in an address to the British Association in 1882 his intention of extending the systematic redetermination of the fundamental units of nature from electrical to chemical science. Prout's law or rule, that the atomic weights are fairly exact multiples of that of hydrogen could hardly be fortuitous. It was not sufficient to accept without criticism the atomic weights that had been determined by experiment. One must 'reprobate strongly the importation of a priori views into the considerations of the question'.

Experimental measurements had their imperfections, and it might be that the accepted figures were inaccurate. The subject was eminently suitable for further research, and the question might be settled by the present generation. The redetermination of the densities of the principal gases was now desirable, and he had himself begun to make some preparations for the under-taking.

Rayleigh discovered that the great experimenter Regnault, who had carried out the classical determinations of the densities of gases forty years before, had indeed made a small error, by assuming that the volume of a glass sphere filled with gas under pressure was the same as when it was empty. This was one of the most striking examples of Rayleigh's intellectual process in research. He looked at information of fundamental importance, but so commonplace that few could bring a critical mind to bear on it persistently. He saw that this commonplace information was so fundamental that it was necessary to be certain that it was correct. When the experiments upon which it was based were examined, the evidence for it was found to be much slenderer than had been supposed.

While still at Cambridge he had started a series of exact measurements of the density of hydrogen, by the careful weigh-ing of glass spheres filled with the gas. The chief experimental error arose from the difficulty of obtaining pure hydrogen gas. Traces of oxygen or nitrogen caused comparatively big errors, as they are much denser than hydrogen.

Rayleigh arranged for his assistant George Gordon to accom-pany him to Terling, to help with these tedious and exacting measurements. He dried the air in the small chamber in which the weighings were made by placing a well-dried blanket within it, a device attributed to Clerk Maxwell. Rayleigh found that the blanket increased by as much as 2lb in weight by absorbing moisture from the air.

After about ten years of work, involving the patient removal of one small cause of error after another, Rayleigh obtained figures which proved that the atomic weight of oxygen was definitely less than sixteen times that of hydrogen.

To most scientists this negative result would have been dis-couraging, and a strong reason for changing to a more promising line of research. However, Rayleigh was not deflected from his plan of enquiry into fundamentals. He proceeded to measure the density of nitrogen gas. He prepared various specimens from the atmosphere, and found his measurements of their densities agreed very well among themselves.

Again, he did not stop at this definite result. He decided to obtain nitrogen from some source other than the atmosphere. He consulted the chemist Sir William Ramsay, who suggested a convenient method, in which the nitrogen was derived in part from ammonia. Rayleigh found that this nitrogen was lighter by one part in a thousand than nitrogen from the air.

He was puzzled and annoyed by the discrepancy, which he thought might be due to lack of skill as a chemist. 'One's instinct at first is to try and get rid of a discrepancy, but I believe that experience shows such an endeavor to be a mistake . . .' He wrote a letter to *Nature* describing his results, with the idea that someone with more experience in chemical analysis might help to clear up the contradiction.

In the spring of 1894, when Rayleigh came to deliver his lectures at the Royal Institution as professor of natural philosophy, he discussed the discrepancy with Sir James Dewar, the Director of the Laboratories there. Dewar recommended him to read Henry Cavendish's experiments on the composition of the atmosphere published in 1799. Cavendish had attempted to remove the nitrogen from a specimen of air by sustained electric sparking, and had found that no matter how long the sparking was continued, a bubble remained which was not more than $\frac{1}{120}$ part of the whole of the nitrogen. He had envisaged the possibility of more than one kind of nitrogen, and had in fact isolated the rare gas argon, though of course he did not realize this. His experiment was, in any case, sufficiently marvellous.

Rayleigh repeated Cavendish's experiment with an improved apparatus which removed the nitrogen thirty times faster than Cavendish's had done. Even then, it was extremely tedious. Admiration for Cavendish's genius rose still higher.

Following Rayleigh's publication of the discrepancy in the density of nitrogen, Ramsey had looked into it for himself, and independently came to the conclusion that it was a new kind of chemically inert gas. He and his chemical colleagues, with their great skill as analysts, presently discovered other inert gases in the atmosphere, forming a whole new group of chemical elements.

Rayleigh announced his discovery at the Meeting of the British Association at Oxford in 1894. The president in that year was Lord Salisbury, who was stimulated by Rayleigh's work to make far-sighted speculations about the implications of the periodic table of the elements, and the evolution of matter.

Meanwhile, the announcement of the discovery of argon was received with much incredulity, not only in Germany, France and other countries, but also in Britain, which annoyed Rayleigh.

By 1895, however, the reality of the discovery had become incontrovertible and excited wide public as well as scientific interest. Its implications were vast. Without the discovery of the rare gases, Rutherford and Soddy might not have been able to work out their revolutionary theory of radioactive disintegration.

In the engineering field, the fixation of nitrogen by the electric arc process, with its implications of unlimited supplies of nitrogen compounds for agricultural fertilizers and explosives, might not have been developed if Rayleigh's researches had not revived interest in Cavendish's electrical method for removing nitrogen from the atmosphere.

The respective parts of Rayleigh and Ramsay in the discovery of the inert gases became a subject of some controversy. Rayleigh's complete openness had perhaps fostered it. Unlike so many of the professionals, he had not become secretive when he had recognized that he had discovered a fact of fundamental importance. Rayleigh was pre-eminent in the intellectual part of the discovery. The situation was solved perfectly by their collaborating in the classical paper on the great discovery, and the simultaneous award of the Nobel Prizes for Physics and Chemistry to Rayleigh and Ramsay respectively in 1904.

VI

THE PIONEERING MIND

The modern development of aviation may be said to start from a letter Rayleigh published in *Nature* in 1883, in which he showed how a bird might maintain itself in the air without doing muscular work. In 1895 Otto Lilienthal wrote to Rayleigh that after reading this letter he had been constantly engaged in experimental research on long-distance gliding. Lilienthal made notable progress, and it was his work which aroused the interest of the Wright brothers.

Rayleigh encouraged the young scientist and American naval cadet A. A. Michelson, to resume and persevere with his famous experiments on the speed of light. Michelson did so, and provided the starting-point from which Einstein created the theory of relativity.

Again, Clerk Maxwell threw out the first hint that the phenomena of radiation from molecules might not be explicable by Newtonian mechanics. This was made more definite by Rayleigh in 1897, when in a discussion of the theory of spectra he gave reasons why it was to be doubted 'whether the analogue of radiating bodies is to be sought at all in ordinary mechanical or acoustical systems vibrating about equilibrium'. Nernst said that Rayleigh was the first to place his finger, as it were, 'on the open wound in theoretical physics', which was healed by Planck's proposal of the quantum of energy.

Rayleigh never succeeded in accepting Planck's theory completely. In 1911 he said: 'Of course I have nothing against following out the consequences of the [quantum] theory of energy—a procedure which has already in the hands of able men led to some interesting conclusions. But I have a difficulty in accepting it as a picture of what actually takes place.' He was then sixty-nine. His mind had been formed in the era of fluid and material models of natural phenomena, and he was too old to dispense with them. Yet, though he had difficulty in accepting the quantum theory, his mathematical methods of handling physical problems were utilized by his successors in creating modern quantum mechanics.

Rayleigh's approach to the use of mathematics in physical research was influenced by the methods of Lagrange, which are particularly useful in the investigation of vibrations and wave-motions. His interest in the scattering of light concentrated his attention on the mathematical handling of the interactions between waves and particles. In 1932 Niels Bohr adopted Rayleigh's mathematical treatment of the scattering of light by particles to show why interactions between neutrons and electrons are so rare, which in turn explained why the neutrons had remained for so long undiscovered.

Rayleigh investigated such problems as the location of the sources of sounds by the ears, and the difficulty of seeing small objects in the dark. He found that in the dark he became temporarily short-sighted. He drew attention to the probable difference between the colour senses of men and insects.

He remarked in 1884 'how many of the playthings of our childhood give rise to questions of the deepest scientific interest', instancing the top, the kite and soap bubbles.

Rayleigh had an inventive strain. He made an improvement in Grove's fuel cell, now so important in space research and the possible replacement of the petrol by the electrically driven motor-car. He increased its output by using platinum gauze instead of platinum plates, and obtained a considerable current using coal gas as fuel.

He advanced the mathematical analysis of the fundamental discoveries of fluid flow, made by Osborne Reynolds. Rayleigh's insight into both hydrodynamics and thermodynamics enabled him to suggest in 1898 that the liquefaction of gases might be achieved most efficiently by a turbine. 'It seems to me that the future may bring great developments in this direction and that it may thus be possible to liquefy even hydrogen in one operation . . .' This idea has been realized by Kapitza and others, and forms one of the most remarkable technical advances in low temperature physics.

His comments on scientific engineering in his Presidential Address to the British Association in 1884 were aptly expressed and far-sighted. He gave a striking description of W. Siemens's regenerative furnace, in which heat is stored in bricks and released subsequently for preheating, on the same principle as the electric storage heaters of today.

His papers are generally short, lucid, and often with the minimum of formulae. They are written in very clear good English, and many of them could be read by non-specialists. These features made Rayleigh's work stimulating to a wide range of workers in many different subjects. He did not follow fashion, but investigated those things that caught his attention, whatever they might be. His unconcerned style and choice of subjects owed something to his social situation. He considered he had no need to bother much about what other people were doing. His style is free from any academic or professional strain.

Rayleigh revealed much about his own scientific mind in his many comments on his scientific hero, Thomas Young. One of his most memorable lectures was on Young, in the centenary celebrations of the Royal Institution. Young calculated the range of molecular forces by comparing the surface tension with the tensile strength, and concluded that it must be about $\frac{1}{250}$ millionth of an inch, and deduced that the diameter of a molecule must be 'between the two-thousand and the ten-thousand millionth of an inch'. This kind of fundamental reasoning, with its remarkable results, appealed profoundly to Rayleigh.

Rayleigh virtually anticipated the Raman effect, thirty years before Raman demonstrated it in 1928. He proposed in 1887 the method of colour photography, which G. Lippmann carried out. Both Raman and Lippmann received Nobel prizes for their discoveries. In 1895, Rayleigh referred to the possibility that argon, the inert gas, might be found to react with fluorine. He had not tried it, because the chemical technique was too difficult. In 1961 the existence of fluorine compounds of argon and xenon was demonstrated.

His researches into the properties of electrical circuits, such as coupled circuits, proved long after to be of great importance in developing modern electronics. His calculations on oscillations in clouds of electrified particles, published in 1906, are used now in investigating the interruption of radio communication between astronauts and the ground, when they are coming down through the ionosphere on returning to the earth. His mathematical theory of the whispering gallery in acoustics has been adapted in studying the effect of nuclear explosions on the ionosphere.

Rayleigh's inclination to allow his intellectual imagination to rove over the whole of physical nature led him to consider how a mathematical method worked out to solve a problem in one branch of physics could be applied in others. When he had solved a problem in, say, the theory of sound, he was apt to look for the analogous problems in optics, hydrodynamics and electricity.

His mind worked so well that he often sent the original solution, just as he had written it out for the first time, straight to the journal for publication. Nevertheless, his mind was not swift and facile. He said that he never understood another person's experiment when it was explained to him for the first time.

Rayleigh expressed significant thoughts on the general problems of science, besides the methods of solving physical problems. He referred in 1874 to the growing problem of the communication of scientific knowledge, in a review of Todhunter's *History of the Mathematical Theories of Attraction and the Figure of the Earth*. He said that: 'Scientific men must often experience a feeling not far removed from alarm, when we contemplate the flood of new knowledge which each year brings with it. New societies spring into existence, with their Proceedings and their Transactions, laden with the latest discoveries, and new journals continually appear in response to the growing demand for popular science. Every year the additions to the common stock of knowledge become more bulky if not more valuable; and one is impelled to ask, Where is this to end? Most students of science who desire something more than a general knowledge, feel that their powers of acquisition and retention are already severely taxed. It would seem that any considerable addition to the burden of existing information would make it almost intolerable . . .'

Rayleigh saw the solution to this in new fundamental discoveries that resumed vast areas of knowledge in a compact form; simple formulae based on profound ideas. True progress consisted as much in complete assimilation of what was already known, as in discovering new things.

Rayleigh's life and work may be regarded as one of the major products of British imperial culture. He was born in the British ruling class at the height of British power, and exemplified some of its most outstanding qualities, and also some of its limitations. He conceived his cultural duty in individual terms. He worked largely by himself, and with the simplest of materials.

J. J. Thomson remarked after a visit to his laboratory at Terling in the 1890's that everything seemed to be fastened together with 'string and sealing wax'. His phrase has since become the classic description of the early period of modern experimental physics. Rayleigh had little taste for team work, though his research on the determination of the electrical units shows that he considered it necessary, and would participate in it as a social duty.

According to C. R. Strutt, after the death of his father, Robert Strutt the fourth Lord Rayleigh, none of the obvious British institutions, such as the University of Cambridge, Trinity College, and the Royal Society or the Royal Institution exhibited interest in acquiring the unpublished working papers of his grandfather and father. Consequently, these were auctioned. The most important of them were purchased ultimately by the U.S. Air Force, which created special Rayleigh Archives at their Research Laboratory at Bedford in Massachusetts.

When they were dedicated on 30 March 1966, Brigadier General Ernest A. Pinson, the Commander of the U.S.A.F. Aerospace Research, remarked that the establishment of these archives was an event almost without precedent in a military research laboratory. He described it as marking in a special sense 'the coming of age of the management of science by the Air Force'. He pointed out that the scientific administrator who 'does not honor the distinct set of values of the community of science', who looks on science merely as a resource from which ideas and information for technological development may be mined, would defeat his own aims. An archival collection was a trust to preserve things of value not only for one organization or nation, but for all mankind. The inauguration showed that the U.S. Air Force was no longer an intruder in science, but a fully participating member in the scientific community. It showed that the U.S. Air Force and science were dedicated to mutual values.

Brigadier General Pinson's interesting comment on this highly significant acquisition of the Rayleigh archives is a striking demonstration of how the scientific achievements of the old British are being taken over by the new American imperialism.

VII

A MAGISTERIAL SCIENTIST

Rayleigh's Conservative political friends tried to involve him in conventional politics because of his scientific prestige. He was inveigled into such posts as the Lord-Lieutenancy of Essex, and then regretted the time spent on local functions, which he felt had been stolen from science.

He was drawn into public work as a scientific adviser. Two of his most influential activities were as Chairman of the Committee to consider the estabishment of the National Physical Laboratory, and Chairman of the Government's Explosives Committee. He participated in the negotiations for Bushy Park as the head-quarters of the National Physical Laboratory, and the choice of R. T. Glazebrook as its first Director.

Glazebrook said that Rayleigh's most important service subsequently was the influence he was able to bring to bear. He was trusted by everyone in matters both of science and administration. He could approach ministers and high officials with ease. His brother-in-law A. J. Balfour was prime minister, and H. H. Asquith was one of his personal friends. When he retired from the chairmanship of the executive committee in 1919 he had presided at 165 out of its 185 meetings in his period. He had seen the institution grow from a laboratory with a staff of 15 in 1901, and an annual expenditure of £8,000 to one of 400, with an expenditure of £100,000.

His work as chairman of the Government's Explosives Committee was yet more important, though the details of it have still not been published. The war in South Africa had revealed serious erosion in the British artillery, due especially to unsatisfactory propellant explosives. Lord Landsdowne and Lord Goschen at the War Office and the Admiralty were disturbed by the situation. Landsdowne happened to meet R. B. Haldane in a railway compartment, and conversation turned to this problem. Haldane suggested that a scientific committee should be set up to investigate it, on the lines of a committee in France under the eminent chemist Berthelot. Haldane suggested that Rayleigh should be chairman.

Landsdowne pressed Rayleigh to accept, which he did. The other members were Sir Andrew Noble, chairman of Armstrongs, Sir William Roberts-Austen, Chemist to the Mint, and Sir William Crookes, with Captain Tulloch as secretary. Haldane,

Crookes and Roberts-Austen spent a week-end at Terling to discuss their prodecure.

The committee was in being for five years, and accomplished much work, before it was dissolved. The full importance of the committee in the development of the relations between science and the state in Britain was not generally known until fifty years after it had been dissolved, when the late Sir Henry Tizard referred to it in his Haldane Lecture in 1955. He said that it was the first definite move to use science in the modern manner in British military affairs.

The committee investigated such problems as the best shape of propellant charges. Rayleigh himself worked on this, but apparently his results were not adopted. It was said that the committee introduced the use of trinitrotoluene as a high explosive, and made extensive researches on the best ways of keeping high explosives under tropical conditions.

Rayleigh's service as chairman of the Advisory Committee on Aeronautical Research was also of prime importance for the public. This committee, formed on Haldane's initiative in 1909, was the parent of the government research in aeronautics, which proved of decisive importance in the Second World War. A major part of its work was on the experimental foundation of aerodynamics, based on the resistance of models in streams of air. Rayleigh himself contributed to the application of the theory of dynamical similarity, which was one of his subjects of research, to the deduction of an aircraft's resistance to the air, from the resistance of its model. He took the chair at 96 of the committee's 126 meetings.

In 1901 Rayleigh's brother-in-law Gerald Balfour, then President of the Board of Trade, offered him the post of Chief Gas Examiner. The work was light and the pay good, and at first Rayleigh feared to accept it, as it might have laid him open to charges of nepotism. However, he did accept, and no trouble arose on that score. Rayleigh greatly admired the ingenuity with which the directors of certain gas companies fought against the policy of their workers' trade union.

He was appointed chairman of a committee in 1901 to investigate the vibration in houses caused by the new Central London tube. They found that it was due to bad design of the electric locomotives. Rayleigh's former assistant Arnulph Mallock was employed to measure the vibrations in the houses and tunnels, arising from the locomotives, irregularities in the lines and wheels, and other causes.

In practical invention Rayleigh's insight was less sure than in science. When the newly-invented telephone was demonstrated to him in 1882, he was deeply impressed by its simplicity and perfection of performance, but he thought it 'not likely to come into practical use'.

He succeeded Tyndall as scientific adviser to Trinity House, and supervised much work on fog-horns. It might have been expected that his mastery of the theory of sound would have made this work particularly fruitful, but it was not very successful. It was development rather than research, and Rayleigh's weakness in this direction was an example of the British research and development effort in general.

Rayleigh began the publication of his collected papers in 1899, on the initiative of the Cambridge University Press. As his son subsequently remarked, a number of distinguished scientists had never done this; it made their work difficult to find, and was 'a serious detriment to science'.

Four more volumes appeared during the next thirteen years, and the sixth and final volume was published posthumously in 1920. When Rayleigh proposed to issue his works under the motto: 'The works of the Lord are great, sought out of all them that have pleasure therein', the Cambridge University Press at first demurred to it, on the ground that there might be misunderstanding about which Lord was being referred to. Another biblical quotation which Rayleigh used as a motto was from *Wisdom* XI.20: 'Thou hast ordered all things in measure and number and weight.'

The six volumes containing his 446 papers, republished under his personal supervision, were a splendid monument of achievement. He was a concise writer, besides being an original and stimulating discoverer over an immense range of physical science. He was not facile in writing or research. He admired Faraday's capacity for thinking in front of his apparatus, and remarked that he could not do that himself. When he came to a difficulty, he had to stop, go away and think it over. He was not apt at giving off-hand judgments. He did not quite agree with the usual rating of Faraday as a scientific conceptual thinker. He considered his views on electrolysis less clear than might have been expected of him.

Rayleigh did not have much confidence in the application of mathematical statistics to the interpretation of observations. He thought it a good thing to learn the statistical theory of errors of observation, but forget it afterwards.

Larmor noted Rayleigh's 'caution in theoretical speculation, and his gentleness in criticism. He was most anxious that ability, of whatever kind, should not be discouraged or overlooked.' Rayleigh discovered J. J. Waterston's neglected paper of 1845 in the archives of the Royal Society, in which the work of Joule, Clausius and Maxwell on the kinetic theory of gases had been anticipated by ten to fifteen years. He caused enquiries to be made. Waterston had been a Scottish civil engineer and teacher in the navy of the East India Company. The Society's referee had described the paper as 'nothing but nonsense, unfit even for reading before the Society'. Rayleigh elicited that Waterston had retired to Edinburgh in 1856. 'He was of a most social, kind disposition, enjoying the society of young people', but avoiding that of scientists. He knew what the Royal Society had thought of his work, and in his comments on the Royal Society 'he returned the compliment in no measured terms'. Rayleigh saw to it that, after half a century, the Royal Society did publish the great paper.

Rayleigh was very cautious in dismissing any widely held belief as being without foundation. It was easy to arouse his interest in dubious phenomena, but very difficult to secure his final opinion on them. He was easy to impress, but difficult to convince. He said that if he had difficulty in finding water, he would certainly employ a water-diviner. He had a deep sense of the mystery of existence, and did not believe science was approaching a solution of them. He said to his son that the world is strange, and that the strangest thing of all is that we are here to discuss it. He found it inconceivable that when any mathematical problem was solved, some kind of mind had not solved it before.

Rayleigh went to great lengths in avoiding dependence on anyone, and making use only of what was at hand. He co-operated only when it served his own research end. This did not mean that he was selfish or refused to help others; all that he wanted was to do his own work in his own way. He was very ready to help others in theirs, but he did not readily adopt other people's methods. His position as an English country gentleman reinforced his individualism. He was in a position to manage his time and resources so that he could work entirely according to his temperament. His close and powerful web of social connections provided him with an unofficial organization; he had only to drop a hint to his relatives the Balfours, or the Salisburys, or the Gladstones, or the Asquiths, or the Haldanes, to secure the most influential attention to anything that he desired. He was an individual worker, but backed by a connection which, in his time, had great social power. These circumstances helped his genius to achieve its magisterial performance.

In spite of his delicate health, Rayleigh lived into his seventy-seventh year. He finally became frail, and on 30 June 1919, he died in a heart attack.

Rayleigh received the distinctions and medals usual to a scientist of his achievement. Besides receiving a Nobel Prize and the Order of Merit, he was President of the Royal Society from 1905 to 1908.

THOMAS YOUNG

1773–1829

I

DEEPLY LEARNED AND HIGHLY ORIGINAL

THOMAS YOUNG, the chief innovator of the wave-theory of
light, decipherer of the Egyptian hieroglyphics, and most learned
of English creative investigators, was particularly admired by
Clerk Maxwell, Helmholtz and Rayleigh, yet he has not become
as well known as his eminent admirers. How is it that Young's
fame came slowly, and within a circle that was limited, however
eminent? What kind of a scientist was he, and what could have
been done to facilitate the impact of his genius, and make it more
immediately fertile on behalf of mankind?

Young probably had a wider range of deep creative learning
than any other Englishman in history. Some may have read more,
but there was none who also made important discoveries in so
many directions in virtually everything that he studied. As
Clerk Maxwell said, his 'acquaintance with all branches of science
was as remarkable for its extent as its profundity'. A single
illustration of the penetration of Young's genius is seen in the
award of the Nobel Prize for Medicine in 1967 to R. Granit,
H. K. Hartline and G. Wald, who, by modern physiological research, have, among other contributions, 'unequivocally sub-
stantiated' the Young-Helmholtz theory of colour vision.

Besides possessing extraordinary intellectual and creative
power, he was a tall handsome athletic man, with attractive social
accomplishments. He was not a recluse or bookworm. Yet with
all these qualities an aura of misunderstanding surrounded him.
His priority in his greatest discoveries was disputed in national
and international circles, and general recognition came slowly.

Fortunately, the biography of Young was undertaken by
George Peacock, who was only eighteen years younger, and
himself one of the most important British figures in mathematics
and educational affairs in the first half of the nineteenth century.
Peacock had joined with John Herschel and Babbage in the reform of Cambridge mathematics, and had had a prominent

part in the reform of Cambridge University. He was so busy that twenty years passed before he completed the biography, which was also delayed by such accidents as the burning of nearly the whole of the first impression in a warehouse fire. Peacock had access to documents which seem since to have disappeared. When the biography was published at last in 1855, it contained information not now available from any other source, and a critical appraisal of Young by a scholar who was himself extensively learned, creative, and experienced in affairs.

Peacock thought that the details of the education which had produced such a man as Young were of interest and value 'not merely as explaining the formation of his own intellectual habits and character, but as illustrating the progress of the human mind in one of the most remarkable examples of its development'.

Young was fundamentally individual in his method of work. Though he had an active social life, he thought intellectual problems out entirely by himself. He attended various colleges and universities, but instead of being trained by them, he made such use of them as he thought fit. He was generally better informed than his professors. When he went to a school or university there was a reversal of the usual position. He did not so much submit himself to the course of instruction as instruct those fellow-students and professors who were prescient enough to seek his instruction. He managed his own education from infancy, and was in a sense an autodidact. It did not prevent him from having fruitful exchanges, though these were of an unusual character, and he was not cut off from the usual sources of knowledge. He did not evolve discoveries from his inner consciousness.

His very individual way of working fostered his originality but not his powers of co-operation. Having thought things out from first principles, and being satisfied with the correctness of his conclusions, he left them to speak for themselves. He did not put them into the conventional forms which would have led to immediate acceptance.

On the one hand, there was his prodigious intellectual achievement, on the other his lack 'of that intellectual fellow-feeling (if the phrase may be used) which is so essential to form a successful teacher or lecturer, or a luminous and interesting writer', nor did he ever feel the necessity nor appreciate 'the value of those formal processes of proof which other minds require'. Peacock ascribes great importance to Young's early upbringing in the strict principles of the Society of Friends in the formation of his particular mental habits. Principles which 'recognize the immediate influence of a supreme intelligence as a guide in the ordinary conduct of life' are calculated to 'encourage feelings of self-confidence and pride in the achievement of intellectual as well as moral triumphs'. Indeed, if the principles are not 'well-regulated', they may stimulate excessive intellectual and moral pride.

Young himself attributed his remarkable habit of perseverance in overcoming intellectual difficulties largely to the operation of those Quaker principles which had been instilled in him from infancy. Like Newton and Edison, he mentioned persistence and perseverance first in trying to explain how he had achieved so much.

Peacock said it would be difficult to point out the causes of Young's success in applying mathematics to physical problems. One of the features of his work in this field was the remarkable simplicity of the mathematics by which he solved difficult problems. In general a desultory education in mathematics leads to unsoundness in application. Young was an exception to this rule. He read books on mathematics in the same way that he read books on other subjects. His notes show that he understood them. This was particularly evident in his notes on Newton's *Principia*, which is a difficult book to read without assistance.

Young's individual exertions led to great discoveries, but his obscurity, departure from conventional forms of proof, and detachment from other people's point of view caused serious misunderstandings. People did not read his works. For example, Young's theory of tides, on which he particularly prided himself, was not read by Airy until he had done his own work on the subject, and still more remarkable, Proudman in the twentieth century did not read Young until he had completed his own noted researches.

Larmor described Young's course of lectures at the Royal Institution as 'the greatest and most original of all general lecture courses'. They were published when Young was thirty-four. From the perspective of content Larmor's opinion may be correct, but the actual lectures at the Royal Institution were not very successful. Young was lacking in the power of communication; his audiences had difficulty in following him.

Several of Young's most astonishing contributions were in engineering and technology. He wrote an important memoir on the strength of bridges, and claimed to be the only Englishman to have written seriously on the theory of carpentry. In the course of these researches, he propounded his famous modulus of elasticity. He was well-informed on steam engines, and was the first to define energy in the modern manner.

But he had little idea of how to make these discoveries useful in practice. He was against the planning of scientific research, and did not understand organization.

On account of his eminence, Young was appointed Scientific Secretary of the Board of Longitude, one of the tasks of which was to produce astronomical tables for navigation. According to Bowden, Young advised that there would be no advantage in superseding human computers with calculating machines of the type invented by Babbage. Right at the beginning of this crucial development, Young was on the wrong side, and must bear some of the responsibility of the British failure to develop it.

Young moved on from one problem to another as they caught his interest, and did not stop to develop his solution of them in a form that could be easily understood and utilized by others. The effect of this was very well expressed by the French scholar Peyron, who wrote to him: 'I have always felt and so do many others, that you are a man of rare and superhuman genius with a quick and penetrating vision . . . there is universal regret that your versatility is so widely engaged in the sciences—medicine, astronomy, analysis, etc. etc. that you are unable to press on with your discoveries and bring them to that pitch of perfection which we have the right to expect from a man of your conspicuous talents . . .'

Young's deficiencies delayed the recognition of his genius, and hindered the utilization of his discoveries. How could they have been mitigated, so that the full force of his discoveries could have been utilized more quickly? What kind of institutional arrangements would have enabled his unparalleled combination of abilities to have functioned with at least as great fertility, but with far more immediately fruitful effect?

II

A ROBINSON CRUSOE OF THE INTELLECTUAL WORLD

Thomas Young was born at Milverton in Somerset on 13 June 1773. He was the eldest of the ten children of Thomas and Sarah Young, who were members of the Society of Friends. His father was a cloth merchant who also did a little banking, or perhaps more accurately, money-lending, probably because the Somerset cloth trade was declining. His mother was related through marriage to the eminent Quaker physician Dr Richard Brocklesby, an old school-fellow and close friend of Edmund Burke.

Young was brought up strictly in the principles of the Society of Friends, and attributed his habits and success largely to his early training. In mature manhood, however, after he had seen something of the world and acquired a reputation, he left it.

According to his own account, Young spent most of his first seven years in the family of his maternal grandfather, Mr Robert Davis of Minehead, 'a merchant of great respectability'. Thomas was probably sent away because of stringency in his own family, increased by its growing size. He became rather detached from them, and there appear to be few references to the more intimate side of their relations. He retained tender feelings for his mother. His father showed signs of perturbation when uncle Brocklesby began to influence his eldest son. His virtual separation from his parents may have affected his deeper feelings, and have contributed to Young's self-sufficiency, and his difficulty in relations with ordinary people.

Brocklesby offered to make him substantially his heir if the direction of his life was given to him. His father said he did not wish to offend Brocklesby, but did not think his offer should be accepted, if it was 'to the exclusion of myself and his other kind Friends having the oversight of him'. He thought his association with his uncle might cause him to study excessively. He was not enthusiastic about a medical career for his son. He did not object to his attending some chemical lectures, 'if he is not exposed to improper company'. He thought he ought to spend some time in an apothecary's shop, in order to gain a better knowledge of pharmacy. It may well be that his father's judgment was correct, and that Young should never have entered the medical profession, for which he was not very well fitted as a practitioner. Young may have felt that he was bound to take up medicine in deference to the wishes of his uncle, who did so much for him. In this his Quaker course of duty may have misguided him. It would have been better if Young could have pursued medical research in the modern manner, as an independent discipline, not necessarily connected directly with practice.

Young recorded that by the age of two he had learned to read fluently. Under the guidance of an aunt and a village school-mistress he read the Bible through twice before he was four. He read *Gulliver's Travels*, which left an indelible impression on his mind. He acquired the habit of committing long poems to memory, and at the age of six learned the whole of Goldsmith's

THOMAS YOUNG

Deserted Village. He began Latin grammar at the age of five, and
started to learn writing.

Young loved his aunt, who looked after him with such care
and affection. He was a great favourite with his grandfather, who
was fond of classical learning, and did everything he could to
encourage his taste for study.

Young said that the principles he imbibed and the habits he
formed under the guidance of these dear and excellent relatives
determined his character for life. His great talents were successfully launched, before the age of seven, in those directions in
which they were to be so fruitful. Evidently, a happy and successfully cultivated infancy was of decisive importance in his history.
He provides evidence for the claim that rearing and education
up to the age of seven determine the character.

It was well that he received such a start, since he was sent to
'a miserable boarding-school' just before he was seven. He was
there for a year and a half, and on the whole very badly taught.
But even at this stage he had begun to be his 'own teacher'. He
read various grammars, and books from *Robinson Crusoe* to
Tom Telescope's Newtonian Philosophy. Then he was brought
home for half a year. His father's neighbour Mr Kingdon had
daughters who had always treated him with great kindness, so
that he had been very fond of going to their house. Mr Kingdon
was an ingenious man who had been a tailor, but raised himself
by his talents and good conduct to the respectable position of
surveyor and steward of estates. Little Thomas found in his
house many books relating to science, and 'particularly a Dictionary of Arts and Sciences, in three volumes, folio', which he
began to read with 'the most intense interest and delight'. He
also found various scientific instruments, which the kind daughters and an obliging nephew showed him how to use.

Before the age of nine he was sent to a school in Dorset conducted by Mr T. Thompson, a man of 'liberal and enlarged
mind'. Mr Thompson had a good collection of English and
classical books, and allowed his pupils initiative in making use of
them. Thomas committed most of the Westminster Greek Grammar to memory, and read many Greek and Latin classics. He
read various textbooks on mathematics, but carefully omitted
the sections on 'gunnery', though he did not disdain to learn
book-keeping.

The school usher was an ingenious young man named Josiah
Jeffrey, who lent him *Lectures on Natural Philosophy,* which
particularly delighted him because it contained 'many detailed

4

rules for the practical construction of optical instruments'. Jeffrey made scientific apparatus, including an electrical machine, which Thomas used frequently. He taught him how to turn with a lathe, mix colours, practical drawing, and book-binding. Jeffrey used to sell paper, colours and various oddments to the boys for small sums. When he left Young took over this part of his activities, and during the year 1786 continued to collect 'as much as five shillings' from such sales. This, together with half a guinea from his parents, he invested in books, which Mr Thompson let him have 'at extremely low prices'. By this time he was already 'enamoured of Oriental literature', on which he had read various compendia. He purchased for five shillings Montanus's Hebrew Bible, and before he left Mr Thompson's school he had got through six chapters of it.

In the school holidays he made the acquaintance of 'a saddler of the name of Atkins, a person of considerable skill and ingenuity', whose meteorological observations were published in the *Transactions* of the Royal Society. Mr Atkins lent him a quadrant, with which Thomas measured various eminences during his walks. Morris Birkbeck stimulated his interest in botany; this led him to construct a miscroscope, which diverted his attention from botany to optics. In order to make the microscope he procured a lathe, and presently turning objects in the lathe supplanted his interest in optics. A reading of a copy of Priestley on *Air*, which his father had happened to buy, first aroused his interest in chemistry. Seeing the symbols of fluxions in a book, he remained unsatisfied until he had read a short introduction to them. He got up earlier, and went to bed later than his school-fellows, using the time saved for his private studies.

He left Mr Thomson's school when he was twelve, and devoted himself to turning, making telescopes, and studying Hebrew. 'That most excellent man, Mr Toulmin,' heard of his studies and, unknown to him, provided Hebrew, Chaldee, Syriac and Samaritan grammars for his use. Thomas read these with great diligence. Mr Toulmin also lent him 'The Lord's Prayer in more than 100 Languages', the examination of which gave him 'extraordinary pleasure'. He also read a fair amount of Persian grammar.

As Peacock commented, there may be even more remarkable examples of acquirements by extraordinary boys, but extremely few in which the development did not cease at an early age, as if the organism had been exhausted by premature growth.

Young's desire for knowledge, power of acquisition and per-severance in overcoming difficulties and solving problems increased with age.

Peacock suggested that Young was saved from being paraded as a prodigy, 'a fate to which wonderful boys have been more or less commonly exposed, in order to gratify the impatient vanity and ostentation of their friends', by the sufficiency of his economic position, Quaker principles, and social connections.

At the age of fourteen Young came to the notice, through a friend of an aunt, of David Barclay, a member of the famous Quaker family of merchants and bankers, and a part-owner of Barclay & Perkins' Brewery. He had collaborated with Benjamin Franklin, in endeavouring to secure the independence of the American colonies peacefully, and was joint founder with John Fothergill of the Quaker school at Ackworth. He liberated the slaves on his Jamaican property and sent them to Philadelphia, arranging for them to receive craftsman's training under fair conditions.

David Barclay was making arrangements for the education of his grandson Hudson Gurney, and Thomas's youthful interest in Oriental languages inspired the suggestion that he would be a good pupil-companion for Hudson, who was twelve and a half. A tutor was engaged, but immediately afterwards he found a more permanent post, and did not come. Barclay said that Quakers had difficulty in finding Quaker tutors, owing to the lack of encouragement for scholars and scientists in their Society; an interesting opinion, for many would have considered that Quaker interest in science and learning was higher than the average, as demonstrated by the number of Quaker Fellows of the Royal Society. When the tutor failed to arrive Thomas volunteered to act as temporary tutor to Hudson in Latin and Greek. Thomas did so well that Mr Barclay continued this arrangement even after he succeeded in securing the services of the able young John Hodgkin as supervisor. He did not think that Thomas was old enough to exercise general supervision over Hudson's education.

Hodgkin himself, who was completing his own education, and became a classical scholar of note, presently received helpful advice and assistance in his own classical studies from the marvellous boy. Thomas, for his part, benefited from Hodgkin's advice and assistance.

Young lived with the Barclays from 1787 until 1792, when he was nineteen. He regarded these years as the most profitable of his life. He saw little of his own family, and went to London rarely, in the main to visit bookshops and libraries. Through his London visits his uncle Richard Brocklesby became increasingly interested in him. Thomas had already become a master of accurate and beautiful penmanship, especially in Greek. One of Brocklesby's friends asked the boy for a specimen of his writing, whereupon Thomas wrote a sentence in several languages in his best style. Some say it was in four or five languages; Peacock said it was in fourteen.

He read a range of books in classics, Oriental and modern languages, mathematics, physics, biology and English literature, of which he kept detailed records, so that what he did is exactly known. To any ordinary judgment, the number of books he read appears large. Nevertheless, this did not seem so to that eminent scholar Peacock, who says: 'The number of books which he read was very small, but he adhered strictly through life to the principle of doing nothing by halves. Whatever book he began to read he read completely and deliberately through; whatever study he commenced he never abandoned; and it was by steadily keeping to his principle, a most important one in education, that he was accustomed, in after life, to attribute a great part of his success, both as a scholar and a man of science.'

Young was seriously ill when he was sixteen, and consumption was suspected. He was put on a rigorous diet, and carefully looked after by Mrs Barclay, under the medical supervison of Dr Brocklesby and Baron Dimsdale, the Quaker doctor who had formerly been physician to Catherine the Great and had successfully inoculated her.

Brocklesby treated his 'dear Tommy' with the perspicacity of a distinguished physician. He pointed out to him that as one who seemed in all things to set himself above ordinary humanity, his errors would be counted all the more reprehensible. Tommy refused to eat sugar, because it was a product of the slave trade. Brocklesby told him that his 'prudery' in abstaining from sugar on this account would in anyone else be altogether ridiculous. He might be allowed such whims, as long as he kept 'free from spiritual pride or too much presumption' in the facility of acquiring language, 'which is no more than the dross of knowledge'. Brocklesby's late excellent friend, Mr Day, the author of *Sandford and Merton*, had abhorred the base traffic in negroes' lives just as much as Tommy did, and had in addition done immense service in the struggle against the infamous trade, and yet he ate as much sugar as he did himself. Mr Day had argued that

60 millions of British capital were invested in the West Indian
sugar trade, and the activities of such an economic power could
not be affected by the action of one or one hundred individuals
who decided not to eat sugar on this account. 'Reformation must
take its rise elsewhere, if ever there is a general mass of public
virtue sufficient to resist such private interests.' Uncle Richard
advised Tommy to 'read Locke with care'.

During his last two years with the Barclays, Young read Simpson's *Fluxions*, the whole of Newton's *Principia* and *Optics*, 'the
great work of Bacon *De Augmentis Scientiarum*', Lavoisier, Black,
Linnaeus, Boerhave and others, besides pursuing his linguistic
studies. He also read Blackstone's *Commentaries on the Laws of
England*, and Burke's *Reflections on the French Revolution*. But
he made 'few or no sacrifices to the pleasures of the imagination,
and was contented to rest in almost entire ignorance of the
popular literature of the day'. He read nothing hastily. His
memory was tenacious, and what he had once learned he never
forgot.

Brocklesby showed some of Tommy's Greek translations of
Shakespeare to Burke, who requested that he should render
'Lear's horrid imprecations on his barbarous daughters' into
Greek. Burke said he should study Aristotle's *Logic* and *Poetics*,
and Cicero's moral and philosophic works. He remarked that
his mind was 'not yet strained to any false principles', and he
should be reared and cultivated in the best manner, so that he
would be formed 'to emulate a Bacon or a Newton in the maturity
and fullness of time'. A comprehensive mind should be 'dis-
regardful of any pecuniary emoluments of a profession'. If such
a mind is inclined to 'enlarged and useful speculations', a small
competence would suffice.

Brocklesby talked to him now as if he were already 'strong in
the manhood' of his mind. He advised him only to try his powers,
and follow the bias which might enable him to do the best for
himself, his country, and mankind. However, he was to be careful
not to become puffed up with vanity, because of the frankness
with which he was being treated. He requested him to write
frequent moral essays, for his own perusal and for Mr Burke,
who had 'taken a great fancy' to him.

Young met Porson and other scholars through his uncle when
he was eighteen, and discussed fine points of classical scholarship with them. He was now approaching his departure from the
Barclays' household, and the close of his youthful education.

Peacock posed the question of why 'an education conducted

for so many years with so little communication with other minds', and 'so little assistance from extrinsic sources' should have been so successful. He thought the principal causes included 'the peculiar constitution of his own mind', that is, inborn and genetic qualities; great industry; his conviction that what one man could do, so could another; and his determination to master every branch of knowledge that he thought necessary.

Young himself had little faith in any peculiar gifts of genius, 'believing the original difference between human intellects to be much less considerable than it was generally supposed to be'. His temper 'was singularly unruffled and tranquil', he had no boyish tastes or amusements; he was not seduced by imaginative dreaming from the assiduous cultivation of the understanding.

His clear and beautiful penmanship, which reflected keen observation and an artistic appreciation of form, increased his power and sense of exactitude in scholarship. Its influence was later to be seen in the exquisite copies he made of the Rosetta and other inscriptions, which led to his decipherment of the hieroglyphs.

Peacock thought Young an almost unique example of an un-assisted student acquiring a rigorous knowledge of grammar and syntax. Young himself informed his brother Robert that there is 'very little that a person who is seriously and industriously disposed to improve may not obtain from books with more advantage than from a living instructor'. An instructor may give guidance about the best path to be followed, but it is 'the strength of the traveller and not of the guide that must conquer the difficulties of the journey. Masters and mistresses are very necessary to compensate for want of inclination and exertion; but whoever would arrive at excellence must be self-taught . . .'

As Peacock observed, this self-education, in spite of its success, also had 'very serious disadvantages'. Young had not sufficient opportunity of freely exchanging thoughts, and finding out how the minds of ordinary people worked. He never grasped those points in the communication of knowledge which, though clear to him, were generally obscure to others.

Young's learning in mathematics and physics was even less assisted than his studies in classics. His writings were 'always obscure and generally deficient in elegance and concinnity of form', yet dealt with profound problems, often by remarkably simple means. In these departments of research his genius was particularly striking.

But his lack of sufficient acquaintance with the way in which other people thought led to failures in the communication of his discoveries, both to other scientists and those who followed and fostered the contemporary development of science. There were always a few who fully appreciated his genius, but his limitations delayed general understanding and recognition of what he had done, and diminished its fruitfulness. Several of his great discoveries were not grasped until they had been independently rediscovered by others with greater powers of clear and complete exposition, often long after his time.

Young's transference from his own family to the Barclays and the Brocklesbys was a change from the religious sectarian lower middle class to the wealthy, cultivated upper middle class, even though both groups belonged to the Society of Friends. The Barclays, who were of Scottish descent, were liberal capitalists whose ideology was in the tradition of Adam Smith. Oldham has described Young as a liberal of the Adam Smith school. He engaged in individual enterprise in the realm of learning. He resisted Government influence in science, and external influence on the Royal Society, as interferences with the freedom of science. He was without insight into the forthcoming need for the organization of science.

All his life he worked like an intellectual Robinson Crusoe, picking up and making use of what he found in the environment, in the form of books, instruments and persons, whom he treated in a detached way as if they had something in common with things. He was regarded as charming and amiable by people he knew intimately, but his quick manner of speaking, which sprang from his immense knowledge, was regarded by many as flippant and superior.

He frequently had difficulties in practical and business relations. He tried to regulate aspects of life that should be governed by intuition and social feeling by intellectual considerations. He had little sense of submitting himself to any group of which he was a member, in order to further its aims. He had no feeling for team-spirit, and for being a good member of an organization. Perhaps these traits were enhanced by reaction against Quaker discipline.

III

MAKING UP FOR LOST SOCIAL TIME

When Young started on the study of medicine in 1792, his manners were described as 'very quiet and pleasing'. While he still adhered to outer Quaker forms, he had abandoned its inner tenets. On the advice of Burke, he paid particular attention to Cicero, and presently quoted him as expressing his own aims. 'I think the man, if any such there be, who possessed that strength of mind, that constitutional tendency to temperance and virtue, which would lead him to avoid all indulgences, and to complete the whole career of life in the midst of labours of the body and efforts of the mind; whom tranquillity, nor relaxation, nor the flattering attentions of his equals in age and station, nor public games, nor banquets would delight; who would regard nothing in life as desirable which was not united with dignity and virtue;—such a man I regard as being, in my judgment, furnished and adorned with some special gifts of the gods.'

He read standard medical works, and his practice in dissection led him to discover that the change in the form of the eye, which enables it to deal clearly with both distant and near objects, was caused by fibres in the crystalline lens, which are muscular in nature. This discovery, published by the Royal Society in 1793, had been suspected by Newton's friend Pemberton; after Young's paper, the great John Hunter claimed it. This led to a disagreeable dispute on priority. Sir Charles Blagden, the Secretary of the Royal Society, who was also Henry Cavendish's secretary, and, as Peacock said, was well acquainted with what was passing in the philosophical world, 'and very much given to retailing it', had mentioned the subject at a dinner at Sir Joshua Reynolds's, where Young was a guest, implying that Young was a plagiarist. Young immediately wrote to everyone else who had been at the dinner, and all denied that the subject had been mentioned. Blagden admitted that he was not sure that he had told him of Hunter's work.

Home and Ramsden produced new experimental evidence against Young's work, and in the face of this authority, Young withdrew it. He subsequently extended his investigation by ingenious and difficult experiments, and showed that, after all, his original view was correct.

This early incident was typical of Young's researches. They were profound, difficult and often not obviously conclusive. They easily gave rise to differences of opinion and misunderstandings.

Young made journeys in his vacations for pleasure and instruction. He and his friend Hudson Gurney toured Cornwall, where he was particularly interested in the development of the Cornish mining machinery, which, under the leadership of James Watt, was then the most advanced in the world.

Uncle Brocklesby gave him introductions to his eminent patients and friends. Young was sent to enquire at Bath about the health of the Duke of Richmond, Master-General of the Ordnance, who was knowledgeable in science and engineering, and in command of the Trigonometrical Survey. The Duke reported to Brocklesby that he 'really never saw a young man more pleasing and engaging'. He invited Young to be his private secretary, at a salary of £200 a year, with library and laboratory facilities. Young turned it down, because it would have entailed leaving the Society of Friends, which he was not yet prepared to do.

After his preliminary studies in London, it was decided that Young should go to Edinburgh, and then to Göttingen to take a medical degree. Even this was not regarded as a sufficient qualification, as the fellowship of the College of Physicians in London was at that time restricted to graduates of Oxford and Cambridge, so he was finally to proceed to one of these.

On his way to Edinburgh Young called on Robert Bakewell, the great animal breeder, and made characteristically interesting and exact notes on his famous farm. He visited Erasmus Darwin, who sent him on his way with an introduction to an Edinburgh friend, describing Young as uniting 'the scholar with the philosopher, and the cultivation of modern arts with the simplicity of ancient manners'.

At Edinburgh Young found a number of his London medical student friends. The Medical School was at the height of its fame, with students from many countries. Young made foreign friends who were afterwards helpful to him. He had not much time for scientific research, as he attended the medical lectures assiduously. The most striking aspect of Young's activities at Edinburgh, and later at Göttingen, were not scientific, nor even medical. He began to read general literature, which he had previously neglected, such as Cervantes and Ariosto. He learned German from a German medical student with whom he became friendly. At Edinburgh he began to drop the external characteristics of the Quakers, though he continued some forms, particularly out of consideration for his mother, to whom he was tenderly attached.

This reservation in his change of opinion and social habits caused Young to be criticized by his old associates, and the subject of witticisms by his new friends. Some hinted that he was hypocritical. He was surprised by the speed and degree of the separation from his old friends. The change of aims and associates

4*

which occurs with departure from a strict sect sometimes causes the subject to plunge into dissipation; this did not occur in Young's case, but for such a person he began to devote an extraordinary amount of time, energy and enthusiasm to social pursuits.

He started to study music, and learned to play the flute. He soon mastered the theory, but had not the natural skill to become a good performer. He took lessons in dancing, and went to the theatre, seeing Mrs Siddons in many roles. He was passionately fond of female society, and became an indefatigable participant in parties and dances, 'though not in those indulgences which are only very generally overlooked because they are so common'.

Through attending the medical lectures, and improving his knowledge of German, Spanish, and Italian, and beginning to read lighter literature, he had not much time either for medicine, scholarship or science. Young revelled in the Edinburgh culture. For the first time he enjoyed life free from Quaker constraints. He made tours of the country, armed with influential introductions. Among these was one to the Duke and Duchess of Gordon. Young had a wonderful time dancing with the ducal ladies, while the amiable Duke, who was 'an expert workman', demonstrated to him his splendid collection of lathes and scientific instruments.

In his journal Young wrote: 'I do not recollect that I have ever passed my time more agreeably, or with a party whom I thought more congenial to my own dispositions: and what would hardly be credited by many grave reasoners on life and manners, that a person who had spent the whole of his earlier years a recluse from the gay world, and a total stranger to all that was passing in the higher ranks of society, should feel himself more at home and more at ease in the most magnificent palace in the country, than in the humblest dwelling with those whose birth was most similar to his own . . .'

Peacock noted that the 'warm and liberal hospitality' of Scotland had 'not yet been cooled down by the crowds let loose upon it by steam-boats and railways . . .'

Young was, however, as diligent in writing notes on the Carron Iron Works, and later on Coalbrookdale in the Severn Valley, as on the higher Scottish social life. In his notes on the former he already expressed the opinion, before the end of the eighteenth century, that British industrialists did not attend enough to 'neatness and elegance' in the designs of their products.

After a winter of Scottish medical study he proceeded to

Göttingen, provided with introductions from Burke and others. He attended the usual medical and scientific lectures, but his devotion to dancing and music was more striking. Having been excluded from them in early life he worked at them with a somewhat misplaced thoroughness. He was too old to learn easily the kind of lessons normally given to youths, and his earnestness about them seemed slightly ridiculous to his gentlemanly friends who had acquired these graces years ago. He could not believe his fellow-students when they told him he would never be a really good dancer or musical performer.

He did not appreciate the German professors' lack of hospitality, which impaired his thirst for social experience. They were, in fact, not sufficiently well paid to do much entertaining.

Young took his doctor's degree in 1796. Besides his dissertation he delivered a short lecture. In the latter he described an alphabet of forty-seven letters, designed to express every sound the human organs of speech are capable of making. Such an invention was desirable in order to facilitate universal communication between all the members of the human race. The problem led him to investigate the theory of sound, to clarify his conception of what it is that has to be made by the voice. His experimental and theoretical researches on sound led him to consider the analogous properties of light, and thence to his major discovery of optical diffraction, and his development of the wave-theory of light.

Young intended to spend some time in Vienna, and visit Italy, but the extension of the French revolutionary war restricted him to touring Germany. He was presented at court at Brunswick, where he had his social exchanges with the ladies. However, the riding was not as good as at Göttingen, which Young considered the best school of horsemanship in Europe. He was passionately fond of riding, and attempted many difficult feats of horsemanship.

He was muscularly very strong, and in the habit of leaping over the loftiest gates. He was best known among Göttingen students for gymnastic skill in vaulting the wooden horse.

Young's tour of a number of the then numerous principalities of Germany led him to doubt whether there is such a thing as national character. He noted 'the want of common spirit in Germany'. He thought the multiplicity of independent governments prevented the development of communications and the economy. 'A ready communication with a single animated centre would have more effect than a greater number of less perfect

ones.' The pride of independence of the petty states had led to
the founding of numerous universities and cultural institutions,
but the professors were ill-paid, and he thought the German
university education on the whole superficial; students were
prompted to take courses on every imaginable subject, attempting to retain information by mechanical memorizing. After seeing the German system, he thought there was something to be
said for the English, which was based on a grind at the ancient
languages. This was so severe that they were 'never to be entirely
forgotten'.

There were more learned men in Germany, but the English
had ever had 'some individuals in many branches who are almost unequalled'. The Germans knew more Latin but less Greek,
their commercial men often spoke French and English. They
were making rapid advances in mathematics, chemistry, and
music.

He noted that German spectators in the theatre applauded
with more taste than the English. Their actors had more delicate
touches of nature, but less force in expressing violent passions.
'A poor strolling actress in a barn' excited as much emotion in
him as Mrs Siddons. He thought class divisions were sharper
in Germany. Professional men had much less social standing
than in England. For example, it was wise to conceal one's
qualifications as a medical doctor if one wished to avoid depress-
ing one's social status. 'The idea conveyed by the English word
gentleman cannot be expressed in German.'

He thought the German publishers' system of paying authors
by the sheet caused the multiplication of mediocre books. It
stimulated the impecunious professors to increase their incomes
by writing long books. This system stifled 'the laconic efforts of
brilliant genius' (like Young's own style).

Young returned to England after nine months at Göttingen. He
had had enough of the German university, and also of 'the perpetual pursuit of novelties, which seldom equal expectation . . .'
Young's even-tempered persistent strain of discreet social
careerism made him to some extent a premature Victorian.

After Göttingen, Young had to spend two years at Cambridge,
in order to satisfy the regulations of the College of Physicians.
He entered Emmanuel College, whose Master was a friend of his
uncle. The college was 'at that time the resort of many students
in the higher classes of life'. Young was twenty-four. He had
already published researches, and secured a German doctorate.
When the Master introduced him to his tutors, he jocularly

remarked that he had brought a pupil who could read lectures to them.

Young soon put Cambridge Greek scholars in their place, and he disdained the Cambridge mathematicians, perceiving that they were out of date. Cambridge men, nettled by this lack of esteem, observed that he 'took no delight in the pleasures of the table, and never could either make a joke or understand one'.

Young never pushed himself forward, but when he was asked questions even on the most difficult subjects, answered in a 'quick, flippant, decisive way', as if he were dealing with the easiest things. He never asserted any superiority, or behaved as if there were any credit in this knowledge. He would discuss contemporary writers. 'He was never personal; he would speak of knowledge itself, of what was known or what might be known, but never of himself, or any other, as having discovered anything or as likely to do so.'

He spoke correctly and rapidly, but he used unfamiliar words, and the arrangement of his ideas was seldom the same as those he conversed with. When later he lectured at the Royal Institution to 'a number of silly women and dilettanti philosophers', he had no sense of adapting his style of explanation to his audience. He presumed 'on the knowledge and not on the ignorance of his hearers'.

He still retained some of the Quaker stiffness. He never said or did a rude thing, but was never warmly affable. He was natural without being timid, and easy without being bold. He did not associate much with the undergraduates, who called him with a 'mixture of derision and respect "Phaenomenon Young",' but he was on familiar terms with the dons. He had few friends of his own age, and as he had not been introduced to many of the distinguished members of the university, he did not seek their society, nor they his. Seniors did not like to have to admit the superiority of one in student status.

He did not appear to read much; his room was not covered with books and papers. He sometimes made experiments, but not regularly. He never laid down the law, and though mathematical, did not seem to think abstractedly. 'A philosophical fact, a difficult calculation, an ingenious instrument, or a new invention, would engage his attention, but he never spoke of morals, of metaphysics, of of religion.'

Young, for his part, found Cambridge 'much more civilized and refined than foreign universities'. He said that he was beginning to see the advantages of these English institutions. It was

good to have a body of dons with time and opportunity to associate with students, and 'fill up the void places in their intelli-
gences'.

Young said of himself: 'When I was a boy, I thought myself a
man; now that I am a man, I find myself a boy.'

Owing to the peculiar university regulations, made in the time
of Queen Elizabeth, when undergraduates were boys, a student
could not receive the degree of medical bachelor in less than six
years after entry, and a medical doctorate until five years after
that. Thus Young, already internationally known, did not become
an M.B. until 1803 when he was thirty years of age, and M.D. in
1808, whereupon he became a Fellow of the College of Physicians.

Young had begun medical practice long before, by virtue of
his German degree. The effect of the English system was to delay
medical practice in the higher ranks of the profession until after
a classical education at Oxford or Cambridge, which integrated
them socially with the upper classes. This explained the higher
social status of medicine in England than on the Continent at
that time. Peacock thought that the reform of the old regulations
might lower the status of doctors. If this happened, then it
could only be raised again 'by a liberal distribution of honours
by the Crown'.

Young's eminent uncle Brocklesby died in 1797. He bequeathed
his house, furniture, library, and collection of pictures chosen
by his friend Sir Joshua Reynolds, together with £10,000 to
Young. Brocklesby had already given Burke one thousand
pounds, and had formerly offered Johnson rooms in his own
house and an annuity for holidays in a warmer climate, to protect him from the injurious living conditions in Bolt Court,
Fleet Street. Brocklesby was generous in large things, but somewhat exacting in small ones. He expected deferences and respect,
and was 'rather unreasonably suspicious' when his wishes were
not fully carried out.

Young was now in a position to do very much as he wished.
He continued to observe his Cambridge residence and secure
hospital experience in London. In 1798 he hurt his foot in London, and was confined indoors. He resumed his study of sound,
and succeeded in clarifying the theory of sound waves, elucidating the effects of the interference of sound waves, and applying
the same principles in optics on the assumption that light is
transmitted by waves. He incorporated his discoveries in a paper
on Outlines of Experiments respecting Sound and Light, which
he read to the Royal Society in 1799.

In this paper, Young made derogatory remarks on the famous treatise on Harmonics by Dr Robert Smith, the friend of Newton and founder of the Smith's Prizes. He described the treatise as 'a large and obscure volume', and 'leaving the subject, except for the use of an impracticable instrument, exactly where it found it'. The first comment was not unfounded, but the second was more questionable. Dr John Robison of Edinburgh, the friend of James Watt and an authority on the physics of music, expressed regret that he had undervalued Smith. It may be noted that Rayleigh a century later pointed out that Smith, and Cotes with whom he collaborated, had long been undervalued by their countrymen, who had failed to recognize that they had anticipated some of Lagrange's optical theorems.

Robison asked Young to attend to the admonitions which he had himself given to 'a very young and ingenious gentleman'. This was a reference to the youthful Brougham, who had published a mathematical paper in the Philosophical Transactions, which contained some material that was new, and other material that was new in form but old in substance, together with some errors.

Young criticized the errors tartly in an article published in 1800, which he prefaced by praising the superiority of the geometrical methods of Newton to the analytical mathematics, which had been developed on the Continent. Brougham had used the new analytical methods, in line with the future development of mathematical physics. In choice of method, he was in the right, besides having contributed something new. Brougham was infuriated, and before long attacked Young with all the force of his invective.

However, before this event, Young felt it necessary to reply to Robison, whom he much respected. He wrote a letter to Nicholson's Journal in 1801, explaining his criticism of Smith, and in it made his first announcement of his extension of the principle of interference from sound to light, which proved that light is propagated by waves. He developed his discoveries in three papers for the Royal Society, the first and third of which formed the Bakerian Lectures for 1801 and 1803.

He returned to Cambridge in 1799 for his final term of residence, and in 1800 started medical practice in London. After he had completed his Royal Society memoirs he worked hard at the hospital and in medical studies. He took a house in Welbeck Street, which he occupied for twenty-five years. Owing to his uncle's bequest, he was under no economic necessity to devote himself entirely to medicine, and had the leisure and means to pursue such researches as he wished.

In 1801 he was appointed professor of natural philosophy in the Royal Institution, which had recently been founded, and where Humphry Davy was already lecturing on chemistry. Young developed a course of sixty lectures, covering virtually the whole of known physics. They were published in 1807, and were unique among British treatises on physics for their comprehensiveness; they were packed with new and stimulating knowledge, such, for example, as the first modern conception of energy, but they were not very successful as expositions for general audiences. His style was too condensed, and he lacked insight into other people's approach to the subjects, so that he did not know how to help his audiences to understand him, in spite of all his care in preparation, and demonstration with models and apparatus.

For decades after its publication, other scientists rediscovered things which Young had discovered and described in his book, though not sufficiently clearly to be easily understood. Young compared himself with 'the celebrated prophetess of antiquity, who always told truth, but was seldom understood and never believed'.

His genius was nevertheless recognized by a few. He was elected Foreign Secretary of the Royal Society in 1802, when he was twenty-nine, on account of his command of languages and range of scientific knowledge, and retained this position until his death in 1829. In 1812 he was asked to stand for Secretaryship of the Society, but he declined, on the ground that it might prejudice his medical practice, for patients might in that case believe that he was more devoted to science than to curing their ills. Nevertheless, Young did not sacrifice his intellectual interests to his medical profession.

IV

NATURAL PHILOSOPHY IN ISOLATION

Newton's main objection to the theory that light is propagated by a wave motion was that no example was then known of light waves bending round an obstacle, in the way that the sound waves from guns discharged from behind a hill are audible, even though the guns are out of the direct line of sight.

In May 1801, while thinking about Newton's beautiful experiments on light, Young first clearly perceived that Newton's main objection to the wave theory of light might be removed, if light waves interfered with each other in the same way that waves in water or in air are observed to do.

The idea of interference of waves was not new. Newton himself had given a masterly application of it in the *Principia*, in which he explained the variations in the tides at the East Indian port of Batsha, which had been described by Halley three years before. When the water flowed in, it arrived at the port through various channels of different lengths. Consequently, the wave of the tide arriving through one channel might be high when the wave arriving in another was low, so that they cancelled each other, the water remaining level. Young used the interference of water waves emerging out of phase from channels of different lengths as an analogy to the interference of out-of-phase light waves.

Young's merit was to conceive the interference of light waves clearly, and devise and perform crucial experiments that demonstrated its existence, and hence that light was propagated by waves, and not by particles, as Newton had concluded.

He forecast that the central black spot, which Newton had observed when two curved pieces of glass, or lenses, were pressed together, would under certain conditions be white. When the experiment was performed, this was found to be the case.

He showed, too, that the phenomena of optical diffraction, such as the fringes seen along a sharp edge when suitably viewed, were a result of wave interference.

Young described his experiments on interference and diffraction of light waves, which were often subtle and complicated, in ordinary language. His descriptions were profound and intuitively illuminating, but often difficult to understand, because the complex argument could not be easily followed without using mathematics. For those who were at home with Young's kind of physical and geometrical thinking, or already knew and accepted the argument, Young's descriptions were often deeply suggestive. But he did not use the most suitable mathematical technique to convince the unconvinced.

Young had already in 1798 made discoveries in harmonics which were unknown to the English mathematicians, and, consequently, he thought original. But then he found that some of these results had already been discovered and demonstrated by the continental mathematicians. This led him to note at this time that Britain was 'very much behind its neighbours in many branches of mathematics', and that if he were to devote himself to mathematics he would follow the French and German school, but the field was 'too wide and too barren' for his taste.

Peacock, who had personally been the first to introduce the Continental notation for the calculus into the Cambridge examinations, and thus had a foremost part, together with Babbage and John Herschel, in the reform of Cambridge mathematics, commented that 'it would indeed have been fortunate for [Young's] scientific character, and would have greatly aided the ready reception of his subsequent discoveries, if he had been tempted, at this early period of his career, to study systematically in this school of mathematics, and had adopted the elegance of form and completeness of development for which the work of Euler, La Grange and La Place are so justly distinguished'.

Young's method of thought was suitable for a powerful mind working in isolation, and his circumstances were such that he was never under decisive pressure to make himself intelligible to others. His uncle's support and fortune relieved him from making any fundamental adaptation to others, and to other schools of thought. He indicated that he had resigned from his Royal Institution professorship because of the claims of his medical practice, but he never fully devoted himself to medicine, and did not possess the subtler qualities in dealing with people that are necessary in an outstanding practitioner. This suggests that the deeper or unconscious reason for his resignation was that he was unable, or unprepared to change his extremely individual methods of thought and behaviour. His frustrations and his lack of immediate recognition were due basically to his excessive intellectual individualism.

This, however, was not adequately recognized at the time. It was ascribed primarily to the anonymous criticisms of his early papers on wave theory by Brougham, who had smarted under Young's patronizing criticism. Brougham wrote as a self-appointed counsel for the Newtonian theory of light, taking it for granted that the Newtonian theory was correct. He ridiculed Young's daring to differ from Newton, and made play with obscurities, and points that he represented as such. Brougham's method and tone were the reverse of objective, passionless consideration of the facts. When Brougham was confronted with a particularly clear experiment, such as the disappearance of the diffraction fringes thrown by a fine wire placed across a sunbeam in a darkened room, on obliterating the rays on one side of the wire, he simply asserted that Young had made an experimental error.

Peacock said 'it would be difficult to refer to another example where the irresponsible power of anonymous criticism has been so unscrupulously exercised, or where the effects which it produced were so long and so injuriously felt'.

This has long been the conventional assessment of the quality and the effect of Brougham's criticism, but it is not wholly correct. Clues to the deeper reasons for the delay in the wider recognition of Young were provided by Peacock himself. He said that Brougham was 'unjust and intemperate', and the theory he was supporting was 'utterly erroneous'. He had, however, expressed himself 'generally in language so choice and felicitous as could hardly fail to charm an ignorant or indifferent reader'. But his arguments were 'intermixed also with passages which are remarkable for the correct and comprehensive view they express for the proper mode of conducting philosophical inquiries, and quite worthy of those varied powers, the application of which, during a long and eventful life, will make the name of the great man to whom they have been commonly attributed, for ever memorable in the civil, the political and the literary history of this country'.

Young replied to Brougham's criticisms in a closely argued pamphlet, which was virtually ignored. As Peacock remarked, it appeared that no effective effort was made to make it generally known. Young thought it sufficient to leave it to speak for itself. It did not seem to occur to him that the persuasion of opinion required more than mere objective explanations. His friends brought his pamphlet to the notice of Canning, Brougham's political oponent, who 'read it with great attention', and commented on the Edinburgh Reviewer's malice and want of candour.

As an individual with considerable private means, who could follow his own impulses without much attention to others, Young naturally drifted into association with political conservatives. He appealed to a few superior persons, and failed to recognize the weight of general opinion.

The limitations of Young's method and outlook led to the main credit for the establishment of the wave-theory of light going to the French school, and especially Fresnel, who presented a more comprehensive and intelligible exposition. Fresnel had been educated in the school of mathematics at the Polytechnic in Paris, the first great school in the world for training professional scientists. He was a more disciplined and professional member of scientific society than Young. He fully recognized the priority of Young's discoveries, though he remade them independently.

Fresnel was opposed by Laplace, who, like Brougham, was a vehement supporter of Newton's particle theory of light. He found an effective supporter in Arago, and together they subsequently strove for adequate recognition for Young. In 1816 Arago and Gay Lussac visited Young in Worthing, and informed him in detail about Fresnel's work. In particular, they told Young of one of Fresnel's experiments disproving the Newtonian theory. They were astonished by Young's quiet reception of the news. Presently, Young told them that he had published the same experiment in 1807 in his lectures on natural philosophy. In the meantime, Mrs Young had disappeared from the room. She returned with the volume, opened at the appropriate place.

During the visit, Arago told him of his experiment showing that rays of light polarized in planes at right angles to each other would not interfere. In 1817 Young wrote to Arago, pointing out that the phenomenon could be explained if the light waves were transmitted by tranverse vibrations. Polarization was due to the restriction of the tranverse vibrations to a particular plane.

The same thought had occurred to Fresnel, but he hesitated to accept it, as it appeared to be difficult to reconcile with his previous physical conceptions. Fresnel said: 'M. Young, however, more bold in his conjectures, and less confiding in the views of geometers, published it before me, though perhaps he thought of it after me.'

Some years afterwards, when Fresnel was dying prematurely, Young with his well-meaning tactlessness wrote to him that while he had planted the tree, Fresnel had gathered the fruit. The sick Fresnel was nettled, and replied that it appeared to him that what he had done in optics was as difficult as what Young had done; 'You have gathered the flowers; may I be allowed to say, with English modesty, I have dug down laboriously to discover the roots.'

As Foreign Secretary of the Royal Society Young had the satisfaction of informing Fresnel two years later of his election as a foreign member of the Royal Society and the recipient of its Rumford Medal. Young said in his letter that he felt that the compliment paid to Fresnel was tacitly also made to himself, but as his own main experiments had been made a quarter of a century ago, he could 'only feel it a sort of anticipation of *posthumous* fame, which I have never particularly coveted'. Fresnel died a few weeks later, at the age of thirty-nine.

The two volumes of Young's Royal Institution lectures contained a multitude of discoveries and speculations about the general properties of matter, heat and electricity, but were not easy to read. Besides all this, they contained a catalogue of twenty

thousand scientific papers, selected as valuable by his encyclo-
paedic mind and intuitive understanding. With this catalogue
the reader enjoyed the personal guidance of a first-rate mind
through the forests of scientific literature.

Young's study of optics led him to consider the mechanism
of the vision of colour by the eyes. There are between one and
two hundred distinguishable colours in the spectrum, and Young
found it impossible to believe that there could be an equal number of points sensitive to all of these at each place on the retina.
He suggested that all colours are produced from combinations
of three primary colours: green, red and violet. He published
this theory in 1802. Helmholtz and Maxwell became interested
in it fifty years later. Helmholtz said he had sought for such a
theory for years, before learning of Young's work. He said that
Young 'was one of the most acute men who ever lived, but had
the misfortune to be too far in advance of his contemporaries.
They looked on him with astonishment, but could not follow
his bold speculations, and thus a mass of his most important
thoughts remained buried and forgotten in the Transactions of
the Royal Society until a later generation by slow degrees arrived
at the rediscovery of his discoveries, and came to appreciate the
force of his arguments and the accuracy of his conclusions.'

Young was prepared to attack any problem from first principles.
He made a thorough and important investigation of the theory
of the strength of bridges, taking into consideration the physical
properties and strength of the materials used. He was a scientific
adviser to insurance companies, and worked on the theory of
insurance, trying to construct empirical formulae which would
take into account a wide range of factors affecting the length of
human life. He investigated hydraulics, especially in its bearing
on the flow of blood in the arteries. He regarded his researches
on the theory of the tides as the most original and successful of
his physico-mathematical investigations. He published it, as
usual, anonymously in 1813, and for long it was virtually ignored.

The range and depth of Young's investigations were prodigious, but it is important to notice that they did not necessarily
have to be attacked to be ignored. Their acceptance was hindered
by their form. As Peacock put it, he had an 'extraordinary capacity for solving the most difficult problems in the applications of
mathematics to natural philosophy, by processes apparently the
most inadequate to the purpose'. He never confined himself to
the beaten track of systematic investigation. He did not use sym-
metrical formulae or analytical refinements. He did not seek

after generalities, but freely resorted to every expedient, however
irregular and unusual, if it served his purpose. He took difficult
steps without proof as obvious, dropped tiresome mathematical
terms as insignificant, and advanced analogues in place of proofs,
and at the end of a short space, seemingly only sufficient for a
preliminary consideration of a difficult problem, the reader is
surprised to find the correct answer. He arrived at correct results
by simple arguments, in which mathematical subtleties and pit-
falls were evaded by a profound sagacity about how nature works.
This quality fascinated Maxwell, Helmholtz and Rayleigh, who
possessed the same kind of sagacity, but, fortunately, were more
skilful in the exposition of their discoveries.

V

GENTLEMAN AND DOCTOR

Young prosecuted his medical practice more seriously after his
marriage in 1804 to Miss Eliza Maxwell. She was an 'extremely
young' lady of aristocratic Scottish descent. Their marriage
proved very successful, though they had no children. He wished
to increase his income, so that he could cultivate his circle of
relatives in addition to his friends, and entertain on a larger
scale.

After his marriage he used to spend the summer months at
Worthing, for the benefit of his medical practice, but also as a
pleasant quiet place where he could pursue studies with less
interruption. During the Napoleonic wars the higher classes went
to British watering places because they could not go abroad, so
there were plenty of well-to-do patients. Peacock remarked that
such places were not yet subject to 'the intrusion of the mobs of
tradesmen and others, whom the increased facilities of communication have since introduced'. Worthing had not yet had its
approaches 'blocked up by those irregular suburbs, equally injurious to the public health and architectual beauty and order',
which had sprung up in all the large towns, in the absence of
'salutary and necessary interference of the legislature'.

Young enjoyed this high-class society as a source of pleasure
and patients. He danced, performed instrumental music, and
sang heartily.

In London he prepared medical lectures and sought important
medical appointments. His lectures gave a comprehensive view
of medical science. They were far too concentrated for ordinary
students to follow, and his audiences were small.

After various attempts he became a Physician to one of the famous hospitals, St George's. He retained this position to the end of his life, even after he ceased to be dependent on medicine for the extra income he thought necessary to uphold his position as a gentleman who could reciprocate visits with the best society. He was not successful with the medical students, who considered him deficient in warmth and earnestness. He did not easily realize what points they found difficult, because they presented no difficulty to himself. They said that 'Dr Young was a great philosopher, but a bad physician'. In fact, Young was technically successful, but not popular.

His medical critics said he was inclined to be more interested in the disease that the patient, and gave too qualified and complicated advice. Patients wanted to be told simply and clearly how to get well. Young was unable to do this, partly because of the subtlety of his mind and his scientific objectivity, but also because he did not express himself in a way that ordinary people could easily understand and appreciate.

He composed an immense *Introduction to Medical Literature*, and sold all the rights for one hundred pounds, remarking that 'it was too good a book to be worth more'.

VI

DECIPHERING THE EGYPTIAN HIEROGLYPHICS

Young behaved as if he considered it his duty to give first place to medicine in the moral importance of his occupations, though he had less success in it than in his other two main activities: natural science and literature. He wrote of medicine with a solemn sense of responsibility, and of natural science with a level respect, but of literary scholarship with love and affection. His attitude was reflected in the series of biographies he wrote for the *Encyclopaedia Britannica*. These were distinguished for their grasp of the intellectual merit of their subjects, of difficulties with which they were confronted, and how they overcame them. Young was gifted in formulating difficulties as problems to be solved. This enabled him to deal with the essence of a man's contribution in a brief entry.

Young's own characteristics were reflected in his biographies. His most elaborate was on Henry Cavendish, who privately pursued perfection, without thought of publication, under conditions of wealthy and aristocratic leisure. There were similarities in their modes of thought and attitude to physics, but there were also differences. Cavendish behaved as if he was frightened of the public, and as if his discoveries were his own private property. Young kept his researches anonymous for reasons arising from his moral preoccupations. These were due in the main to the results of his abandonment of Quakerism. Like many apostates, he was left with a permanent residual strain in his conscious and his unconscious mind. This was an important factor in his repeated failures of adjustment to situations, in spite of his almost unparalleled talents.

His biography of Porson was the most successful; he wrote of him, and of Greek scholarship with a love and affectionate grace which showed that he was emotionally at ease with the man and the subject. Literary scholarship had been his first intellectual devotion while he was still an earnest Quaker child. At the age of eighteen he had been able to bandy Greek emendations with the great but bibulous scholar, famous for pouring himself, in the midst of inspired suggestions, yet one more drink from an empty bottle.

Young had been consulted on the interpretation of damaged documents from Herculaneum, which had been fused together under the heat and pressure of volcanic ash. He worked on them textually, and also as a scientist to detach the layers in as intact a form as possible. His researches in this field caused him to be consulted when analogous problems arose.

In 1814 the fragments of an Egyptian papyrus, which had been soaked in seawater, were sent to him. This interested him in the problem of deciphering Egyptian hieroglyphics. As he was about to leave for his usual summer vacation at Worthing, he took with him copies of the inscriptions on the famous Rosetta stone, and existing material on their decipherment. There are three inscriptions, one in sacred language, another in common language, and a third in Greek. Porson and others had already effectively restored the missing parts of the Greek inscription, but not much progress had been made on the other two. Scholars such as de Sacy, Akerblad, and Champollion had deciphered isolated features.

During the summer of 1814 Young succeeded, with intense labour, in deciphering the second inscription. He became very impatient to read Champollion's book *L'Égypte sous les Pharaons*, published in 1814, to see exactly how far he had got. He had already been warned by de Sacy to be careful in any dealings with Champollion, who was liable to appropriate other people's ideas without acknowledgment. When he received a copy of

Champollion's book he saw at once that Champollion had made little progress.

Young printed an account of his work in 1816, which was circulated among scholars in the field, but not published until 1821. Champollion, also in 1821, published a memoir with the title *De l'Écriture Hiératique des Anciens Égyptiens*, in which he announced as an original discovery one of the conclusions Young had announced five years before, and made an error which showed that he had not yet properly conceived the existence of phonetic hieroglyphics. Champollion withdrew and tried to suppress this work, and then sent copies of the plates, without the dates and letter-press to Young, who was left in ignorance of the fact that these had been published in 1821.

After the publication of Young's work in 1821, Champollion made great progress in the decipherment of the hieroglyphs and Egyptian literature. He was primarily an Egyptologist. It was his main occupation, and he was a scholar of vast knowledge and intense industry. It seems conclusive that he got the main key to the hieroglyphs from Young, and then, with his single-minded concentration, overtook him. Young, or course, had his major fields of natural science and medicine also to pursue.

Champollion had great difficulty in admitting his indebtedness to anybody. He and his followers tried to establish their independence and priority of Young, and the national friction between England and France exacerbated the conflict. Champollion made an outstanding contribution, but he appears to have suffered from the megalomania, which sometimes afflicts scholars, of claiming to have discovered everything of importance in his own field.

In 1815 Young had written to a friend: 'My translation is printed: it is anonymous, and must for some time remain so: but everybody whose approbation is worth having will know the author.' The document which he circulated in 1816 was a revision of this decipherment. He had hoped that it would appear more quickly. 'The printers at Cambridge are models of slow and dignified deliberation. I made it a condition in August last that my paper should be immediately printed. It was accepted; and now, in January, the three sheets are not yet worked off; but it is of little consequence, or rather none at all . . .'

One of the most difficult problems in the interpretation of hieroglyphics was the discovery of how primitive pictorial characters were modified in order to give them sound, or phonetic, as well as pictorial significance. Young had noticed that the

Egyptian and Chinese characters for sun, moon and country were virtually the same. He concluded that Chinese was a very ancient language. The original characters were modified by a variety of signs, in order to add sound values to them. Young therefore suspected that a similar thing had happened in Ancient Egyptian, and this led him to the first major advance in its interpretation.

He gave a substantial account of his researches in an article on *Egypt*, published in 1819, in the *Encyclopaedia Britannica*. He signed his articles with an abbreviated Latin pseudonym, which indicated that he considered that his success in his own profession had not been equal to his hopes, and that his researches were esteemed more in Europe than in his own country.

Fresnel, great man as he was, handsomely acknowledged Young's priority in the wave-theory of light, as soon as he became acquainted with the facts, though he had worked independently, and had done more than Young to extend the theory and make it acceptable. His conduct was in marked contrast with that of Champollion. The French Academy of Sciences admirably recognized Young's achievements, electing him in 1827 one of its eight Foreign Associates. The other candidates included Bessel, Robert Brown, and John Dalton.

Young tried in his conscious mind not to give much attention to priority, but he was much concerned when it was not duly accorded to him. For all his comprehensive and creative genius, he had rather bald deficiences of mind and personality in some directions. His individuality was so marked that it was a hindrance as well as an advantage.

VII

GENIUS, LEARNING AND INEPTITUDE

Young's ineptitude in managing his relations with the world, exemplified by his contradictory attitudes on priority and on anonymity was repeated in his scientific activities on behalf of the state. He held that he was exempt from anonymity in these activities, because they were on behalf of the public. His conduct on, and of, government commissions was similar in its virtues and defects to his work in science and scholarship. Intellectual investigation was always well and often profoundly done, but there was a deficiency in the handling of the social and political aspects of the scientific and political questions under consideration.

His great scientific abilities and high social and political connections caused him to be invited to join and conduct commissions on technical and scientific problems of concern to the state.
One of the earliest of these was on the design of ships. A new
form of ships' frame had been proposed by an able master shipwright, or naval architect. Young investigated the theoretical
mechanics of the design thoroughly, and confirmed that it had
many advantages. In the process, he investigated the general
principles of naval architecture, and incidentally, the strength of
wooden structures constructed according to the usual carpenter's
principles. His report, upon which he based a memoir in the
Philosophical Transactions in 1814, enraged the conventional
shipwrights, showing that they were out of date, and at the same
time embarrassed the Admiralty, who informed him that 'though
science is much respected by their Lordships, and your paper
is much esteemed by them, it is too learned'.

Young was appointed secretary of a Commission set up in
1816, for ascertaining the length of the seconds pendulum, com-
prising the metre and the yard, and considering the adoption
of a more uniform system of weights and measures in the British
empire. The length of the seconds pendulum was at first believed to be so accurately determinable that a permanent standard
measure of length might be based on it, but this was presently
found not to be so. Peacock remarked that 'the pride of philosophy was destined to encounter a similar rebuke' to that suffered by the French inventors of the metre, when they believed
they had based it on the supposedly immutable and accurately
known size of the earth.

The Commission declined to recommend decimalization, but,
observed Peacock, 'their successors in 1837 came to an opposite
conclusion, which public opinion has already sufficiently confirmed, and which cannot fail before long to receive the sanction
of the Legislature'. More than a hundred years passed before
Peacock's forecast was confirmed.

Young was appointed a member of a Committee of the Royal
Society in 1814 to advise the Home Office on the dangers arising
from the introduction of the use of gas. Experiments made on
behalf of this committee showed that flame did not pass easily
down fine tubes, a discovery Humphry Davy subsequently
applied in the invention of the miner's safety lamp.

In 1818 Young was appointed superintendent of the Nautical
Almanac, and Secretary of the Board of Longitude. The Nautical
Almanac, which had been started in 1765 for the benefit of

mariners, nevertheless had been so full and accurate as to be useful to astronomers. In latter years, however, the quality of the computing had declined, and the number of errors in the tables had increased. Young proceeded to take steps to eliminate errors which would endanger navigators, but he adhered strictly to the view that the Almanac was primarily for mariners, and did not improve it in directions desired by the astronomers who had come to use it. The astronomer F. Baily drew attention to these shortcomings in a temperate article, but they were dismissed by Young as 'superfluous and frivolous' in the Journal of the Royal Institution. Young's critics thought this not an appropriate place for the publication of astronomical matters.

In 1828 the Board of Longitude was dissolved, and its functions taken over by the Admiralty. They appointed Young as superintendent of the Nautical Almanac, together with Faraday and Sabine as his scientific advisers. This strengthened the position of Young, and annoyed the astronomers still more. The latter presented their criticisms to the Prime Minister, the Duke of Wellington. Young adhered to his position, but he was already ill, and died two months later. The Admiralty thereupon asked the Royal Astronomical Society to report on the Nautical Almanac; following this, it was entirely reorganized.

Peacock commented that it would be difficult for Young's warmest admirers to justify his conduct of this matter. His argument that the astronomical improvement would involve the Government in expense was 'absolutely unworthy of notice', and his argument that it would put in the hands of seamen more information than they required could hardly be regarded as an embarrassment to navigation. Nor was there substance in Young's argument that astronomers had no claim for such public financial aid. 'It is precisely in those cases, where private enterprise must necessarily fail, or where no effectual co-operation can be other-otherwise secured, that it becomes the duty of a government to interpose; for, by such interference wisely and judiciously exercised, the great body of the people will be taught to regard the machinery of government not as designed for the interest of particular classes and parties, but as essentially necessary to the attainment of much higher objects, the promotion of science, of education, of the public health, and of rational progress in whatever concerns the good of the community.'

So commented Young's eminent biographer in 1855. Young's views on the relation between government and science led him to resist the introduction of computers for calculating the nautical tables, on the ground that human computers were cheaper. They contributed to the national failure to develop Babbage's great invention, as important for the future as James Watt's steam engine and Faraday's electromagnetic induction.

In 1829 Young became ill with what he believed was asthma. His condition steadily declined until, on 10 May, he died in his London home. His genius had been fully recognized by a comparatively small number of eminent persons and organizations, and a medallion to his memory was placed in Westminster Abbey.

TEACHERS

THOMAS HENRY HUXLEY

THOMAS HENRY HUXLEY
1825–1895

I

MASTER OF THE WORD

THOMAS HENRY HUXLEY'S talents were particularly suited to the situation in which he found himself. In 1859, when Darwin's *Origin of Species* appeared, he was thirty-four. He had already published seventy scientific papers. His intellectual powers were mature, and his position as a research scientist in anatomy was assured. He had shown outstanding ability as a lecturer at the School of Mines in Jermyn Street, which he had joined in 1854, especially in those courses designed for working men. 'I am sick', he wrote, 'of the dilettante middle class, and mean to try what I can do with these hard-handed fellows who live among facts.'

Huxley was splendidly equipped to understand and expound Darwin's revolutionary theory of evolution. These qualities were, however, only a part of his total talent. He might have been effective only within comparatively limited circles, but he had other qualities that enabled him to enlighten and influence the broad public. He regarded public exposition as a serious and responsible task. He said that his public lectures should be described as 'People's lectures . . . *Popular* lectures I hold to be an abomination unto the Lord . . .' He carried conviction because of his human qualities as well as his intellectual competence. Most people could not help liking him. The poet Tennyson wrote in 1871 that he 'was charming. We had much talk. He was chivalrous, wide, and earnest, so that one could not but enjoy talking with him.' People commented on his power of putting different kinds of persons at their ease, and inspiring them to talk.

Huxley spoke with an element of command as well as scientific authority. He taught the public what they had to believe, as well as why they should believe it. He had started life as an assistant naval surgeon, and no doubt he had learned as an officer how to give orders. Huxley regarded his naval experience as one of the most formative influences in his life. He retained some of the best qualities of the officer, and when he became the head of a laboratory he was known among his assistants as 'the General'.

He acquired his extraordinary clear and pointed style of writing and speaking slowly, by prolonged effort. It was the product of the severe self-discipline of an exceedingly swift and incisive mind, which had functioned originally with chaotic intensity. Huxley's mental intensity was associated with a violent temper, and he had learned to control both. His tautness of expression had an elegance which derived from internal tension, like the elegance of a modern bridge derived from pre-stressed steel. His contemporary, the physicist Stokes, was also celebrated for a clear, calm, impressive style. He had a rock-like imperturbability, and his friends were surprised to learn that when he was a boy he had been violent and uncontrollable. People felt that Huxley and Stokes, in spite of their calm manner, had strong emotions, and were not to be trifled with. This increased their authority.

Darwin did not possess the qualities required to achieve the quick conversion of the broad public prejudiced against his ideas, which was necessary in the interest of the progress of science and civilization. Huxley learned only from experience that he possessed them. The critical moment came at the Meeting of the British Association at Oxford in 1860. It was expected that Darwin's new theory would be discussed, and a crowd of conservatives assembled under the leadership of the Bishop of Oxford, Samuel Wilberforce, to ridicule it. Wilberforce was a fluent and insinuating speaker, known in some quarters as 'Soapy Sam'. He was regarded as being qualified to speak on science as he had taken a first-class degree in mathematics in his youth.

Wilberforce, who had been coached by Richard Owen, the anatomist and anti-evolutionist, on the biological details, attacked the new theory flippantly. At the end of his address he turned to Huxley and 'begged to know, was it through his grandfather or his grandmother that he claimed his descent from a monkey'. Huxley exclaimed to his neighbour: 'The Lord hath delivered him into mine hands.' He waited until he was invited to reply, and after dealing with the biological arguments which Wilberforce had retailed, said that 'a man has no reason to be ashamed of having an ape for his grandfather. If there were an ancestor whom I should feel ashamed in recalling it would rather be a *man*—a man of restless and versatile intellect—who distracted the attention of his hearers from the real point at issue by eloquent digressions and skilled appeals to religious prejudice'.

Wilberforce expressed the attitude of the old social ruling class dominated by the gentry and the Church of England. He and his followers had taken it for granted that they were in social authority, besides having the better arguments. The unexpected discomfiture of the champion who slunk out of the hall abashed, as if he had 'forgotten to behave like a perfect gentleman', left his followers taken aback.

Huxley's social victory was even more important than his scientific victory. It marked a shift in scientific authority from one class to another. He had exposed the representative of the old ruling class as a vulgarian; this was much more damaging than the exposure of his scientific deficiencies.

Huxley's defeat of the opposition in the presence of an important and intensely involved audience made him aware of the scope of his powers. When he made this speech he was not an elder statesman of science in his sixties. He was thirty-five. To have made that speech in that situation at that age showed a very unusual capacity. Huxley said that the Oxford experience had changed 'my opinion as to the practical value of the art of public speaking, and that from that time forth I should carefully cultivate it, and try to leave off hating it. I did the former, but never quite succeeded in the latter . . .'

Huxley had a balanced endowment of scientific and literary ability. He explained the fundamental relation between science and literature long ago, also in 1860, when he said that 'science and literature are not two things, but two sides of one thing'. He did not write easily. He told his sister Lizzie in 1854: 'My pen is not a very facile one and what I write costs me a good deal of trouble.' Twenty-eight years later he remarked that 'My own way is to write and re-write things, until by some sort of instinctive process they acquire the condensation and symmetry which satisfies me. And I really could not say how my original drafts are improved until they somehow improve themselves.' He said that 'it is an excellent rule always to erase anything that strikes one as particularly smart when writing it . . .'

He was over sixty before he began to enjoy writing. He remarked in 1889 that 'You can't think how I enjoy writing now for the first time in my life.' The subject on which he wrote so relievedly was Agnosticism, his personal kind of religion without theology. His preoccupation with religion and his relief in writing about it suggest that some of his internal tension and his early difficulties in mastering expression in speech and writing were connected with feelings of childhood guilt and religious complexes. His English style was deeply influenced by the English translation of the Old Testament. He advocated the study of the Bible in the education of the people. He said that 'the mass of the people should not be deprived of the one great literature which is open to them.' He shocked some of his ardent anti-clerical friends by giving this as his reason for supporting the study of the Bible as a cultural work in the new Board Schools of the 1870's for the masses.

He became to evolutionary theory what Paul had been to Christianity. His friend Herbert Spencer noted his clerical attributes. He was, among other things, an inspired preacher. He presently entitled a collection of his addresses *Lay Sermons*.

Huxley's scientific reputation was firmly established before he emerged on the public stage. He had accumulated a very large amount of new anatomical information during his voyage in the *Rattlesnake*. This was important in itself, but his interpretation of it was still more so. Richard Owen had interpreted the structure, or morphological type, of animals in terms of the notion of an 'archetype'. He supposed organisms were constructed according to a sort of blue-print in the primordial mind of Nature, or an idea in the mind of God. The notion was derived from the Platonic concept, according to which things were regarded as concretizations of the Idea. According to Plato, the Idea was prior to the Thing, and Matter was based on Mind. Theologians and theologically-minded men like Richard Owen found this idealist philosophy very acceptable.

Huxley started from the opposite philosophical position. He believed that the notion of an animal type must be derived from the study of concrete specimens. The Thing came first, and the Type or Idea was derived from it. His philosophical position was realist, or as some might say, materialist; in fact, it was Baconian.

He was very sceptical of hypotheses on general relationships between animals, until Darwin had provided adequate evidence for them in the *Origin*. This made Huxley's subsequent support for Darwin all the more effective.

In his first years at the School of Mines he worked out his system of teaching biology, which was very widely adopted. It was based on the thorough study of a few kinds of animals, carefully chosen so that comparison would enable general biological principles to be drawn from them.

As the School of Mines was concerned with the strata of the earth and their contents, Huxley was naturally involved in the study of fossils. Before 1859 he had already published about twenty papers on their anatomy, especially of fossil fishes. He compared these with living species, and his work on these vertebrate animals led him to the study of the anatomy of the skull. He had already founded the modern approach to this by 1858. In the previous year, Richard Owen had contended that man has a unique brain and skull. This fitted in with those who believed that man was specially created by God.

Huxley made a thorough comparative study of the anatomy of the skulls of man and the higher apes. His lectures on this subject were published under the title of *Man's Place in Nature* in 1863. It stirred deep popular attention. Weldon has expressed the opinion that this made Huxley more than ever conscious of his duty as a teacher of the people at large. What he said of Joseph Priestley he began to feel himself: 'It seems to have been Priestley's feeling that he was a man and a citizen before he was a philosopher and that the duties of the two former positions are at least as imperative as those of the latter.'

In spite of his increasing public activities, Huxley published about fifty technical papers between 1860 and 1870. His *Manual of the Comparative Anatomy of Vertebrated Animals* involved enormous anatomical labours. His study of the anatomy of birds revealed their relationship with the reptiles. He started work on the classification of the races of mankind. His *Elementary Lessons in Physiology*, published in 1866, became the best known of all elementary textbooks on biology This work, the first textbook on physiology in the English language, was written in the midst of multitudinous and pressing duties. His grandson A. F. Huxley has described how his own mother possesses 'an amusing copy of this first edition'. It is a small green volume externally exactly like the famous textbook, 'but if you look inside every page is totally blank'. It was specially made up by his publisher and sent to Huxley 'to remind him to hurry up with the manuscript'.

An illustration of the acuteness and depth of T. H. Huxley's knowledge is seen in his account of the structure of muscle in his textbook on *The Crayfish*. The ablest microscopists of the second half of the nineteenth century had similar conceptions, but by the middle of the twentieth century these had been dismissed as figments of the imagination. Then, in 1953, H. E. Huxley showed with the electron microscope that the old conception was indeed substantially correct.

When he became professor at the Royal College of Science at South Kensington, he elaborated his system of instruction with the assistance of Michael Foster, Ray Lankester, Thiselton Dyer, and W. Rutherford. It became the pattern for many of the world's universities.

Huxley's influence penetrated deeply through his colleagues and pupils. Michael Foster went to Cambridge and founded the now world-famous Cambridge schools of physiology and biochemistry, which have inspired numerous men of genius, including C. S. Sherrington and F. Gowland Hopkins.

II

'I AM DARWIN'S BULLDOG'

Great gifts of exposition were not sufficient for Huxley to accomplish what he did for the theory of evolution. The ancient belief that the history of the world and man had been short and was static had been passed on from an earlier social order, and was irrelevant to the contemporary society. It was like a huge pile of ideological refuse, to which reactionary sections of society clung as an anchor against the ideological changes which reflected the overtaking of the old social order by the new.

The body of opinion attached to the old ideas was not merely misguided. It was almost insufferably complacent, and its opponents when challenged could be nasty as well as superior; they felt that their social position as well as their ideas were being undermined.

Huxley had the fighting spirit to stand up to ill-natured opposition, and the tenacity to hold on until ignorance and obstinacy were overcome. His description of himself as Darwin's bulldog epitomized these qualities in himself.

He described Darwin as quite another sort of dog. He considered Darwin's mind 'conspicuous for its powerful humility and strong gentleness'. He had 'a marvellous dumb sagacity about him—like that of a sort of miraculous dog'. He said that his own mind and Darwin's were characterized respectively by 'mere vulpine sharpness and genius'.

He once advised Darwin to leave sharp passages out of a paper, for 'if I say a savage thing, it is only "pretty Fanny's way"; but if you do, it is not likely to be forgotten'. He wrote of Darwin in 1882 that 'he had a clear rapid intelligence, a great memory, a vivid imagination, and what made his greatness was the strict subordinating of all these to his love of truth'. Darwin's mind was free from the kind of inhibitions that restricted Huxley's action on his own creative ideas.

Before the publication of the *Origin of Species*, Huxley had already begun to act as Darwin's intellectual agent, but he had profound original thoughts of his own. He wrote to Lyell early in 1859 on the problem of whether the changes in species were continuous or discontinuous. He said that 'the fixity and definite limitations of species, genera, and larger groups appear to me to be perfectly consistent with the theory of transmutation. In other words, I think *transmutation* may take place without transition.'

He continued: 'I may illustrate what I mean by a chemical example. In an organic compound, having a precise and definite composition, you may effect all sorts of transmutations by substituting an atom of one element for an atom of another element. You may in this way produce a vast series of modifications—but each modification is definite in its composition, and there are no transitional or intermediate steps between one definite compound and another. I have a sort of notion that similar laws of definite combination rule over the modifications of organic bodies, and that in passing from species to species "Natura facit saltum".' (Nature proceeds by leaps.)

Here he anticipated Mendel's fundamental ideas, and those of modern molecular biology. He was aided in arriving at them by the engineering and structural characteristics of his mode of imaginative thought. He said of his great friend Tyndall: 'a favourite problem of his is—given the molecular forces in a mutton chop, deduce Hamlet or Faust therefrom. He is confident that the Physics of the Future will solve this easily . . .'

He asked in 1861: 'Why does not somebody go to work experimentally, and get at the law of variation for some one species of plant?' Mendel had in fact begun just that in Brno.

Huxley was prodigiously busy at the time, but occupation with other things is not a completely adequate explanation of why he did not pursue his fundamental ideas himself. If they had weighed on him as heavily as Darwin's ideas weighed on Darwin, he would have put other things on one side. There was a psychological censor in addition to other deterrents.

Darwin would never have dreamt of putting other things in front of research. Huxley was concerned at least as much with implications as with discovery. Primarily, Darwin's genius was for discovery, while Huxley's was for teaching, which he carried out on a magnificent scale. He taught in the lecture room, in the debating hall, in the working-men's institutes, in the Government offices of Whitehall, in the meetings of committees and Royal

Commissions. He wrote incessantly in the newspapers and magazines. He participated in the founding of scientific journals for the instruction of the public. He worked out methods of teaching biology, and compiled formative textbooks. He wrote about ninety essays on science, which constitute a classic of English literature. To all this he added the force of personality, which made his opponents feel the sharpness of his arguments. They hesitated to attack the science defended by this highly accomplished debater, who combined the qualities of a biologist, a philosopher and a bulldog. Among the many lessons taught by Huxley's achievement, the role of character in ensuring the proper understanding and use of science was one of the most important.

III

RELIGION AND CLASS

Huxley said that the only religion that appealed to him was 'prophetic Judaism'. His style owed a great deal to the incisive magisterial clarity of the Old Testament prophets. Through the medium of the Biblical style he was able to reach the masses in the only educated accent that they then knew. Up to that time the literary education, such as it was, had been restricted largely to what they had learned through Bible classes and Sunday schools. The technical knowledge they had acquired in crafts and industry was passed on in a dialect virtually of its own, different from that of the conventionally literate.

As the clarity of Huxley's agnosticism was facilitated by the expulsion of theology from religion, his literary style was enhanced by severe rationalistic pruning. He redoubled criticism and self-criticism. Through this he became an ancestor of movements which were a good deal different from those in which he had worked and created himself. The middle class to which he belonged took over his ideas, and various movements in it developed them in their own ways, which differed from his. His son said that he had a 'strong sense of the decencies of life, appearing elsewhere in his constant respect for the ordinary conventions and his dislike for mere Bohemianism as such'.

Huxley's high degree of identification with the middle class was a fundamental element in his influence. If it had been less, his influence would have been much less immediately effective. It has been said that teachers should never be too much in front of their publics, if their work is to have quick recognition and effect. Orthodoxy in wide social, political and cultural areas facilitated Huxley's effectiveness in changing opinion on those matters on which he was unorthodox. In his private life he was a model of middle-class virtues. He was a delightful and adored parent. He sold the gold Royal Medal, presented to him by the Royal Society when he was twenty-seven, to raise £50 to help the impoverished widow of his brother George.

The teacher cannot be effective unless there is a large area of agreement between the audience and himself, however violent the initial difference may be over some special point, such as biological theory. This is why Huxley often seems today a surprisingly conventional figure. For example, he thought Joseph Priestley a bit of a bore, and Thomas Sprat superficial. Though he strongly sympathized with working-men, he never dreamt of regarding himself as one of them.

He was a Protestant, who wanted the ruling class to adopt more up-to-date ideas, make itself more efficient, and raise its moral standards. He was not concerned with changing the social system, except as it might be modified in the long run by such forces as education and science.

He was very active in promoting scientific research and education, but even in these fields his ideas were not unconventional. He regarded pure science as the paragon of scientific activity, and Faraday as the model scientist. In spite of his promotion of technical education, he believed that technology must look to pure science for fertilizing ideas. He did not stress the equally important point that it should develop itself in its own right, on a basis of equality with pure science.

At the Royal College of Science his influence worked in the direction of improved teaching of science in the spirit of Faraday, rather than towards the creation of the kind of technological university which Britain really needed. The influence of his teaching of science as an essential element in culture persisted longer through the influence of followers such as Sir Richard Gregory and H. G. Wells. They continued his work of educating the public, but on the possibilities and proper use of science, rather than primarily aiming at the change of the organization of science, and of the social order of which it was a manifestation.

In a less direct way Huxley's literary influence also continued through such figures as Sir Leslie Stephen, and the Bloomsbury intellectuals of the twentieth century. Their culture, manifested in its most powerful form in Maynard Keynes, inherited much from Huxley's scientific rationalism. But unlike Huxley they were distant from, as well as outside the masses. Huxley's grandson

5*

Aldous might be regarded as an inheritor of the literary part of his talent. Huxley could not have written such a negative work as Aldous's *Brave New World*. If he had addressed himself to the same problems, he would have had something positive and constructive to say. Aldous was closer to the Bloomsbury writers than the scientific mainstream to which his grandfather belonged.

Huxley's grandson Julian has inherited his positive, constructive, expository spirit. Julian has expounded with a similar talent the bearing of biology on major social problems, such as those of population, and the preservation of wild-life. He has dealt with these in a way which the public, besides specialists, can understand and appreciate.

Huxley was detached in his attitude to the exploited peoples in America and elsewhere. He sided against the South in the American Civil War, but not on sentimental grounds. He wrote to a sister who was living in Tennessee, and whose son was serving in the Confederate Army, that he had 'not the smallest sentimental sympathy for the negro; don't believe in him at all, in short. But it is clear to me that slavery means, for the white man, bad political economy; bad social morality; bad internal political organization, and a bad influence upon free labour and freedom all over the world. For the sake of the white man, therefore, for your children and grandchildren, directly, and for mine, indirectly, I wish to see this system ended. Would that the south had had the wisdom to initiate that end without this miserable war!'

Two years later he joined the committee formed to prosecute Eyre, the Governor of Jamaica, on a charge of murder, for having executed Gordon, a Negro political leader, under martial law. Gordon was a member of the Assembly, and accused of promoting a Negro rising which had been suppressed by force. English upper class opinion was sharply split. Many held that the Governor had acted justifiably in the interests of the security of the state.

Huxley's study of the evidence convinced him that this was not so, and a dangerous precedent was being established. Eyre was personally friendly with some of Huxley's friends. Huxley told his own friends with the utmost frankness that the personal qualities of Eyre and Gordon had nothing to do with the question. Eyre might be a most charming person, and Gordon might be a 'poor type of small political agitator', but there was no sound evidence that he was involved in the rising. Darwin, Spencer,

Huxley, Lyell and J. S. Mill were for the prosecution of Eyre, while Tyndall, Carlyle and Tennyson were against.

Huxley told Tyndall that it was evident that the American Civil War had shown that their political principles were fundamentally different. On these they must agree to differ, and if both of them were strong and wise enough, they would be able to preserve 'that love for one another which I value as one of the good things of my life'.

Huxley also took an unsentimental view of the Irish troubles. When violence broke out and was attributed to the Fenians, he said that it should be 'our business to disappoint them first and extirpate them afterwards'. In this, he and his friend Tyndall were not in disagreement.

IV

ORIGINS

Huxley's father was the son of an innkeeper in Coventry. He became a not very successful schoolmaster. At the time when Thomas Henry was born, on 4 May 1825, he was an assistant in a semi-public school at Ealing, which was then a quiet country village outside London. The school had been brought into a prosperous state by a vigorous headmaster, but declined after his direction. In its palmier days it had educated J. H. Newman, the future cardinal. Huxley said: 'I can hardly find any trace of my father in myself, except an inborn faculty for drawing, which unfortunately, in my case, has never been cultivated, a hot temper, and that amount of tenacity of purpose which unfriendly observers sometimes call obstinacy.'

Huxley may have considered that he had not inherited much from his father, but to others it may not appear so inconsiderable. In fact, Huxley's skill as a draughtsman in making anatomical drawings was an essential element in his early success as a scientist.

He felt, however, that he was very much a mother's son. As a child he loved her passionately, and used to cry secretly in bed at night, from a morbid fear that she might die. Her praise or blame was joy or misery to him. His mother, whose maiden name was Rachel Withers, bore his father eight children, of whom Thomas Henry was the seventh and youngest surviving child.

Huxley said: 'Physically and mentally I am the son of my mother so completely—even down to peculiar movements of the hands, which made their appearance in me as I reached the age she had when I noticed them . . .' The not inconsiderable traces of his father were almost completely overshadowed by these striking maternal characteristics.

'My mother was a slender brunette of an emotional and energetic temperament, and possessed of the most piercing black eyes I ever saw in a woman's head. With no more education than other women of the middle classes in her day, she had an excellent mental capacity. Her most distinguished characteristic, however, was rapidity of thought. If one ventured to suggest she had not taken so much time to arrive at any conclusion, she would say, "I cannot help it, things flash across me". That peculiarity has been passed on to me in full strength; it has often stood me in good stead; it has sometimes played me sad tricks, and it has always been a danger. But, after all, if my time were to come over again, there is nothing I would less willingly part with than my inheritance of mother-wit.'

His mother was restless, talkative and untiring until she died at the age of sixty-six. She was as active and energetic as a young woman, almost to the end.

In a sense, Thomas Henry Huxley was to some extent to have his time over again, through the reappearance of these characteristics in his grandson Sir Julian Huxley, who possesses a quite exceptional rapidity of thought, and a gift of instant common-sense reaction allied to mother-wit, which made him an unsurpassed broadcaster on science. Julian Huxley combines with these qualities a most attractive tone of voice which contributes to his broadcasting talent. Perhaps he has inherited this voice from his grandfather; if so, one may conclude that quality of voice was also among Thomas Henry Huxley's gifts as a speaker, and that he would indeed have been a marvellous radio and television teacher in the university of the air.

As the son of a schoolteacher, Thomas Henry received particularly odd schooling. He had virtually no systematic instruction. At the age of eight he was sent to the semi-public school in its declining condition. He was there for two years, until it disintegrated. After this, his father returned to Coventry, where he eked out an existence as the manager of a savings bank.

Referring to his two years at the disintegrating school, Huxley said that 'though my way of life had made me acquainted with all sorts and conditions of men, from the highest to the lowest, I deliberately affirm that the society I fell into at school was the worst I have ever known. We boys were average lads, with much the same inherent capacity for good and evil as any others; but the people who were set over us cared about as much for our intellectual and moral welfare as if they were baby-farmers. We were left to the operation of the struggle for existence among ourselves, and bullying was the least of the ill practices current among us. Almost the only cheerful reminiscences in connection with the place which arises in my mind is that of a battle I had with one of my classmates, who had bullied me until I could stand it no longer. I was a very slight lad, but there was a wild-cat element in me which, when roused, made up for lack of weight, and I licked my adversary effectually. However, one of my first experiences of the extremely rough-and-ready nature of justice, as exhibited by the course of things in general, arose out of the fact that I—the victor— had a black eye, while he—the vanquished—had none, so that I got into disgrace and he did not. We made it up, and thereafter I was unmolested. One of the greatest shocks I ever received in my life was to be told a dozen years afterwards by the groom who brought me my horse in a stable-yard in Sydney that he was my quondam antagonist. He had a long story of family misfortune to account for his position, but at the time it was necessary to deal very cautiously with mysterious strangers in New South Wales, and on inquiry I found that the unfortunate young man had not only been "sent out", but had undergone more than one colonial conviction.'

In 1860, when he was profoundly distressed by the death of his first son at the age of three, he wrote a revealing letter to Charles Kingsley, in which he said of himself that he had been 'kicked into the world a boy without guide or training, or with worse than none, I confess to my shame that few men have drunk deeper of all kinds of sin than I. Happily, my course was arrested in time—before I had earned absolute destruction—and for long years I have been slowly and painfully climbing, with many a fall, towards better things.'

This concern with redeeming himself was one of the strongest preoccupations of his life. It enhanced his persuasive power, and was reflected in his literary style.

He told Kingsley that this drive did not arise from any hope of immortality or future reward. 'No, I can tell you exactly what has been at work. *Sartor Resartus* led me to know that a deep sense of religion was compatible with the entire absence of theology.' Science had given him a resting-place independent of authority and tradition, and love had opened up to him a view of the sanctity of human nature, and had impressed him with a deep sense of responsibility. If he was 'not a worn-out debauched, uselesss carcass of a man', it was because these agencies had been at work on him.

Huxley put Carlyle, a literary figure, as the first influence in his redemption. As will presently be seen, Carlyle had a comparable influence on Tyndall. However, when the theory of evolution was promulgated by Darwin, Carlyle became one of its bitterest opponents, and never forgave Huxley for expounding its bearing on man, in *Man's Place in Nature*. When Carlyle was near the end of his life, Huxley happened to see him one day walking along the opposite side of a street, frail and lonely. He crossed the street and greeted him. Carlyle looked up, stared and said: 'You're Huxley, aren't you? The man that says we are all descended from monkeys', and then walked away.

Huxley said he learned from Carlyle to hate shams and humbug, and was inspired by him to teach himself German. This had the unforeseen consequence later on that he was one of the few young English scientists of the day who could follow the very energetic development of German science in its own language.

He also probably acquired some of the vigour of his style from Carlyle. Unfortunately, while Carlyle stimulated the young scientists of the 1840's, he was unable to provide them with an adequate intellectual philosophy.

Huxley started to educate himself by reading his father's books. When a boy of twelve he found a copy of Hutton's *Geology*, and read it in the middle of the night by candlelight. He was fascinated by Sir William Hamilton's *Logic*, which strengthened an early interest in philosophy. This Sir William Hamilton had a remarkable English style, to which Huxley no doubt also responded.

Huxley said that his great desire was to be a mechanical engineer, but the fates were against it. He was drawn to study medicine because his two brothers-in-law, who were doctors, took an interest in him; in short, he studied medicine because it was the direction from which he could get help. He said that he was not sure that he had not through all his life been at heart a mechanical engineer, who had been unfaithful to his profession. He said he was subsequently rather horrified to think how very little he had ever known or cared about medicine as the art of healing. 'The only part of my professional course which really and deeply interested me was physiology, which is the mechanical engineering of living machines.'

There had never been much of the genuine naturalist in him.

He never collected anything, until he started on gentians in his last years. 'What I cared for was the architectural and engineering part of the business, the working out the wonderful unity of plan in the thousands and thousands of diverse living constructions, and the modifications of similar apparatuses to serve diverse ends.'

Huxley's talent for research into the structure of the tissues of organisms seems to have been inherited by his grandson Professor A. F. Huxley, the younger half-brother of Julian, who received a Nobel Prize in 1963 for his researches on the structure and mechanism of nerves.

This passionate interest in structure led to Thomas Henry's being taken, at the age of thirteen or fourteen, to a post-mortem. He worked with intense absorption for two or three hours, and did not cut himself, but became very ill. He presently recovered, but ever after suffered from hypochondriacal dyspepsia. How far Huxley's illness was physical and how far psychological the medicine of the day never determined.

His medical brother-in-law gave him some instruction, and then he was sent to Rotherhithe in the London docks to work as an assistant, before going to medical school. He was horrified by the social squalor, and the living illustrations of the conditions which he was reading about in Carlyle's denunciatory works. Then he was apprenticed to his other medical brother-in-law in North London, and began to attend medical classes. At the age of seventeen he competed in an examination, and came second. If he had come first, he would have won an exhibition which would have almost certainly led him into medical practice, and he would not have become a scientist. Huxley's father applied at Charing Cross Hospital for free scholarships for Thomas Henry and his elder brother James Edmund. One of the references he gave for his boys was the former pupil of the Ealing school, John Henry Newman.

The Huxley brothers began their studies at Charing Cross in 1842. Thomas Henry soon came under the influence of the excellent teacher of physiology, Wharton Jones, who gave him his first thorough scientific training. Equipped with this, Huxley looked into things for himself. He discovered a membrane in the root of the human hair which had not hitherto been noticed. It became known as Huxley's layer. Wharton urged him to publish his discovery, and helped with the revision of his English. Huxley said that at that time, and for many years afterwards, he detested writing, and would take no pains with it.

To have made and published a scientific discovery at the age of nineteen, while a student, was a clear mark of ability. At about the same time he conceived a plan for a perpetual motion, and summoned up courage to ask Faraday for his advice. When he arrived at the Royal Institution he was told that Faraday had just gone out. He gave the porter a letter containing his plan and turned to leave, when Faraday happened to return. The porter gave Faraday the letter, and he kindly invited the youth to come in. Huxley confusedly tried to explain his idea. Faraday listened courteously, and told him in effect that if the perpetual motion were possible, it would have occurred spontaneously in nature, and overpowered all other forces. Huxley thanked him, but departed unconvinced.

He passed his first medical examination in 1846. A fellow-student, Joseph Fayrer, suggested he should apply to the Director-General of the Naval Medical Service for an appointment. He was called for an interview and told to hold himself ready for an examination. He passed this, and found himself in the Service. He was entered in the books of Nelson's old flagship, the *Victory*, for duty at Haslar Hospital.

His chief at Haslar was Sir John Richardson, a noted naturalist and famous Arctic explorer. He ignored Huxley's presence for several months, to his intense disgust. Then Richardson suddenly stopped him in the hospital square, and said he had not been able to get him a resident post, but intended to keep him until he had got him one he would like. Huxley now realized why he had not been sent to any of the out-of-the-way posts.

After some months Richardson stopped him again, and told him that Captain Owen Stanley was leaving in H.M.S. *Rattlesnake* on an exploratory expedition, and wanted an assistant surgeon who knew some science; would he like the job? Huxley jumped at the offer. So, at the age of twenty, Huxley became assistant surgeon on a notable voyage that was to last four years. Among his messmates at Haslar he had become acquainted with Andrew Clark, Alexander Armstrong and John Watt-Reid, who, like his still earlier friend Fayrer, all became famous doctors. It seems that the Navy was a magnet for ability, a reflection of the rising power of Britain. However, the ability was largely wasted, as the ruling political ideas were opposed to state expenditure on science. Britain had had the chance to create a strong scientific organization, but her rulers failed to take it.

V

H.M.S. RATTLESNAKE

The *Rattlesnake* sailed in 1846 and returned in 1850. She spent about three years in Australian waters, and was at Sydney for nearly a year. The passage within the Great Barrier Reef was surveyed as a route for ships proceeding from India to Sydney, and other surveys were made in the region, off New Guinea and elsewhere. Owing to the death of Captain Stanley, the ship returned without completing all its programme.

Huxley became acquainted with peoples in different stages of civilization, and a vast wealth of animals and plants. He used his skill as a draughtsman to record new and instructive material; he concentrated on anatomical drawings of organisms floating near the surface of the sea. These organisms were not easily preserved, and consequently not well known in Europe. He sent a stream of papers on his findings to Professor Forbes in London. The ship was out of touch with ports for months at a time, and received mail rarely. Years went by, and Huxley received no acknowledgment of his papers. In 1849, in desperation, he drew up a memoir on the *Medusa*, a jelly-like organism. He drew attention to parallels between its structure and that of other organisms in the same family, but he also made the capital observation that it had a feature similar to those found in the embryos of animals with backbones. His mind had been prepared to see this from his reading of Baer and other German literature, and the discovery proved to be of profound significance in the theory of evolution of organisms from lower to higher forms. His knowledge of German had been crucial in enabling him to make this discovery, which was so significant for himself as well as for biology.

When he arrived back in England in 1850 he found that the Royal Society had received and published the work, and a large packet of separate copies was awaiting him. The Royal Society had started to implement the reforms carried through in 1847, aimed at making it a more professional organization restricted to working scientists, and more concentrated on the stimulation of research. Rising young men were looked for and encouraged. The young Huxley was just the kind of man they were looking for, and Forbes proposed him for election. Thus Huxley became a fellow of the Royal Society before he was twenty-six. In the same year he first met his lifelong friend and fellow protagonist of science, John Tyndall.

Forty-three years later Huxley wrote that 'Personal, like national, history has its epochs; brief seasons, during which life is fuller than usual, and the present is more obviously pregnant with the future than at other times. For me the year 1851 constitutes such an epoch.' The Royal Society gave him still more encouragement, by awarding him a Royal Medal in 1852.

Huxley said that he owed a great deal to his naval experience, especially the discipline it imposed on his impulsive manner of working. The hard, close and intense life on the small naval vessel gave him a deep experience of different kinds of men. He observed that his fellow officers were admirable characters, and yet they had little respect for science. It did not follow that men who despised science were to be despised. The scientist had to secure the interest in, and appreciation of science by men who were, as men, at least as good as himself. The naval experience taught Huxley a proper deportment towards non-scientists with superior human qualities, which was invaluable to him later, when he became involved in public affairs.

Another important quality which he acquired, perhaps without knowing it for he does not seem to have commented on it, was the art and habit of command. In four years of giving orders he learned how this had to be done, if it was to be effective. His naval experience gave him an insight into the lower as well as the upper deck. Nevertheless, for all the gain in understanding, it also integrated him with the upper deck. He became a member of the officer class, albeit a liberal one. His attitude to the working class was always that of an understanding superior.

Huxley's habit of command was of essential importance when he started on his campaign of education in the academic and the public world. His audiences responded to his authority as well as his arguments.

The diary which Huxley kept during the voyage of the *Rattlesnake* was found about forty years ago among a pile of old laundry books, where it had lain more or less overlooked for about an equal period. His son Leonard had never had the heart to go through all the mountain of documents that his father left, and the presence of the diary in the material where it ultimately turned up could scarcely have been suspected. The work was edited by Julian Huxley, and first published in 1935.

Charles Darwin had also started his scientific life by a celebrated voyage, of which he kept a diary. The contrast between Huxley's diary and Darwin's was very striking. Huxley's revealed him deeply preoccupied with psychological problems and feelings of failure, to which the scientific notes and beautiful drawings gave second place. In Darwin's diary scientific preoccupation dominated its content from the first page. Darwin suffered severely from illness during his voyage, and remained more or less an invalid for the rest of his life, perhaps from some disease he had contracted. Yet these sufferings always gave second place to science. His mind was remarkably free from strain, however much his body suffered. He described the experiences and observations which gave him the clue to his theory of evolution, and made his diary a scientific classic.

Huxley's diary was comparably remarkable, but as a personal document. It was as introvert as Darwin's was extrovert. Huxley believed that the illness he had contracted at his first post-mortem when he was a boy had been the cause of his lifelong attacks of depression. The character of his diary suggests rather that he had some inborn or early acquired psychological pecularity, which contributed to his melancholia and self-questionings.

He seems to have always been struggling with himself, subduing discordant impulses. His victory over himself helped him to success in struggles with others, both with opponents and the public.

Darwin's social position was quite different. He was on board the *Beagle* primarily as a gentleman naturalist, not a naval officer. It was not his business to order people, and he would never have dreamt of doing it. He left people and arguments to speak for themselves. He was free from Huxley's kind of internal conflict, and devoted his energies almost entirely to the problems of science.

This may help to explain why Darwin was absorbed in research, while Huxley became a master-teacher.

VI

EARNING A LIVING

Huxley's swift and resounding scientific success after his return from the voyage by no means solved his personal problems. He found that in England, then at the height of her power, a scientist 'may earn great distinction, but not bread'. He could receive every kind of invitation, but not enough income to pay his cab-fares. Nothing but what was absolutely practical would then go down in England, and even then one could not earn a decent livelihood, except by working like a galley slave, and intriguing like a courtier. Scientific merit alone was very little good; it had to be backed by tact and knowledge of the world.

Huxley and his friend Tyndall, whom he had met in the train on the way to the British Association Meeting at Ipswich in 1851, applied for the chairs of Natural History and Physics at Toronto, but they were passed over. The same thing happened with regard to the corresponding chairs at Sydney in Australia.

Huxley was loth to leave London, for he regarded it as then '*the* place, the centre of the world'. He advised and pushed Tyndall into securing the chair of Natural Philosophy at the Royal Institution. 'This is where, as I told you, you ought to be—looking to Faraday's place . . . What they want, and what you have, are *clear powers of exposition*—so clear that people may think they understand even if they don't. That is the secret of Faraday's success . . .' Tyndall was appointed to the Royal Institution in 1853.

Though Huxley's pen was not very facile, and writing cost him a good deal of trouble, he began writing regular articles on Contemporary Science for the *Westminster Gazette*, in order to increase his meagre income. This was the beginning of his scientific journalism, which he continued through the rest of his life, contributing to many journals and magazines, and initiating and supporting projects for new journals. The founding of *Nature* owed much to his sustained pioneering in this field. His work as a scientific journalist set a pattern and standard which were followed by Ray Lankester, Chalmers Mitchell and others. In 1854 he got Tyndall to collaborate in the articles for the *Westminster Gazette*.

Huxley was spurred in his intense efforts by his desire to get married. When he had first visited Sydney in 1847, he met Henrietta Anne Heathorn, who was about two years his junior, and was managing her sister's household. He fell in love with her almost at first sight, and they became engaged. They remained in that relationship for all his three years in the region, and for five more years after he returned to England. They held that they could not marry until he had a proper job. At last, in 1854 he was appointed lecturer in Natural History at the School of Mines in Jermyn Street, only a few minutes from Tyndall at the Royal Institution in Albemarle Street, at £200 a year. He was making a further £200 a year by writing articles, books, making translations and giving other lectures. He could now marry.

Miss Heathorn and her parents arrived in England in 1855, but Huxley was shocked to find her very weak after an illness, much more so than he had gleaned from letters. He secured the best attention for her, and she recovered. They were married later in 1855, his friends Tyndall and Hooker attending the wedding. Charles Darwin wrote: 'I hope your marriage will not make you idle; happiness, I fear, is not good for work.' Their marriage was particularly successful. Mrs Huxley bore him three sons and two daughters, and sustained him in his intense labours and the fits of depression which afflicted him.

Huxley's feeling for his children was expressed in a letter to Haeckel in 1868. He said that they worked a greater metamorphosis in men than any other agent. They ripened one wonderfully, and made life ten times better worth having. He enjoyed playing with his children, and delivering lectures to child audiences.

Huxley met Darwin for the first time soon after his return to England, and with the confidence of youth told him of his belief in the sharpness of the division between species, and the absence of transitional forms. He did not know that Darwin had been studying the problem and he was puzzled and haunted by the gentle smile with which Darwin explained that that was not altogether his view. By 1858 he had had many talks with Darwin, and learned a great deal more from his own researches, but he was still not convinced. In that year, however, Wallace's promulgation of the theory stimulated Darwin to write out his argument in the *Origin of Species*, which was published in the following year.

The copy sent to *The Times* for review went to a member of the staff. This excellent man enquired who might help with the review, as he knew nothing about the subject. He was recommended to Huxley, who was only too anxious to help. Huxley wrote the review at white heat, faster than anything he ever wrote in his life. He said it was worthless as a scientific review, but he hoped it might influence the 'educated mob', that got their ideas from *The Times*. He was not mistaken; it was one of the most influential newspaper book reviews ever written. From this moment, he became the most effective literary advocate of the new theory.

VII

THE STRAIN OF ACHIEVEMENT

Huxley's activity in research, speaking and writing proceeded with increasing intensity. He left home early in the morning and generally returned late at night. His family saw little of him, in spite of his attachment to them. He also felt the lack of contact with his personal friends, and in 1864 founded a small dining club, where they could continue to meet together at intervals. There were nine members, and they called themselves the x Club. The others were G. Busk, E. Frankland, T. A. Hirst, J. D. Hooker, J. Lubbock, H. Spencer, W. Spottiswoode and J. Tyndall. The club survived for twenty-eight years, and produced three successive presidents of the Royal Society. None of its members were Oxford or Cambridge men. It became a medium of influence of the more professional middle class scientists who had emerged in the 1850's. Government informally asked scientists who happened to be members for their advice. For example, the Minister Goschen consulted Huxley and Spottiswoode on the headship of the new Naval College, and they independently suggested T. A. Hirst.

Various of their members had connections with industry, finance and government, so that all were able to secure informed advice over a wide range of matters. This helped Huxley to support his far-sighted views with good information. He became acutely conscious of the chaotic condition arising from the flood of new science. He wrote to Haeckel in 1865 that 'It is the organization of knowledge rather than its increase which is wanted just now'. In 1866 he told the British Association that he was sure that the important question for England 'was not the duration of her coal, but the due comprehension of the truths of science and the labours of her scientific men'.

The year 1851, which Huxley regarded as the most pregnant of his life, had also been the year of the Great Exhibition. The profits from its success were devoted, under the influence of the Prince Consort and Lyon Playfair, to the foundation of a new centre for science, at South Kensington. The Prince had envisaged a national, and indeed an international centre of science and peace. His ideas were far in advance of the British ruling classes, and at first were only very partially realized.

It was proposed that the School of Mines in Jermyn Street should be moved to the new centre, together with other institutions. To these, fresh ones should be added, until a comprehensive group of scientific institutions had been formed, adequate to the national needs. These ideas provoked sharp differences of opinion in the School of Mines. Should it, or should it not, become part of such a comprehensive scheme, and should it leave the socially very convenient site in Jermyn Street for what was then the somewhat distant and arid suburb of South Kensington?

Huxley, with his intelligence, common sense and energy,

became keenly interested and involved in the School of Mines' policy and administration, and, as Bibby has shown from his studies of the minutes of its council, he rapidly acquired much influence in its affairs. He was a good committee man. He was elected to audit accounts and sign cheques. In 1859 he secured the appointment of Tyndall as professor of physics. He was asked to recast the prospectus, and consider the form of the students' examination.

When the School was criticised in 1868 for the small number of qualified men which it produced, Huxley replied pungently by laying the blame on the British industrialists, who failed to recognize the need for trained technical staff.

Huxley advocated the amalgamation of the Royal College of Chemistry in Oxford Street, made famous by the great A. W. Hofmann, with the School of Mines, as a step towards a comprehensive college of science. Then, the Duke of Devonshire's Commission on Scientific Instruction and the Advancement of Science, of which Huxley himself was a member, reported in 1871 in favour of amalgamation and the establishment of a general School of Science at South Kensington.

In the period between 1850 and 1870, with the new fundamental advances such as the theories of evolution, and the conservation of energy, the lack of adequate scientific institutions prevented the people from benefiting from the new knowledge, which Huxley had so passionately expounded. These considerations stimulated his interest in elementary and technical education. He found elementary education grotesquely inefficient, and its content of science virtually zero. There was no proper supply of science teachers.

These facts were well known to many others, some of whom had pointed out in the 1860's that Britain was already losing the industrial supremacy which the Great Exhibition of 1851 had demonstrated. The discontent led to the introduction of the Education Act of 1870, requiring that a system of elementary education should be instituted.

In London this was carried out by the formation of a School Board, whose members were to be elected. Huxley became a candidate for Marylebone, and was elected after a strenuous campaign of meetings. Many of the other elected members were philanthropic and religious persons, who felt a duty to the poor, but were horrified by Evolution. Huxley's charm, tact, obvious love of children, intellectual superiority and committee skill soon gave him a remarkable influence with them. He knew, and could explain clearly and persuasively, exactly what he wanted. Together with this, he had a wide network of influence through such contacts as the x Club. In the extraordinarily short time of fourteen months he persuaded them to accept a series of innovations which were to transform the teaching of elementary science to London's 500,000 children, and set the pattern for large numbers more in the provinces. Huxley himself worked on methods of teaching science to children, and of training science teachers, and wrote, and inspired the writing of, appropriate new types of elementary textbooks.

Huxley's intense efforts not suprisingly were accompanied by bouts of ill-health. The first serious one occurred in 1872, after his work on the School Board, when he was forty-seven. He was advised to take vacations abroad, and he found walking in hills and mountains helpful. He had no difficulty in restoring his appetite, but found it very hard to dispel lassitude and depression.

In 1873 Darwin and seventeen other friends presented him with £2,100 to relieve him from financial anxiety, and help him to regain his health.

As Dean of the Royal College of Science Huxley received only £800 per annum. From 1881–85 his income was increased by £700 as Inspector of Fisheries. When he was forced to retire in 1885 the Government fixed his pension at £1,200.

Huxley persistently overworked, and did an enormous number of things himself. He seems not to have had an adequate conception of the kind of organization required for the development of science. He was not a creative thinker in the crucial realm of science organization. The building at South Kensington in which he had his department and which now bears his name, the Huxley Building, though solid, is one of the most unsatisfactory scientific buildings in England. He was not outstanding on the administrative organization of science. His ideas in this field were not to be compared with those of his far-seeing contemporaries, Lyon Playfair and Alexander Strange.

He had grown up in a period when a scientist like Faraday was regarded as the ideal type, and he ever afterwards acted as if this were so. He recognized that more organization was necessary, and fought for it, but he still held individual genius infinitely above the means necessary for its successful expression.

With this belief, he depended too much on personal effort, and not enough on creative organization. This put an excessive strain on him, and was one of the causes of his somewhat obscure illnesses.

The same principles governed his activities in the Royal
Society. He became biological Secretary from 1871–80, and
devotedly sought to sustain and increase its influence. When the
Government invited the Society to plan the famous *Challenger*
expedition, Huxley worked on it extremely hard and well. But
no adequate ancillary organization was provided to help in such
tasks: Huxley did a vast amount of the work himself.

With regard to his presidency of the Society, to which he was
elected in 1883, he said: 'I may say that I accepted the office
inter alia for the purpose of getting people to believe that such
places may be properly held by people who have neither riches
nor station—who want nothing that statesmen can give—and
who care for nothing except upholding the dignity and the freedom of science . . . I will not, if I can help it, allow the chair of
the Royal Society to become the apanage of rich men, or have
the noble old Society exploited by enterprising commercial gents
who make their profit out of the application of science.'

In other words, he had a set of principles which were admirable
for dealing with science as the sinews of intellectual culture, but
were not so suitable for securing from statesmen the kind of
support for science that only they can provide, and for dealing
with it as a major factor in modern industry, society and politics.

It would have been necessary for him to enter politics, if he
had desired to shape and lead political action on science. He was
invited to do so, but declined, saying that he desired to remain
outside, where he could exert influence irrespective of the party
in power. Though he believed that science ought to ally itself
with the radicals, he was not himself prepared to become politically active.

When Huxley's health revived after the breakdown of 1872,
he became very active in the cause of technical education. The
social discontent had made the ruling classes aware that something must be done. Indeed, the social situation provided the
motive force which enabled Huxley to accomplish so much so
quickly. He held that technical education must be provided to
enable the nation to survive in a world of industrial competition;
but, as he expressed it later, it must be broad in character and
not merely vocational, for 'the savage of civilization is a more
dangerous animal than any other wild beast . . .' Any social
organization that allowed them to accumulate would ultimately
'be torn to pieces by them'.

The City companies, with their large accumulations of wealth
which were not being used to much useful social purpose, feared

that they might be attacked. Huxley was deputed to ask them
for financial help for technical education. He persuaded them to
devote considerable sums to the construction of new technical
colleges in the City and in South Kensington, and provide funds
for awards on the basis of examinations in technical subjects.

The movement developed less quickly than he had hoped, but
he steadily pressed it forward. In 1889 the Technical Institution
Act gave local authorities power to levy rates for technical education, which enabled local technical colleges to be founded in the
chief towns of the country.

Meanwhile, by 1881, the Government had decided that a
general school of science should be founded at South Kensington.
Huxley was invited to be professor of biology and its head, as
Dean of the professors. For the first four years he carried out the
full duties of the position, and impressed his ideas on the new
college. Then, by 1885, his health again became so bad that he
had to retire from the presidency of the Royal Society after serving only two years, and he desired to retire from the College. It
was arranged, however, that while he retired from the professorship, he would continue as Dean, with few administrative duties,
so that his advice and guidance could be retained.

Huxley expressed his conception of how such a higher scientific institution should be conducted when he said that: 'the
modern university looks forward, and is a factory of new knowledge: its professors have to be at the top of the wave of progress.
Research and criticism must be the breath of their nostrils;
laboratory work the main business of the scientific student;
books his main helpers.

'The lecture, however, in the hands of an able man—will still
have the utmost importance in stimulating and giving facts and
principles their proper relative importance . . .'

Many years later someone asked Rutherford how he managed
always to be on the top of the wave of discovery. 'I made the
wave, didn't I?' he replied.

Huxley described the ignorance of the so-called British
educated classes as stupendous, and in the hands of men like
Gladstone it was 'a political force'. He said in 1886 that 'anxious
watching of the course of affairs for many years past has persuaded me that nothing short of some sharp and sweeping
national misfortune will convince the majority of our countrymen that government by average opinion is merely a circuitous
method of going to the devil; and that those who profess to lead
but in fact slavishly follow this average opinion are simply the

fastest runners and the loudest squeakers of the herd which is rushing blindly to its own destruction'. Evidently, he would not have been in favour of government by public opinion polls.

In 1887 he expressed his disappointment with the newly-founded Imperial Institute. He had hoped it would play a role with regard to industrial science that the Royal Society had played with regard to pure science. He had hoped that the capitalist and the artisan would meet in it on equal terms, and pursue the systematic study of the higher questions of industry and commerce. It should have provided a 'foundation for that scientific organization of our industries which the changed conditions of the times render indispensable to their prosperity'. The country was entering the most serious struggle for existence. The country was embarked on an industrial war far more serious than any military war. Better instructed competitors were arising in Europe, and better-endowed ones in America. 'To those who reflect seriously on the prospects of the population of Lancashire and Yorkshire—should the time ever arrive when the goods which are produced by their labour and their skill are to be had cheaper elsewhere—to those who remember the cotton famine and reflect how much worse a customer famine would be, the situation appears very grave.'

He thought that State socialism was best exemplified by the societies of the bees and ants. Belief in majorities was not rooted in his breast. If he found all the world against him he would thoroughly examine his views, but it would not in itself make him forsake them.

He thought the belief that all babies were born good, and became evil only through the influence of a corrupt society, was a liberal illusion.

Huxley was, however, against government by professors. 'The fact of their being specialists is against them. Most of them are broad-minded practical men; some are good administrators. But, unfortunately, there is among them . . . a fair sprinkling of one-idea'd fanatics, ignorant of the commonest conditions of official relation, and content with nothing if they cannot get everything their own ways. It is these persons who, with the very highest and purest intentions, would ruin any administrative body unless they were counterposed by non-professional, common-sense members of recognized weight and authority in the conduct of affairs.'

Huxley spent most of his last days at Eastbourne, cultivating and studying the genetics of gentians, and enjoying the walk up the hill to Beachy Head. His health finally decayed, and he died in a heart attack on 29 June 1895.

Huxley received all the main honours open to a British scientist, and a multitude from abroad. He was eminent in research and in scientific affairs, but as a teacher of the meaning and facts of science he was a genius.

JOHN TYNDALL
1820-1893

I

EXPOSITOR AND MOUNTAINEER

TYNDALL combined outstanding gifts for teaching and expounding science with major achievements in mountaineering. He became the most famous public lecturer of his generation on physical science; the new demonstration experiments he invented for teaching physics dominated textbooks for half a century; and he was the first to ascend the Weisshorn.

He would have been a splendid type both for television science, and for making the first landing on the moon. Today, no scientific type is more important than that exemplified by Tyndall: a good scientist who can explain science to the people, and lead a growing point of contemporary endeavour, such as the exploration of space. Talents such as his should be sought and recognized in providing for the modern need for extending knowledge of science from the thousands of Tyndall's day to the millions of our own; and to have pioneer reports from the moon and planets by investigators who are scientists as well as athletes.

Tyndall found scope in the situation arising out of the Industrial Revolution, which created the need for the systematic teaching of science. Though he sprang from the very heart of the nineteenth-century industrial development, the foundation and construction of the first railway system, he did not particularly relate his activities to this social situation. He regarded his efforts to promote a new grasp of science among the people in theological rather than social terms. He aimed at destroying and replacing old ideas on nature which conflicted with the new science. He strove to destroy what he conceived to be scientific errors. In fact, what he was doing was to destroy old notions on science which belonged to the feudal era and were a part of the old ideology, and replace them by the new notions on science produced by the new capitalist society.

He regarded his tempestuous exposition of science as primarily

a campaign of truth against error, rather than as the supersession of old by new ideas. Though he was interested in history,
he did not clearly see his efforts in a perspective of social history.
Yet the social significance of his efforts was great, in spite of his
incomplete awareness of its nature.

It was necessary that the increasing numbers of skilled men,
engineers and scientists required to operate the new technological
industry should receive appropriate education, and in the course
of a hundred years institutions were created to provide it. Public
lectures on science and mechanics became popular, especially in
the new industrial cities. Mechanics' institutes were founded to
meet their social, cultural and scientific needs.

The Royal Institution was one of the most outstanding of these
new institutions for fostering science, and informing the public
of its progress. Its success was a measure of the social pressure
for what it provided; this in the first place was for knowledge of
what was happening in science.

The Royal Institution was established through its expository
function. Its lectures attracted a loyal audience drawn from
several social classes, from the aristocracy to skilled mechanics,
which provided the lecturers with a modest security, and the
opportunity for research. Davy and his successor Faraday added
to the Institution's services to the public a series of discoveries
which, in the long though not in the short run, consolidated the
Institution permanently.

When Faraday was at the height of his creative work, he was
much concerned for the future of the Institution. His great discoveries, though contributing to the Institution's fame, did not
attract immediate financial support. This was one of the reasons
why he devoted so much attention to the lecturing side. He
feared that if this was not kept up to the highest standards, the
Institution might have to close.

He gave particular attention to the problem of the qualities of
his successor, and was determined that skill in public exposition
must be high among them. He perceived in John Tyndall a
possessor of this skill in the highest degree, so he secured his
appointment as Professor of Natural Philosophy in the Institution in 1853, when Tyndall was thirty-three years old. In due
course Tyndall described how for fifteen years he had enjoyed
Faraday's friendship, and then, after his death in 1867, 'reverently
but reluctantly' took his place as Superintendent. On returning
from one of his Alpine expeditions, he found at the entrance of
the place that had been occupied successively by Davy and

Faraday, his name upon the wall. It was to him 'more of a shock than a satisfaction'.

Tyndall was Faraday's choice as an expositor of science. He combined a gift for inventing elegant lecture demonstration experiments with exceptional command of language and eloquence. His demonstrative experiments influenced hundreds of thousands who never heard him speak, owing to their adoption in textbooks.

His wife gave an excellent description of his appearance. 'Tyndall was of middle height, sparely built, but with a strength, toughness and flexibility of limb which qualified him to endure great fatigue and achieve the most difficult feats as a mountaineer. His face was rather stern and strongly marked, but the features assumed an exceedingly pleasing expression when his sympathy was touched, and the effect was heightened by the quality of his voice. His eyes were grey-blue, and his hair, light brown in youth, was abundant and of very fine texture . . .'

Oliver Lodge, who was born in 1851, largely self-educated and himself a masterly expositor, was particularly well qualified to assess Tyndall. Lodge was in his youth when Tyndall was at the summit of his activity and influence. He saw him as the colleague of Huxley in the battle to make 'the new standpoint of modern science part of the accepted philosophy in general life'. To the ordinary Englishman he became the typical professor of physics. 'His strong, picturesque mode of seizing and expressing things gave him an immense living influence both in speech and writing.' He disseminated a popular knowledge of physical science that had not previously existed, and was 'perhaps the greatest popular teacher of natural philosophy of his generation'. Herbert Spencer particularly emphasized the 'scientific use of his imagination' in Tyndall's exposition.

Tyndall was more at ease in speaking than writing. He told his friend Hirst, while at work on his first book *The Glaciers of the Alps*: 'I think I shall never undertake to write a *book* again. If one were a scamp, the work would be easy enough, but for an honest man it is dreadful.' He nevertheless went on to write more books. He said that 'To forget one's self and to be simple is the highest quality of the Scientific Writer'.

Tyndall was keenly interested in the history of science, and the relations between science and the various theologies, such as Protestantism and Catholicism. He did not, however, give much attention to the interactions between science and social and political ideas. He did not relate the science of the past to the social environment in which it had developed. His biographers commented that he did not perceive clearly the social and political changes which the new technology would bring.

The feudal element in Tyndall's views was reflected in his attitude on the American Civil War. He said he was a Southern sympathizer, 'not with slavery, but with bravery, during their fight'.

His friends felt that Tyndall never fought for his own hand. He was always a champion for others, and ignored obloquy. He sprang into controversy from generosity and love of a fight, not from ambition. Though he had started life as a poor man, he later earned a good deal of money, with which he was exceedingly generous. He refused to take any payment for his very successful lectures in America, and devoted the proceeds to American science. In spite of his unconcern over money, he left twenty thousand pounds at his death.

His preference for the life of science over that of gain inspired his friend Hirst, like him, to abandon his career as an engineer and become a scientist. As with Faraday and Huxley, it separated him from the profit-seeking spirit in the contemporary society.

Those who did not like Tyndall deprecated what they described as 'his love of posing, his occasional straining after effect, his tendencies to humour the foibles of a fashionable audience, and to fall in with every passing whim . . .' No doubt these were reflections, in part, of his inclination towards the aristocracy.

He did not, however, lose his sense of values. After he had become popularly famous as a scientist and a mountaineer, he said that his greatest climb was from the banks of Barrow to the banks of Thames, that is, from obscurity in Southern Ireland to a professorship at the Royal Institution, within a period of thirteen years.

II

SON OF A PROTESTANT POLICEMAN IN SOUTHERN IRELAND

Tyndall came from outside the English university system. He was largely self-educated, and his power of exposition was developed in the course of trying to explain things to himself. The circumstances of his youth strengthened the freshness of his view and the independence of his expression.

He was born at Leighlin Bridge in Southern Ireland on 2 August 1820. His father was descended from an English family who had settled in Ireland in the seventeenth century. He was a shoemaker and leather dealer, who had married Sarah McAssey, the

JOHN TYNDALL

daughter of a neighbouring farmer. He was an ardent Protestant and Orangeman, and treasured a scrap of flag alleged to have been flown at the Battle of the Boyne. An enthusiastic student and debater of politics and theology, he possessed a considerable number of books on these topics. His business was not very successful, so he joined the Irish Constabulary, in which he became a sergeant.

Tyndall's mother was a gentle imaginative woman, more cultivated than most women of her class at that time. She had acted as an assistant in a school to Miss Lecky, an aunt of the famous historian. Her background was not unlike that of Rutherford's mother.

Tyndall grew up in an atmosphere of argument, reading and combat. He was very much in the open air, and was remembered for fighting with his school friends, for the sheer fun of it. He adored his father, who appreciated his first signs of intellectual ability, manifested by satirical doggerel in the local newspaper. He told his son how much he regretted being too poor to be able to send him to university.

Tyndall senior did not scruple, however, to send his boy to the National School in a town four miles away, which was directed by a Roman Catholic teacher. This man, Mr. John Conwill, was an exceptionally good teacher of mathematics. The first book on arithmetic which he gave to Tyndall was by Thomson, the father of the William Thomson who became Lord Kelvin. He grounded Tyndall in algebra, geometry, trigonometry and conic sections, giving him a good deal of personal instruction.

The Protestant friends of Tyndall's father queried the propriety of his son receiving instruction from a Catholic, but the police sergeant did not allow his theological convictions to hinder his son's education. Tyndall's teacher lived about half way between the school and his house, so they often used to walk home together. They discussed problems, and sometimes drew diagrams in the snow to asist their concentration. Tyndall became aware that he had an exceptionally powerful visual imagination. He could see three-dimensional diagrams in his head, and argue about them as easily as if they had been represented on paper.

This gift contributed to his subsequent power as a lecturer. He had a quiet, unhurried, certain and confident style. He was in fact reading from what he could see before him in his mind. He did in his mind what many television performers do today with the assistance of legends and scripts which they can see, but which are concealed from the audience.

6

His teacher Mr Conwill used to send the boys out to make simple surveys, as exercises in practical mathematics. So Tyndall grew up, mathematics being associated in his mind with the open air life and physical exercise. He was being unconsciously prepared for his future combination of Alpine climbing with the scientific study of glaciers.

There were two main strands in Tyndall's early education, the debate and reading inspired by his father's political and theological passions, and the good instruction he received from his mathematical master. Tyndall referred to these two strands of language and science in education in an address to the students of University College in 1868.

He said that the object of education was, or ought to be, the wise exercise of man's bundle of inherited capacities and tendencies, so that he may contribute to the usefulness, beauty and nobleness of his life. He conceived the object of education in individualistic terms, as the attainment of his friend Tennyson's

> Self-reverence, self-knowledge, self-control
> These three alone lead life to sovereign power.
> Yet not for power (power of herself
> Would come uncalled for), but to live by law,
> Acting the law we live by without fear;
> And, because right is right, to follow right
> Were wisdom in the scorn of consequence.

He said that two rival methods of education solicited attention. 'These two methods are the classical and the scientific method. I wish they were not rivals; it is only bigotry and short-sightedness that make them so; for assuredly it is possible to give both of them fair play. Though hardly authorized to express an opinion upon the subject, I nevertheless hold the opinion that the proper study of a language is an intellectual discipline of the highest kind. If I except discussions on the comparative merits of Popery and Protestantism, English grammar was the most important discipline of my boyhood.'

The analysis of Milton's tortuous grammar was to him 'a source of unflagging delight', and knowing the value of English so well, he would be 'the last to deny, or even to doubt, the high discipline involved in the proper study of Latin and Greek'.

He thought, however, that the study of the evolution of the cosmos and of living things provided a discipline equal to or even surpassing that derivable from the study of languages, because it revealed not merely an extraordinary collection of facts, but a

panorama of phenomena instinct with law, which could be ascertained by the motions of the intellect, proceeding inductively
and deductively. So he believed 'it would be possible to so limit
and arrange the study of a portion of physics as to render the
mental exercise involved in it almost qualitatively the same as that
involved in the unravelling of a language'.

However, man could not live by intellect alone. 'The intellectual action of a complete man is, consciously or unconsciously,
sustained by a current of the emotions.' His emotions, which
had provided the motive power of his later scientific life, had
been provided by Carlyle, Emerson and Fichte. He remembered
gratefully that Carlyle had 'through three long cold German
winters' caused him to bathe in his tub at five o'clock in the
morning, before the ice was broken, bracing himself to face each
day's difficulties freshly and cheerfully. 'I never should have gone
through Analytical Geometry and the Calculus had it not been
for those men. I never should have become a physical investigator.'

His subsequent scientific career had been due to their moral
impetus. 'These three unscientific men made me a practical
scientific worker.' They announced the need and duty to act, and
he hearkened to them, though he took the liberty of deciding for
himself the direction he would take.

Thus, just a hundred years ago, Tyndall had discovered the
two cultures, and shown that there was no necessary conflict
between them. In fact, one of the sources of his power as an
expositor of science was that he was aware of this, and, like Huxley, held literature and science in different but equal regard.

III

RAILWAY SURVEYOR

Tyndall's early education had been limited in scope, but he had
been able to continue it up to the age of nineteen, which was
unusual then in his social class. He had conceived an ambition
to become a civil engineer, and considering that surveying might
provide a path to that profession, followed the suggestion of a
young officer friend in the Royal Engineers, Lieutenant George
Wynne, that he should join the Ordnance Survey at Youghal in
County Cork. This he did before he was twenty years old. Wynne
became one of his intimate friends, and rose to be a general.

Tyndall started as a draughtsman, but picked up the calculating
and computing side of the work. His friend Wynne enabled him

to undertake work in the field; he observed his desire for improvement and did all he could to help. On an occasion when all of the men skilled in trigonometrical surveying were absent, Tyndall volunteered to undertake such observations, on the strength of the instruction he had received at school. After some hesitation and chaff, he was provided with a quite complicated theodolite. He carefully mastered its operation and adjustments in the office, and then went out into the field with two assistants. He had first to determine some measurements which were very accurately known. Bets were made against his success, but his results proved to be good enough.

He was paid less than a pound a week, but it was sensible work. One of his first surveys was along the tidal reaches of the neighbouring sea shore. He sent to his father fine descriptions of the wild scenery and the Atlantic roar, wading barefoot through the mud for miles. He said he had become as strong as an ox, and his feet were beginning to resemble horses' hooves. He corresponded with his father on politics and theology, and was recommended by him to read Jeremy Taylor on the *Confutation of Transubstantiation*.

He went to evening school three nights a week to learn drawing, and became an accomplished and beautiful draughtsman. Then, in 1842, the Ordnance Survey moved him to Preston in England. He completed his journey there with his first experience of steam railway travel. He was thrilled by the experience, and by the beauty of the Lancashire countryside, enhanced, as he thought, by the numerous factories and chimneys.

However, life was hard. He worked from 6.30 a.m. to 5 p.m., and attended evening lectures and used the library at the Preston Mechanics Institution. There John Clay, chaplain to the House of Correction, lectured on mechanics. Various lecturers dealt with astronomy, physics, chemistry, botany and physiology. The surgeon Mr Corless lectured on respiration, and Tyndall saw for the first time the familiar demonstration of turning lime water milky by breathing through it. Corless had forecast what would happen. The experiment excited the audience, and made an impression on Tyndall that he never forgot. He later was to excel at inventing this kind of visual demonstration.

Tyndall did not like the way the Preston Ordnance Office was run, and life in the town was hectic. He found himself surrounded by the thousands of unemployed and half-starved workers struggling for the Workers' Charter. He began to feel that he could have no future in such surroundings, and he wrote to a well-to-do relative in America, asking whether there was opportunity for him there. He was discouraged by the reply, which was apparently restricted to prospects in surveying. Tyndall rightly thought that he could have turned his hand to almost anything, and that there must be all sorts of jobs in the new country for a healthy and adaptable young man. He said he was ready to be anything from a cowboy to a Congressman. As for England in 1843, he wrote to his father: 'There is no hope in this country—too much *competition* . . .'

Fortunately, he received no encouragement to emigrate. Instead of scuttling off to the United States, like so many a century later, he stayed, and began to look the contemporary social situation in the face. Through the window of the Ordance Survey office in Lune Street at Preston, Tyndall and his colleagues could see the processions of the thousands of hungry workers who had been sacked from the silent mills. 'In their helplessness and misery they had turned out, so that their condition might be seen of all. Well, in Lune Street, down which we could look from our office the tumult one day became unmanageable. Heated by its own interaction and attrition, the crowd blazed out into open riot, and attacked the bakers' shops. Soldiers had been summoned to meet this contingency. Acting under orders, they fired upon the people, and the riot was quelled at the cost of blood.'

Carlyle's *Past and Present* was published at about this time, and extracts from it were printed in one of the Preston newspapers. He described the condition of the famished weavers in searing phrases, and appealed to the campaigners against slavery to divert their attention from miseries abroad to those at home.

'In thee too is a kind of instinct towards justice, and I will complain of nothing. Only, Quashee [a West African negro] over the seas being once provided for, wilt thou not open thine eyes to the hunger-stricken, pallid, yellow-coloured "Free Labourers" of Lancashire, Yorkshire, Buckinghamshire, and all other shires? These yellow-coloured, for the present, absorb all my sympathies. If I had a twenty millions, with model farms and Niger expeditions, it is to them that I would give it. Why, in one of these Lancashire weavers, dying of hunger, there is more thought and heart, a greater arithmetical amount of misery and desperation, than in whole gangs of Quashees.'

These were the first words of Carlyle that Tyndall ever read, and he said that 'after the rattle of musketry and spatter of bullets, among the weavers and spinners of Lune Street', they rang with a strange impressiveness in his ears.

When Tyndall unveiled Carlyle's statue on the Embankment in 1881, he remarked, in recounting this incident, that Carlyle's pity was vast, though his division of it between black and white might be called in question. Carlyle became Tyndall's revered friend, but Tyndall was not blind to his limitations. He referred to him humorously as 'the old brute'.

Tyndall was inclined to the Radical Conservatism propagated by Carlyle and Disraeli in the 'Young England' movement of 1842. Marx and Engels in the *Communist Manifesto* referred to it as feudal socialism, 'half lamentation half lampoon, half echo of the past, half menace of the future; at times, by its bitter, witty and incisive criticism, striking the bourgeoisie to the very heart's core, but always ludicrous in its effect; through total incapacity to comprehend the march of modern history.

'The aristocracy, in order to rally the people to them, waved the proletarian alms-bag in front for a banner. But the people, so often as it joined them, saw on their hindquarters the old feudal coats of arms, and deserted with loud and irreverent laughter.'

Like even the greatest of his companions in this movement, Tyndall never entirely lost the slight atmosphere of ludicrousness which infected their activities. His generous and courageous spirit prompted him, however, to rebel against the social oppression, which had also penetrated to the Preston office of the Ordnance Survey. Their hours were long, pay was low, and sick-pay non-existent. They protested against their conditions, but their formal protest, signed by Tyndall and all the best draughtsmen, was rejected, and they were sacked.

The dismissed men proposed to send a deputation, including Tyndall, to see Sir Robert Peel in London, then the Master General of Ordnance. Tyndall did indeed reach London, but Peel refused to see him.

Meanwhile, his father was horrified by his opposition to the Government. Tyndall was deeply hurt by his strictures, and asked him in his now fully-developed clarity and forcefulness of style, whether he expected him to depart from those principles of honest and forthright conduct which he had so earnestly inculcated in him.

Tyndall exposed the shortcomings of the Survey of Ireland in a series of articles in the *Liverpool Mercury*. He said that it was to have taken seven years at a cost of £300,000. Actually, it had taken seventeen years and cost nearly £750,000. Many of the results were inaccurate and useless. He attributed much of the trouble to the system of civilian officers working under military direction, which caused friction, and was very inefficient.

Unable to find work, he had to return home to Ireland. He kept up the study of mathematics and French during this unsettled time, until in 1844 he heard of a new surveying post in Preston. He applied for it, and was appointed, but it turned out to be no good.

Then he went to Manchester, where he secured a job with one of the many engineering firms involved in the feverish competition for the rights for the construction of the railways, at the height of the railway mania. The work was well paid for those times—three to four guineas a week, but it was desperately hard. Plans for lines had to be deposited by certain dates at the Board of Trade, and surveyors often had to work twenty-four hours of the day, in the field during daylight and drawing plans during the hours of darkness. They were kept awake with coffee, brandy and chicken, racing to get their plans finished, to be delivered by special train in London, in time to catch the closing date at the Board of Trade.

He surveyed for the lines projected between Bedford and Ely; and between Manchester, Stockport and Chester. When these and others were done, he went to Halifax to survey for the projected West Yorkshire line. His work proved far more accurate than that for a rival line; however, the two rival lines came to terms and merged. Tyndall at first found himself out of a job, but was presently taken on by the line formed by the merger. He oscillated between surveying in the fields around Halifax, and rushing to London to help with evidence in the Committee Rooms of Parliament on Bills for new lines.

While at Halifax, Tyndall met in the engineering office where he worked, a youth ten years his junior, Thomas Archer Hirst, and formed a friendship with him that became significant for British science. Tyndall and Hirst inspired each other, and their mutual help was probably the decisive factor in settling both of them in the scientific life.

Hirst was to follow Tyndall's example. He abandoned engineering after his apprenticeship, and, like Tyndall, went to Marburg, and later to Göttingen and Berlin, to graduate in mathematics and science. A score of years later he succeeded Augustus de Morgan as professor of mathematics at University College, London, and had a leading part in consolidating the

London Mathematical Society, which has been the chief organ of British mathematics during the last hundred years.

Hirst had taken his doctorate in mathematics at Berlin, after studying under Gauss and Dirichlet, and probably knew more than any other man in England at that time of the kind of mathematics which was to lead the development of European mathematics during the next half-century. Hirst ultimately became a Fellow of the Royal Society and, as has already been mentioned, first Principal of the Royal Naval College at Greenwich.

One of Tyndall's last pieces of field work was on the taking of a line of levels from the town of Keighley to the exposed village of Haworth in Yorkshire.

'On a certain day, under grave penalties, these levels had to be finished, and this particular day was one of agony to me. The atmosphere seemed filled with mocking demons, laughing at the vanity of my efforts to get the work done. My levelling-staves were snapped and my theodolite was overthrown by the storm. When things are at their worst a kind of anger often takes the place of fear. It was so in the present instance; I pushed doggedly on, and just at nightfall, when barely able to read the figures on my levelling-staff, I planted my last "bench-mark" on a tombstone in Haworth Churchyard. Close at hand was the vicarage of Mr Brontë, where the genius was nursed which soon afterwards burst forth and astonished the world.'

No doubt the 'mocking demons' that troubled Tyndall were the same as those that tortured the soul of Emily Brontë's Heathcliff. In intervals of toiling among the eerie spirits that accompanied the Brontë genius in the wild Haworth landscape, Tyndall witnessed scarcely less sinister scenes in the Committee Rooms of Parliament, where the lawyers Austin and Talbot were grand and merciless, as they ruined hostile witnesses. The civil engineers Stephenson, Brunel, Locke and Hawkshaw appeared, and the redoubtable George Bidder, who, after being a calculating prodigy in his youth, applied his quickness of mind to supporting clients' cases as an expert witness. He could calculate the implications of technical figures almost instantaneously, and added to that general intelligence and swift retort. Tyndall saw him 'take the breath out of Talbot himself before a committee of the House of Lords. Strong men were broken down by the strain and labour of that arduous time.'

Many pushed through and survived, but others collapsed; some with large fortunes, but with intellects so shattered that instead of taking their place in the front rank of English statesmen, they sought quiet and escape in the retired lives of country gentlemen. Tyndall himself used to snatch five minutes' sleep on a deal table from time to time, using a volume of Babbage and Collet's logarithms as a pillow.

Tyndall described how in this time of mad unrest nothing was spoken of but the state of the share market. From mansions to stables, and magnates to costermongers, the prospects of projected lines were discussed, and the luck of an ostler or pot-boy who had cleared ten thousand pounds by a lucky stroke of business. High and low, rich and poor, joined in the reckless game, and for weeks Tyndall himself suffered agonies. 'It was not defeated ambition; it was not a rejected love-suit; it was not the hardship endured in either office or field, but it was the possession of certain shares which I had purchased in one of the lines then afloat.'

The share list proved the winding-sheet of his peace of mind. He was haunted by the Stock Exchange. 'Then, as now, I loved the blue span of heaven; but when I found myself regarding it morning after morning, not with the fresh joy which, in my days of innocence, it had brought me, but solely with reference to its possible effect, through the harvest, upon the share market, I became at length so savage with myself, that nothing remained but to go down to my brokers and put away the shares as an accursed thing.'

Tyndall's spell of railway gambling ended without loss or gain, and the two to three hundred pounds he had saved during the wild surveying days remained intact.

IV

STUDENT IN GERMANY

The railway mania began to subside in 1847, and railway work slackened. Tyndall looked for other jobs, and a friend put him in touch with Queenwood, a Quaker residential college in Hampshire. The building had been opened by Robert Owen and the Owenite Socialists in 1841 as Harmony Hall, where the Millennium was to commence. The letters 'C of M' were worked in flint in the brickwork of the building.

The Millennium promptly failed to materialize, so Owen had persuaded the Quaker, George Edmondson, to take it over and convert it into a college for boys, and youths of about twenty years of age, described as 'farmers'. Many of the latter were men who had failed at the universities, or for some reason had not

6*

completed any conventional training. They were an unruly and
difficult group.

Queenwood was the first school in England to have laboratory
and practical instruction in applied science. Tyndall's job was to
teach mathematics and surveying, keep the college books and
act as college secretary. He found Edward Frankland, later to
become an eminent chemist, a founder of the theory of valency
and structural organic chemistry and a precurser of Kékule, in
charge of the chemical laboratory.

Edmondson gave Tyndall a copy of Liebig's *Animal Chemistry*,
and requested him to lecture on it to the scholars. Tyndall
found it a 'superb work'. These lectures, and his practical teaching of surveying, fascinated the difficult 'farmers'. Tyndall's
gifts as a teacher became immediately evident. He said that at
Queenwood he learned that a good teacher must be master of
his work, but that this was not all. 'A power of character must
underlie and enforce the work of the intellect.' Some men could
so rouse and energize their pupils as to make the hardest work
agreeable. Without this power, he doubted whether a teacher
could ever really enjoy his vocation. 'With it I do not know a
higher, nobler, more blessed calling . . .'

Tyndall had already heard of German science, and read
Carlyle's references to German philosophy and literature.
Through this, he had come to regard them as 'a kind of revelation
from the gods'.

Frankland was five years younger than Tyndall, but had already published original work on gas analysis. Tyndall went to
his lectures in the college on chemistry, geology, botany, hydrostatics and heat. Frankland and Tyndall experimented on themselves with anaesthetics, and made records of their effects. In
the vacation Tyndall visited his friend Hirst at Halifax, and
heard Ralph Waldo Emerson lecture there, another of the formative experiences of his life.

With Frankland he went on a tour in Northern France. He left
him in Paris and returned to London. Hearing that street fighting had broken out—it was the Revolution of 1848—he went back
to Paris to rescue his friend, but found him safe and sound. They
improved their time by going to hear J. B. Dumas lecture.

Tyndall was paid £200 a year at Queenwood, besides his keep,
which was pretty good for those days. But he found the Edmond-
sons' anti-smoking, teetotal puritanical grimness rather forbid-
ding. He and Frankland used to go off on long walks, for drinks
and smokes in out-of-the-way country pubs. He felt that he must

find a more agreeable occupation. To do this, some academic qualification would be necessary.

He was interested in Germany, and Frankland had already spent three months at Marburg in Bunsen's laboratory. The two friends therefore decided to go to Marburg together, Frankland to work with Bunsen on the chemistry of ozone, and Tyndall to pursue the student's course leading to the usual doctorate of philosophy.

Marburg had not yet been reached by the railway. It was a very picturesque old town, whose orchards and chestnuts blossomed gloriously in the spring. In it Luther and Zwingli had conferred on Consubstantiation and Transubstantiation. William Tyndale, the translator of the Bible into English, and possibly an ancestor of the Tyndall family, had lived there. Papin was in Marburg when he invented the steam digester or pressure cooker.

Bunsen was now the most eminent citizen, but there were other distinguished men in the small university of 300 students.

Tyndall lived in an attic, and got up at five in the morning to start studying. His room was warmed by a stove filled from the outside. This was not lighted until six o'clock, so he obtained a dressing gown lined with catskin to keep warm. From his youth he had been in the habit of sucking coffee beans to keep his brain alert in the early morning hours, and coffee and bread did not arrive until the stove was made.

He learned German by listening to Bunsen, who was a tall and impressive personality with a fine voice, besides exceptional mastery of experiments as well as theory. Tyndall thought him the ideal professor. His assistant at the time was Debus, who became one of Tyndall's intimate friends, and like his particular friend Hirst, also went to the Royal Naval College at Greenwich, where he was professor of chemistry. In one of Bunsen's lectures, Tyndall heard for the first time an appreciative reference to 'the English brewer, Joule'.

The professor of mathematics, Stegmann, gave Tyndall the subject of his doctoral thesis, which was mathematical. It was *On a Screw Surface with Inclined Generatrix, and on the Conditions of Equilibrium on such Surfaces*. Tyndall found this thesis pretty hard work, with the lack of much formal training in mathematics in his youth; he found the calculus difficult.

Mature minds often find mathematics frustrating, for they are apt to perceive its real logical difficulties, whereas the young student is generally more concerned with acquiring facility in its operation. This is more practical, as the logical difficulties are more easily understood after facility in operation has been acquired.

Tyndall's late and laborious acquaintance with mathematics had a significant role in important aspects of his later career. It exacerbated his relations with William Thomson, Tait and others with a Cambridge mathematical training.

He completed his work for his doctorate in two years, instead of the usual three. He overworked, as he continued to do throughout his life, until he undermined his strong constitution. He was very conspicuous as a student at Marburg, being so much older than the usual, yet very lively and juvenile in his social habits.

His Halifax friend, Hirst, was now nineteen years old and in the kind of religious and intellectual difficulties which afflicted Victorian youth. Tyndall, who had not yet received his doctorate and was entirely unknown, wrote to Carlyle for intellectual and spiritual counsel for Hirst. Carlyle sent the letter to one of his friends in Yorkshire, who then befriended Hirst.

After two years at Marburg Tyndall found the savings he had made during the railway mania running out, and contemplated returning to teaching. Hirst, knowing he wanted to continue research at Marburg, helped him with small loans, which enabled him to survive through this period, and definitely pursue the scientific life. He assisted Knoblauch, who had recently come to Marburg from Berlin, in experimental research on diamagnetism. They aimed at extending, with more delicate apparatus, the investigation of this phenomenon, discovered by Faraday in 1845. Tyndall made a number of new experiments, which he interpreted by conceptions somewhat different from those of Faraday. He sent a paper on them to the *Philosophical Magazine*. Presently, early in 1851, he had sadly to say good-bye to Germany, as his small but increasing debts had begun to give him anxiety.

Tyndall subsequently remarked that while the German universities had made an important contribution to German greatness, they were not its cause. This was the steady fortitude and valiant laboriousness, which had triumphed over the gravest natural disadvantages, and it was 'not the result of university culture'. It was the superposition of the informed and disciplined minds trained in the universities on German strength and endurance, which had made Germany great, and 'it is the combination of these elements which must prevent England from becoming small'. England might thank God for able journalists, an orderly Parliament and free press, but she should thank God still more for 'the hardy English root' from which these good things had sprung.

V

CHOPPY SCIENTIFIC WATERS

On coming back to England after his German studies Tyndall called on Faraday, and explained his differences on magnetism and diamagnetism. Faraday replied that it was no matter, he saw he differed not as a partisan, but because of his conviction. At their very first meeting, Faraday said to him: 'Science is not the principal thing; we are men and ought to have human feelings.' Tyndall went on to Edinburgh to read a paper on his work at the Meeting of the British Association. He was already known as a young man who differed from Faraday. Among those who heard him were William Thomson and Stokes.

He searched for a job, and the editor of the *Philosophical Magazine* engaged him to translate important German and French papers at £2 per sixteen pages, to keep him going. The very first paper he received for translation was by Clausius, on the mechanical theory of heat. The best job he could find was a return to Queenwood, where he worked and saved very hard. Debus had come from Marburg to join the staff.

Tyndall sent four titles for papers to the British Association for the Meeting at Ipswich in 1851. As has already been mentioned, in the train to Ipswich he met Huxley, and they became friends for life. They ultimately became so identified in the public mind that when Tyndall married a titled lady, people began to behave to Huxley's wife as if she were titled, and when Tyndall died, Huxley read reports of memorial services on himself.

When the Ipswich meeting started, Tyndall found that the arrangements for the delivery of his papers had been muddled. Faraday expressed a desire to hear one of them, so the programme was rearranged; but then the Prince Consort arrived, and the proceedings were interrupted. Tyndall had to wait until the end of the day before he could read his paper, but Faraday stayed, and discussed it at some length.

At this time Tyndall applied for the Chair of Physics, and Huxley for that of Natural History, at Toronto, when both were turned down. Mrs Tyndall said that the same thing happened to them shortly afterwards, in applying for chairs at the new University of Sydney in Australia. At this critical stage of his career Tyndall, like Huxley, was helped by the Royal Society.

The explorer and geophysicist Captain Edward Sabine was the Treasurer. He was accustomed to scientific work in the open, and could appreciate the characteristics that early railway surveying had installed in Tyndall. As he was an Irishman he could also appreciate Tyndall's temperament, and was interested in his origins.

When asked about these, Tyndall exhibited a social inferiority complex. Sabine told him that he was evidently the architect of his own fortunes, and most sensible people would admire him for it. Some of Tyndall's aggressiveness may have sprung from his consciousness of his humble origin.

Tyndall was elected to the Royal Society in 1852, Huxley having been elected in the previous year. In 1853 Tyndall for the first time heard Faraday lecture; it was to children. Tyndall was thoroughly familiar with the subject. He noted the depth of Faraday's thought, and the sweetness of his disposition. Tyndall himself was asked to lecture on 11 February 1853. He expounded his work on the magnetic properties of crystals, and his difference with Faraday on its interpretation.

He delivered the lecture with outstanding skill, and when he had finished slunk into a corner, expecting a storm of dissent and criticism. Instead, there was a storm of applause, and Faraday came forward, and insisted on presenting him to the President. His reputation as a lecturer was made. It was after this lecture that Huxley encouraged him to aim at succeeding Faraday in the Royal Institution. Tyndall was commissioned to give other lectures, and Huxley told him that the Museum of Economic Geology would also be glad to get him, if they could.

The Royal Institution, under the influence of Bence Jones, Faraday's biographer, offered him its Professorship of Natural Philosophy later in 1853, at £100 a year. The presence of Faraday decided him to accept, in spite of the low salary. He persuaded Hirst to succeed him for a time at Queenwood before proceeding to Berlin to secure his doctorate.

Tyndall studied Faraday's methods of lecturing, and took the greatest pains over his own. He wrote them out, rehearsed them, devised and tested many illustrative experiments, and applied as much care to their production as that of a play in a theatre.

This part of his work progressed splendidly, but he had an unpleasant experience in connection with his researches. At the end of 1853 the Royal Society awarded two Royal Medals. It became known that one was to go to Charles Darwin for biology, and the other to Tyndall for physics. But before the date of announcement opposition arose over the award to Tyndall. Critics said that his work was not entirely original, and owed much to the physicists with whom he had worked in Germany.

Tyndall discussed the situation with Faraday, who told him that when his Government pension was discussed, the Prime Minister, Melbourne, had made some disparaging remarks about the worthiness of pensioners. Faraday rejected the pension, and refused to accept it until he had an apology from the Prime Minister in writing. Tyndall thereupon informed the Royal Society that he would not accept the medal.

When the awards were announced, it was stated that only one Royal Medal would be given in that year; to Darwin. Thereupon Huxley immediately rose, and asked why one of his intimate friends was not sitting beside Darwin. The President replied that the Medal had been awarded to Tyndall, but that he had refused it.

This incident was one of several, in which differences on fine intellectual points were made the occasion for attacks on Tyndall, who never paused to return the fire. The chief criticism came from scientists with Cambridge criteria and mathematical training. An element of national prejudice entered into it, exhibited in opposition to persons educated abroad, and to ideas and work originating there.

Tyndall in the course of his researches begun at Marburg investigated the magnetic properties of nearly a hundred different crystalline substances. In order to discover whether the structure of the crystals had anything to do with the magnetic properties, he ground many crystals to powder, and then compressed the powder into bars, or into shapes like crystals. He compared the properties of his model crystals with their natural prototypes.

He made small spheres of commercial and native sulphur and other minerals, and found the laws of attraction and repulsion of magnetic and diamagnetic substances were the same. He ground spheres out of pieces of spar, crystals of iron carbonate, iron sulphate, and bismuth. He compressed powdered bismuth into spheres, and compared their diamagnetic properties with those of spheres ground out of solid bismuth.

He carried out an immense variety of experiments, and secured observations that had eluded Faraday. He summarized his work in the Bakerian Lecture to the Royal Society in 1855, concluding that diamagnetism was, like ordinary magnetism, a polar phenomenon.

Only one month later Faraday propounded his conception of

the electromagnetic field, through which all the phenomena of diamagnetism were to be explained. Faraday produced one of his master-experiments in support of his conception, which Tyndall tried to confute. Tyndall and others did not perceive the full depth of Faraday's idea, until Clerk Maxwell took it up ten years later, and worked out the electromagnetic theory.

Tyndall accomplished a varied experimental research on diamagnetism with great skill and intense industry. It was a good contribution, even if his theoretical insight was less than Faraday's.

VI

FROM DIAMAGNETISM TO GLACIERS

Tyndall's experiments on compressing materials and powders into spheres and bars, which he had made for his researches on diamagnetism and the magnetic properties of substances, provided him with knowledge and insight into the effects of pressure on solids.

After speaking on his magnetic researches at the Liverpool Meeting of the British Association in 1854, he went on three weeks' holiday, during which he visited the famous Penrhyn slate quarries near Snowdon. The cleavages in the slate do not follow the lines of stratification formed by the layers of fine mud out of which the strata were originally made. They run across the direction of the pressure which compacted the material. This reminded Tyndall of his experiences in the compression of bismuth, wax, and dough. He began to attend to the effects of pressure on materials, and later extended his experiments to the study of such phenomena as the exfoliation of rails under pressure, like that produced by a passing train, or the structure of puff pastry under the cook's rolling pin and fingers; a kind of research which has become of great importance in the development of plastics.

The variety and number of experiments was very characteristic of Tyndall's approach. His influence as an inventor of teaching experiments in science depended as much on his industry as on his inventive talent. He was able to draw upon an enormous range of experiments which he had tried, and select those that he knew to be the best. The number of first-class teaching experiments he published was large, but it was only a small selection from a much larger number of personal experiments. A driving activity was one of Tyndall's characteristics.

Tyndall lectured on his investigation of the cleavage of slate at the Royal Institution in 1856. His friend Huxley was present; it occurred to him that Tyndall's investigation of the structure of slate deposits might help to explain that of glacier ice. He suggested to Tyndall that he should read the Scottish physicist J. D. Forbes's writings on glaciers. Tyndall did so, but was not satisfied with Forbes's theory that ice is viscous or plastic, and that the features of glacier ice are due to the effects of pressure on a plastic material. He and Huxley arranged that they should investigate some of the Swiss glaciers together, to pursue the problem. This was the beginning of Tyndall's serious interest in the Alps.

Tyndall and Huxley visited glaciers near Basle. They noted resemblances between the glacier ice and that of slates, and piles of spilled mortar. After returning to London Tyndall made many experiments on the effect of pressure on ice, and in 1857 he and Huxley published a joint paper on the *Structure and Motion of Glaciers*.

Tyndall's investigation of the properties of ice led him to study the effect of radiation on glaciers. He showed that ice is a fair conductor of heat. He focused a beam of rays from the sun on a point inside a block of ice. He found that the ice was melted at this point by the radiant heat that had been focused there, and had travelled through the ice. A star-shaped cavity appeared at the point, where the ice had been turned into water. As the amount of water was smaller than the volume of ice from which it was formed, a vacuum had been formed. Audible clicks were sometimes heard when the cavity appeared.

Tyndall began to study the whole structure of the glaciers, their mode and rate of movement, their physical environment, and the effects of atmosphere and climate on them. He investigated the effects firstly of pressure, and then of radiation, on various materials. At the same time he became interested in mountaineering. His physical researches and the mountaineering then began to develop on their own, as well as in unison.

The pursuit of the physical properties of matter so posed took him into fields of research far away from glaciers, while the aesthetic and athletic fascination of mountaineering grew on him. The stamina and experience of the former youthful railway surveyor were an excellent foundation for the new geophysicist, and then for the new mountaineer.

Tyndall had been confronted with the problem of the role of the sun's radiation in the formation of glaciers. This involved the effect of the atmosphere on the sun's rays. Most of the preceding exact research on radiation had been on its effects on solids and liquids. Tyndall extended it especially to gases. He found that gases such as oxygen and nitrogen absorbed radiation only slightly, whereas the absorption by compound gases or vapours was very high.

He measured the absorption in a wide range of vapours, from those of alcohol and chloroform to carbon bisulphide and ethyl iodide. He found that the absorption by water vapour was thirteen times that of air. He noted that ozone was markedly absorbent, and that it appeared to be a condensed form of oxygen. This was eleven years before its chemical constitution was finally established by Brodie.

He gave greater precision to the understanding of the role of water vapour in the climate and history of the earth. He commented on features of climate at high altitudes, and in the interiors of Siberia and the Sahara, such as hot days and chilly nights, due to the small amount of water vapour in the air. He said that probably ten to fifteen per cent of the heat radiated from the earth was absorbed within ten feet of the earth's surface. This was evidently of 'the utmost importance to the life of the world'. The water vapour became warmed through absorbing the radiation, 'thus wrapping the earth like a warm garment, and protecting it from the deadly chill which it would otherwise sustain'.

Tyndall began mountaineering at the age of thirty-six; during the next eight years he became one of the famous mountaineers. He exhibited great courage and remarkable powers of endurance. He said he could fancy nothing more fascinating than climbing among such crags and precipices for anyone who was given to it by nature and habit. He was the first to ascend the Weisshorn, and nearly the first to ascend the Matterhorn.

When he did get to the top of the Matterhorn he made reflections very typical of himself. 'Hacked and hurt by time, the aspect of the mountain from its higher crags saddens me. Hitherto, the impression that it made was that of savage strength, but here we had inexorable decay ... When I look at the heavens and the earth, at my own body, at my strength and weakness of mind, even at these ponderings, I ask myself, Is there no being or thing in the immense that knows more about these matters than I do?—What is my answer? ...'

If Tyndall had lived a century later, his combination of qualities might have made him one of the greatest of space-investigators. As an athletic explorer with some knowledge of geology, and the sharp eye of an experimental physicist, his report on the surface of the moon would indeed have been worth having.

When his best climbing days were over, Tyndall built a house in the Alps at a height of 7,000 feet, with a 'marvellously beautiful' view of the Weisshorn and the Matterhorn. He spent three months of the year there, and became the ruling personality of the district, to whom the local peasants referred their problems. He found that if one was just, firm and kind, one could rule almost despotically.

Sociologically, Tyndall had the values of pre-industrial society. Like Faraday and Huxley, he held the life of commercial gain in contempt, but he was not well equipped sociologically to combat it. He remained on the outside of nineteenth-century capitalism, and found congenial social friends in the aristocracy.

VII

NOT WITHOUT DISTINCTION IN RESEARCH

The research on radiation, originally inspired by investigation on the role of the sun's rays in the formation of glaciers, extended into a comprehensive study of infra-red, or thermal radiation, and later on to visible radiation, or light. Tyndall's investigation of the infra-red, or non-visible heat rays, was facilitated by his discovery that a solution of iodine in carbon bisulphide was opaque to visible, but transparent to the non-visible thermal rays. He used this as a convenient filter for obtaining beams of heat radiation from ordinary sources, such as electric arcs.

He focused such beams with refractors made of rock-salt, which is transparent to them, or with mirrors silvered on the front surface. He thereby fused zinc, exploded gun-cotton, and made a variety of experiments with the rays.

He used such a system for heating platinum until it was luminous, and showed how a complete spectrum could be obtained from this light. He called the phenomenon of obtaining short or visible rays from long or invisible rays *calorescence*, the reverse of Stokes's *fluorescence*, in which longer waves were obtained from shorter ones.

He explained the absorption and radiation in and by liquids, vapours and gases, and showed that good absorbers were good radiators. As he did not work with beams of a particular wavelength he did not obtain precise measurements, and was therefore unable to place the theory of absorption and radiation on a quantitative basis. He conceived, however, that absorption was due to the vibration of molecules with a natural period similar to that of the impinging radiation.

He believed that 'not only the *physical* but the *chemical*, in other words the *molecular* condition of bodies, played a part previously unrecognized in the phenomena of radiation and absorption'.

His studies of heat radiation led on to the investigation of the effects of visible radiation. He observed in 1868 that a beam of light could produce a cloudiness in vapour of amyl nitrite, and other kinds of vapour. The beam appeared a brilliant blue when seen from the side. This blue light was polarized, like the blue light from the sky. Tyndall saw that he had produced an artificial sky, and he believed that the blue was due to the scattering of light by particles or drops, formed by chemical reactions between the molecules of the vapour, which had been stimulated by the beam. Rayleigh became interested in his observations, and was able to show theoretically that the blue was due to scattering by the individual molecules themselves.

Rayleigh, like other men with Cambridge mathematical training, was at first rather superior about Tyndall's limitations in mathematical theory. Later on he succeeded Tyndall as professor of natural philosophy at the Royal Institution. He then became more appreciative of him, and deprecated the criticisms of his physical researches from Cambridge-trained circles. Perhaps Rayleigh's experience as a lecturer at the Royal Institution gave him more insight into the nature and magnitude of Tyndall's talents.

Tyndall's method of examining the scattering of light from an intense beam subsequently became part of the standard technique of colloid chemistry, for investigating suspensions of fine particles or drops.

Tyndall's pursuit of the physical and then the chemical properties of radiation, stimulated originally by his research on glaciers, led him on into biology and medicine. When he started the experimental investigation of the effects of radiation on gases, he worked in the laboratories of the Royal Institution, which was situated in the murky atmosphere of the London of the mid-nineteenth century. The intense beams of light which projected through his specimens of air, gases and vapours became disturbingly luminous, owing to the motes floating in them. He showed that the motes could be instantly destroyed by passing through flame, or a very hot platinum tube, and concluded that they must be organic in nature.

This confirmed Pasteur's view that putrefaction of sterile substances was due to organisms coming into them from without. Tyndall gradually evolved much of the technique of the modern operating theatre, in order to avoid contamination from the air. He worked in newly-washed clothes, thoroughly boiled his apparatus, and ultimately erected a laboratory hut on the roof of the Institution, to escape from the heavily contaminated air in the rooms.

He made rigorous experiments to disprove alleged cases of the spontaneous generation of life, showing that in every case, when the experiments were thorough, there was no evidence for it.

He experimented with scores of infusions made from all sorts of organic material, from tongue to tripe, and showed that in 130 different cases, three minutes' boiling produced sterilization. When infection occurred, he tracked it down. He described how he saw through his microscope, in drops from inadequately cleaned apparatus, bacteria darting to and fro, wriggling, rotating longitudinally, and spinning round a vertical transverse axis. 'Monads also galloped and quivered through the field.'

He became involved in controversy with H. C. Bastian, who claimed that life could be spontaneously generated in infusions of hay. Tyndall made many of these infusions, and found that indeed they might be difficult to sterilize. Those made from some old hay from Guildford were not always sterilized after four, or even eight hours of heating.

In 1877 Tyndall wrote to Huxley, who was then a Secretary of the Royal Society, that he had found that repeated discontinuous heating was a very effective method of sterilization. This discovery became of high importance, for it greatly facilitated the practical use of sterilization in research, medicine, industry and commerce.

Tyndall's skilful application of physical technique in bacteriology was a big contribution to the development of that important new science. He recorded in 1870 that Lister had written to him, saying that his lecture on motes in the atmosphere had borne good fruit, for it had suggested to him 'a most simple and most effectual new method for the treatment of wounds'.

Tyndall's own acute observations carried him far. He noted how those potent infusions of old hay had 'introduced a plague into our atmosphere—the other infusions, those of fresh hay included, like a smitten population, becoming the victims of a contagium foreign to themselves'.

In 1871 J. Burdon Sanderson, J. B. S. Haldane's great-uncle, had noted that if common air is bubbled through one of Pasteur's nutrient solutions for cultivating bacteria, *Penicillium* mould always appeared, but no bacteria. Sanderson had concluded that common air contained no bacteria. Tyndall sharply attacked this opinion, and argued that the experiment proved the inability of the mineral constituents in the culture solution to develop the bacteria, not that there were no bacteria in the common air.

In spite of Sanderson's experiment, and Tyndall's own observation of the smiting of whole populations of bacteria by a foreign contagion, it did not occur to either of them that the bacteria being taken into the water with the bubbles of air were being killed by the *Penicillium*, and that that was why the water remained free from bacteria.

Huxley had been deeply interested in the experiments of Pasteur and Tyndall, and himself read a paper on *Penicillium, Torula and Bacterium* to the British Association in 1870, the year in which he was President, and expressed the opinion that life had originated from non-living matter. Huxley's friend Hooker wrote to him with regard to these researches that he had 'always found that it was rather brains and boldness, than eyes or microscopes that the mycologists wanted . . .'

Thus Sanderson, Tyndall, Huxley and Hooker were hovering around the discovering of penicillin. But half a century had to pass before bacteriologists began to be oriented in the appropriate perspective for making the correct interpretation of such observations. It was not until 1928, when Fleming found himself confronted with similar phenomena of bacteria killed by *Penicillium* from the air of Paddington, not far from the Royal Institution, that the correct conclusion was drawn.

Besides contributing fundamentally to the advance and acceptance of bacteriology, Tyndall was the first to speak in England on the work of Robert Koch.

VIII

FACING FACTS

Facing facts, as he saw them, and forcing others to face them, was a continuous feature of Tyndall's personality and life. It was an essential factor in his expository function. Not all explainers are prepared to fight for their views. Many of them prefer merely to put them out and leave them to make their own way. The greatest expositors are distinguished by a more positive approach. They are prepared, not only to state truth, but resist and pursue error and destroy it, even at the sacrifice of repose. This Tyndall did. Tyndall's ability in controversy was of positive importance, and therefore requires consideration as more than an odd quirk of character. Religious and political argument was the chief mental sustenance of his youth in his passionately Protestant Southern Irish family. He was against Catholics, and, as an Irishman, never altogether for the English.

As a young surveyor he fought for the rights of his exploited colleagues during the 'hungry forties'. In his very first appearance on the scientific scene, as a recently-fledged Ph.D., he publicly differed with Faraday on the nature of diamagnetism.

His German higher education enabled him to appreciate the splendid contributions of Julius Robert Mayer to the establishment and development of the principle of the conservation of energy. He vindicated Mayer's achievement, and thereby even assisted him to recover from paranoic insanity caused by non-recognition. Mayer was ultimately given the Royal Society's highest award, the Copley Medal, in 1871, after it had been given to Joule in the previous year.

Tyndall had to contend with the theoretical and experimental authority of William Thomson and Joule, who, for all their outstanding command respectively of applied mathematics and experimental skill, and their independence of discovery, were in fact preceded by Mayer in deducing a reasonably well-founded figure for the mechanical equivalent of heat, and in many imaginative applications of the principle of the conservation of energy in the explanation of the economy of nature.

Clausius himself, who preceded Thomson in the discovery of the Second Law of Thermodynamics, did not read Mayer attentively until Tyndall had asked him for a collection of his papers. In his reply to Tyndall's enquiry, he at first said that Tyndall would not discover much of value in them. When he had collected the papers and looked through them, he wrote to Tyndall that he was astonished by their originality and penetration. Tyndall launched, without a moment's hesitation, into argument with Thomson and his rather undiscriminating friend and adherent, P. G. Tait.

When a unit quantity of a gas is raised in temperature by one degree, the amount of heat required is greater when the pressure of the gas is kept constant than when its volume is kept constant, during the heating. Mayer assumed that the difference was due to the work done against the atmosphere, when the pressure of the gas is kept constant, but its volume is allowed to expand.

It had not yet been experimentally proved that the heat absorbed in compressing a gas was equivalent to the force used in carrying out the compression. Logically, it could be contended that Mayer's argument was unsound, so long as this point remained unproved. Such an attitude was contrary to the logic of original discovery, which nearly always arrived at fundamental new truths long before some of the intervening steps in the argument were demonstrated. But P. G. Tait in particular argued that a proof which was imperfect in a single link was no proof at all.

A century later the fourth Lord Rayleigh commented with regard to this controversy that 'It may well be held that those who enumerate new and important results *which prove to be right in substance* should not be judged by the criteria which would be appropriate in marking an elementary examination paper a generation later . . .'

In 1877 Tait wrote to *Nature* that it was granted to very few men to do the useful work of popularization of science 'without thereby losing their claim to scientific authority. Dr Tyndall has, in fact, martyred his scientific authority by deservedly winning distinction in the popular field. One learns too late that he cannot "make the best of both worlds" . . .' This verged on the impertinent. The opposition to Tyndall was exacerbated by his combativeness, and it was fed by motives other than scientific profundity.

Tyndall expounded his views on the evolution of nature in his Presidential Address to the British Association in 1874. They were received with storms of dissent. He described with clarity and uncompromising force the universe as an assemblage of atoms in course of interaction. These formed themselves into systems of stars and planets. On one of the latter at least, on the earth, the interaction of molecules had proceeded further, and led to the formation of living organisms, which had then proceeded through their own evolution, in the manner elucidated by Darwin and Wallace.

While giving a forceful exposition of this line of thought, he explained very clearly that he regarded it as a limited materialism. He frankly found the mind-matter problem a mystery. There were many things appertaining to man whose prescriptive rights were quite as strong as those of the understanding itself. Among these was the feeling on which religion was based. He said that 'to yield this sentiment reasonable satisfaction is the problem of problems at the present hour'. It must be recognized, however, that this should not be allowed to intrude on the region of objective *knowledge*, but is capable of adding, in the region of *poetry* and *emotion*, 'inward completeness, and dignity to man'. Tyndall did not regard himself as an atheist.

He believed that life had originally arisen from non-living molecules, in spite of the proof by himself and others that all alleged cases of spontaneous generation were spurious.

Tyndall replied to the blame heaped on him 'for crossing the boundary of the experimental evidence' that this 'is the habitual action of the scientific mind'. In his own subject, physics, 'the experiential incessantly leads to the ultra experiential'. The difference between 'the great and the mediocre investigator' consisted for the most part in 'their different powers of ideal extension'. The kingdom of science did not come from observation and experiment alone, but was 'completed by fixing the roots of observation and experiment in a region inaccessible to both, and in dealing with which we are forced to fall back upon the picturing of the mind'.

Passing the boundary of experience did not constitute a sufficient ground for censure. He thought there must have been something in his 'particular mode of crossing it which provoked this tremendous chorus of dissent'. His theory of the step from dead to live matter did not depart from the fundamental method of science, but it antagonized ancient and widespread beliefs.

Tyndall's Belfast Address was a splendid piece of exposition, and more profound and far-seeing than his critics realized. The modern theories of the origin of life are in line with it.

IX

BACHELOR LIFE ENDS

Up to his middle fifties, Tyndall led an exceptionally intense scientific and athletic bachelor life. In spite of frequent attendances at dinners and country-house parties, and sharing a house (which had previously been occupied by T. H. Huxley) with his friend Hirst, Tyndall felt lonely. He suffered almost continuously from headaches and indigestion. These ailments, at any rate in their earlier stages, could not have been of a very serious nature, for even while suffering from them he accomplished major mountaineering feats.

Tyndall replied to those who denounced him as a materialist after his Belfast Address, that in his youth he had regarded his body as a weed, to be sacrificed to what he regarded as higher things. 'The error was not an ignoble one, but this did not save it from the penalty attached to error. Saner knowledge taught me that the body is no weed, and that treated as such it would infallibly avenge itself . . .'

Tyndall married in 1876, when he was fifty-six, Louise Charlotte Hamilton, the eldest daughter of Lord Claud Hamilton, brother of the first Duke of Abercorn, whose wife was the daughter of the third Earl of Carysfort. He had first begun to visit country houses and associate with the aristocracy through the Royal Institution, several of whose Managers and members belonged to it. Tyndall's wife was twenty-five years younger than himself. Her mother, Lady Claud Hamilton, drew Tyndall's attention to her feelings towards him. Lady Claud was a person of ability; Tyndall recommended her to Pasteur as English translator of his son-in-law Valery Radot's biography. Tyndall read the draft translation and contributed a preface. While he profoundly admired Pasteur's scientific genius, he privately deplored his vanity.

Louisa Tyndall conceived her wifely role in terms of Victorian devotion to her husband, combined with the deportment of a dutiful daughter to a father. Her looks were plain, and to the external world she presented an appearance of utter submission. To her duties as wife she added those of cook, secretary and nurse. In spite of her presentation of herself to the world, she and her husband were happily married. Tyndall said that if only Carlyle had been able to enjoy the playful relations with his wife that he did with his, both he and Mrs Carlyle would have been happier people.

In his earlier years Tyndall kept his natural combativeness under a fairly firm rein. If he was always uncompromising, he was rarely rash. The natural judgment which enabled him to avoid foolhardy dangers in climbing the Alps helped him to avoid carrying controversy too far. As he grew older and his health deteriorated, he became irascible, and some people came to look on him as a quarrelsome old man. He squabbled with his neighbours and planted screens of trees to prevent them from seeing into his garden.

His association with the aristocracy strengthened his Protestant Irish opposition to Home Rule for Ireland. He became a rabid Unionist. He described Gladstone as a madman, and the greatest curse ever inflicted on England. He considered standing for Parliament as a Unionist.

During these acrimonious years his health became still more

delicate. He became very sensitive to noise at night, and began to depend on drugs for combating his insomnia and indigestion.

After leaving the Royal Institution he retired to a villa which he and his wife had built on the beautiful heath at Hindhead. It was surrounded by some hundred acres, which ultimately was given to the National Trust, and became known as Tyndall's Park.

Tyndall and his wife worked on his large collection of papers, with the intention of writing his autobiography together. His health deteriorated, and the project proceeded slowly. His wife had to pay more and more attention to his condition. She habitually gave him a sleeping draught of chloral at night, and a dose of magnesia in the morning.

On the morning of 4 December 1893 she confused the two bottles, and measured out what she thought was a dose of magnesia. In fact, it was chloral, and was much larger in quantity than the usual chloral dose. Tyndall gulped it down, and commented on its sweet taste. His wife then realized what had happened, and, horrified, exclaimed: 'John, I have given you chloral.' He replied: 'Yes, my poor darling, you have killed your John!'

Tyndall took charge, got out of bed, and said: 'Let us do all we can. Tickle my throat. Get the stomach pump.' Doctors were sent for. Emetics were tried. He was put to bed with hot-water bottles, and given hot coffee. The doctors restored his consciousness for a time, and he said: 'I know you are all trying to rouse me.' The efforts were unavailing, and he died in the evening.

Tyndall's character was never more clearly exemplified than in his end. His direct recognition of the facts, his immediate and calm practical action in the face of the extremest danger, and the absence of complaining revealed the core of his nature stripped of all superficial weaknesses.

His wife survived him by nearly forty-seven years, dying at the age of ninety-five in 1940. It is remarkable that she was able to bear her situation all that time, and not surprising that she became difficult. She dedicated her long remaining years to the cult of her husband's memory. She desired to complete by herself the autobiography which they had begun together. She wrote an excellent short account for the Dictionary of National Biography, but a comprehensive work proved to be beyond her powers.

She could not bring herself to entrust the task to anyone else. When it became obvious that she would have to have a collaborator, she would not allow the papers to be removed from the house, and insisted that the collaborator must live in her house while he was at work, so that she could keep the whole activity under her personal control.

She received great consideration from Debus, Leslie Stephen and others, but naturally failed to persuade a suitable biographer to work under such conditions.

When she died in 1940 a biography of Tyndall had still not been written. This retarded the recognition of the importance of his gifts and the magnitude of his contribution. These were not adequately appreciated in the first half of the twentieth century, but will be esteemed more in the second.

Tyndall lectured with extraordinary lucidity, animation and charm. He had the gift of stimulating a passion for science in his hearers. Many persons, especially among the poorer sections of the population, gained their first knowledge of science from his lectures and books, and were inspired by them to secure a scientific education. They formed an important part of the scientific teaching personnel in the schools in the second half of the nineteenth century.

The extent of his influence was world-wide. Helmholtz translated some of his lectures into German, and editions were issued in Chinese, Japanese and other languages. His aim was to make intelligible in non-technical language the dominant scientific ideas of the age. By achieving this, he became 'a teacher of mankind'.

AUGUSTUS DE MORGAN
1806–1871

I

INTELLECTUAL QUALITY FOR THE PEOPLE

AUGUSTUS DE MORGAN is a unique figure. He inspired most abstract developments in mathematics, and at the same time carried out a major effort in public education. William Rowan Hamilton found the hint for his invention of quarternions in de Morgan's works, and George Boole was inspired by him to create Boolean Algebra, the language of the modern computer. As the first professor of mathematics at University College, London, and first president of the London Mathematical Society he had a major influence on advanced mathematical teaching, and on policy in mathematical research.

His simultaneous work of public instruction was achieved through the Society for the Diffusion of Useful Knowledge, and the *Penny Cyclopaedia* associated with it. He contributed more than 700 articles on mathematics, astronomy, the history of science, and music to the *Cyclopaedia*. Put together, they make about four of its thirty volumes. He wrote many of them before he was thirty years old, and they constitute a critical appraisal of the standard works of the period. They show him in process of forming his own opinions, and so instruct the reader how to form his. For this reason, they remain first-rate, even when later research has extended and revised the data on which he wrote. As the articles were largely critical expositions of the work of others, they are free from the specialist's tendency to dwell on the things which particularly interest him.

De Morgan published a large part of his extensive works through the Society, including even his *Differential and Integral Calculus*, expressly with the aim of bringing knowledge, and knowledge of high quality, to the people. He was profound by nature and simple on principle, in order to make his contributions intelligible to general and working-class readers. He poured into the pages of the encyclopaedia his critical knowledge of mathematics and science, raising the standard in the British treatment of these subjects, which is a necessary foundation for political action in a scientific age.

While the mode of publication of de Morgan's work increased its social influence by direct communication with the masses, it has hindered the recognition of his achievement. He published so much anonymously that the magnitude and significance of his work are not easily seen; if it had been published in collective form, its importance would have been more spectacularly evident. De Morgan exerted his influence on the people, and on mathematics, science and learning less through a few conspicuous works than an extraordinary number and variety of articles.

The most widely known of his books is his *Budget of Paradoxes*, published after his death, and based on his contributions to the *Athenaeum*, the leading weekly journal of the day. Through this medium he educated the contemporary administrative and ruling classes in the appreciation of minority opinion. He pointed out that 'in every age of the world there has been an established system, which has been opposed from time to time by isolated and dissentient reformers. The established system has sometimes fallen, slowly and gradually: it has either been upset by the rising influence of some one man, or it has been sapped by gradual change of opinion in the many.' His aim was to illuminate the nature of established and dissentient opinion, especially in the field of science, and illustrate the features which distinguish the false from the true.

While de Morgan was conducting his very important public enlightenment, he was an inspirer of the generalized mathematics which is needed to deal with the ideas of space and time required for describing the phenomena of relativity and the atomic nucleus.

De Morgan wrote classical mathematical textbooks in which the logic and quality of presentation were raised to a higher standard that gradually penetrated British mathematical teaching. Among his students were E. J. Routh and Isaac Todhunter, who became great Cambridge teachers of the next generation; and the tempestuous J. J. Sylvester, who attended his classes as a boy, but was expelled from the College at the age of fourteen, for taking a knife from the refectory with the intention of stabbing a fellow-student. Others carried his acuteness of insight into other disciplines, such as the political economist W. S. Jevons, and the political writer Walter Bagehot.

De Morgan's home was a centre of London cultural life. His wife Sophia was the daughter of the noted nonconformist, actuary and mathematician William Frend. He was the tutor of Miss

Milbanke, who became Byron's mathematical wife, and the mother of Byron's mathematical daughter, the future Countess Lovelace, who became one of de Morgan's private pupils, and the expounder of the principles of Babbage's computer. While his younger son, George, had been the chief founder of the London Mathematical Society, his eldest son, William, became a noted artist in ceramics, and at the age of sixty-eight began to publish novels which were to make him famous. These included *Alice for Short* and *Joseph Vance*.

How de Morgan appeared to his students at University College has been well described by Thomas Hodgkin the historian, and cousin of Joseph Lister. 'Towering up intellectually above all his fellows, as I now look back upon him, rises the grand form of the mathematician, Augustus de Morgan, known, I suppose to each succeeding generation of his pupils as "Gussy". A stout and tall figure, a stiff rather waddling walk, a high white cravat and stick-up collars in which the square chin is buried, a full but well chiselled face, very short-sighted eyes peering forth through gold-rimmed spectacles; but above all such a superb dome-like forehead, as could only belong to one of the kings of thought: that is my remembrance of De Morgan, and I feel in looking back upon his personality that his is one of the grandest figures that I have known.'

The historian of University College, H. H. Bellot, says that 'The personal character of de Morgan was as impressive as his force of intellect. He had a temper of great sweetness and liberality, but the masterful and independent cast of his mind, a love of principle, a keen sense of humour, and an athletic delight in mental agility, made a radical and incisive critic whom no solemnity could baulk.'

The range and depth of de Morgan's interests, his concern with the ethics of learning and the conduct of scientific organization in the shape of scientific societies; the variety of media through which he communicated his knowledge and principles; the different classes to which he appealed, made him one of the most influential formulators of public and specialist opinion on mathematics and science. He was a great teacher, scholar, and investigator.

II

ORIGINS OF INDEPENDENCE

Augustus de Morgan was born at Madura, in Madras, India, in 1806. His paternal ancestors had held posts in the military and civil service in India for 150 years. His great-grandfather and his grandfather fought under Warren Hastings. His father was a colonel, energetic in the performance of his duties, with earnest and rigid Evangelical religious views, and a strong sense of propriety in the conduct of affairs.

The colonel's wife, Augustus's mother, was a granddaughter of James Dodson, the author of the *Anti-logarithmic Canon*, a friend of de Moivre, and mathematical master at Christ's Hospital. He was also the chief founder of the Equitable Life Assurance Company, and computed the first tables used by it. De Morgan said that, so far as he could find, Dodson was the first to recommend the use of double-entry in retail trade, which he suggested in a work on book-keeping.

Colonel de Morgan had chosen the command at Madura because it was quiet during a period of unrest in the army. At other places, British officers were being killed by Indian troops, and even at Madura the colonel used to crawl out of bed, at the time his wife was pregnant, in order to spy on the sentries, to learn whether they were passing rebellious messages during the changing of the guard. Some months after Augustus was born, the family returned to England. They travelled in a large convoy of more than thirty ships, in a voyage that lasted more than three months.

Beaufort, the commodore of the convoy, became in later years an eminent meteorologist and admiral; the inventor of the Beaufort Scale of storms. De Morgan and he were friends for years before discovering that, half a century earlier, de Morgan as an infant had been a passenger in his convoy.

De Morgan had been born in India in circumstances of psychological tension. He was exposed to no less serious physical strain; he contracted the disease which commonly attacks the eyes of infants in India. Both of Augustus's eyes were affected, and his right eye was virtually destroyed. The damage to his eyes hindered his normal development. It was a cause of his detachment from conventionality, and his intellectual independence.

The family lived at first in Worcester, and then at various places in the West Country, not settling anywhere. After about two years the colonel returned alone to India, became involved in disturbances in the Madras Army, and was suspended from duty, but subsequently exonerated. He came back to England in 1810, and returned alone to India once more in 1812. He became ill, and was ordered home in 1816, dying off St Helena during the voyage.

De Morgan received his first instruction from his father at the age of four, and then went to a series of schools, according to the

AUGUSTUS DE MORGAN

migrations of the family. He left a list of them, in which he described himself as 'The Victim', indicating his opinion of his early education. However, he admired the last of his teachers, the Rev. J. Parsons, formerly a fellow of Oriel. He was under him from the age of fourteen to sixteen and a half. Parsons was a good scholar, and gave de Morgan a sound training in the classics. He first gained an insight into mathematics through an adult friend, not one of his teachers, who explained to him that the aim of Euclid is logical demonstration.

De Morgan did not take part in any sports because of his poor sight, and was tormented by some boys because of his virtual blindness in his right eye. They would creep silently on his blind side, holding an open knife up to his face, so that when he was spoken to, he would turn involuntarily, and jab his face. This was stopped only by fighting.

Serious effects also followed from the rigid religious convictions of his parents. His father was a passionate Evangelical. He made Augustus learn long Scripture lessons by heart, and attend innumerable services; he was required to make an abstract of every sermon. The effect was to confirm in him a life-long resistance to any kind of intellectual domination, especially when advocated on moral grounds. He became incapable of listening to any continued speaking or preaching.

He entered Trinity College, Cambridge, in 1823, before he was seventeen. His teacher Mr Parsons had wanted him to read classics. His mother, who was responsible for the whole of her family, desired him to become an Evangelical clergyman, and regarded time spent on reading mathematics as wasted. She was deeply distressed when he did not immediately surpass his fellow students, and entreated him not to be 'so wilful' as to devote himself to mathematics.

At Trinity College de Morgan came under the instruction of Peacock, the most academically influential of the three Cambridge mathematical reformers: Babbage, Herschel and himself. Besides Peacock, there were the younger and less radical followers of the reformers: W. Whewell and G. B. Airy, with whom he established lifelong friendships; and a group of less famous but enthusiastic students of the new mathematics.

George Peacock, born in 1791, was the son of a North Yorkshire clergyman. He was one of the men from the North of England, referred to in the Cambridge of the day as *The Northern Lights*. They included Whewell, Sheepshanks and Airy, and they injected the vigour of the new industrial North into the

ancient university. Peacock was intellectually acute, physically
strong and very industrious. He pursued mathematical and
administrative reform with clear vision and steady determination,
describing himself as a reformer by choice.

Shortly before de Morgan entered Cambridge, Peacock had
used his position as an examiner to introduce the modern differential calculus notation into the examination for the university
honours degree. He wrote to a friend: 'I assure you that I shall
never cease to exert myself to the utmost in the cause of reform,
and that I will never decline any office which may increase my
power to effect it . . . It is by silent perseverance only, that we
can hope to reduce the many-headed monster of prejudice and
make the University answer her character as the loving mother
of good learning and science.' His last public act before he died
in 1858 was to attend a meeting of the Royal Commission on the
reform of Cambridge and Oxford universities.

Peacock was a perfect master for de Morgan. He revealed to
him the kind of mathematics which was suited to his talent, and
the example of his character and views strengthened and confirmed his tendency towards critical independence.

Peacock placed the exposition of algebra on a more consistent
logical basis. He pursued this aim in a treatise on the subject
published in 1830, and an influential report written for the
British Association in 1833. He carried the logical treatment
further in his *Symbolical Algebra*. His aim was to eliminate the
restrictions on the rules of arithmetical algebra. Historically,
algebraical symbols had first appeared as representations of
numbers; Peacock showed that they could also be conceived
merely as signs, entities in their own right, which could be mani-
pulated in a logical system, by operations such as addition and
multiplication, when performed according to certain rules or
postulates. De Morgan said that 'Peacock had very nearly attained
the idea of algebra as a *formal science*, in which every result of the
form is to have meaning'.

This formalistic theory of algebra was adopted and carried
further by de Morgan. It had started in a determined effort to
separate algebraic symbols from numbers, and it directed attention to the form rather than the content of the argument.

The criticism of the principles of mathematics by Peacock and
others revived interest in logic. This branch of the Cambridge
critical development was led by William Whewell, who was born
in 1794, and was three years younger than Peacock. Whewell
was Second Wrangler in 1816, but his gifts were more for en-

cyclopaedic scientific learning than mathematics. He conceived the aim of becoming a modern Francis Bacon, and planned a programme of work to that end. His study of Bacon's views on inductive logic and its role in scientific discovery strengthened his interest in logic itself. De Morgan was among those who responded to Whewell's enthusiasm both for logic and for wide scientific learning.

Whewell was the son of a Lancaster carpenter, and a man of extraordinary physique. A pugilist happening to see him in the street, stopped him and said: 'What a man was lost when they made you a parson!' Besides pursuing his mathematical, logical and Baconian studies, he became an active professor of mineralogy, and wrote on the history of architecture, publishing a book on the origin of the Gothic style. One of his most successful contributions was in the invention of new words to describe new scientific ideas. Faraday sought his advice on names for electrical phenomena, and Whewell suggested to him anode, cathode, anion, cation, ion, and para- and dia-magnetic. He suggested to Lyell the geological terms eocene, miocene and pliocene. Most remarkable of all was his invention of the very word 'scientist', for persons who engage in science. In a sense, this invention marked the beginning of the present age, for it implied the recognition of science as a profession.

Whewell's knowledge was vast and varied, but his acuity was uneven. Besides making valuable contributions he also made mistakes. His qualities were seen to best advantage in situations requiring force and courage, as well as learning. He was an outstanding Master of Trinity College, Cambridge, a position which gave his strong personality scope, though the violent intensity of his physical and intellectual energy made him dogmatic and authoritarian. It caused him many tribulations in dealing with people and situations. To undergraduates he was known as 'Whuffler'. His head was bullet-shaped, and his physique enormous. He had the habit of rushing into morning chapel with his face bleeding from hasty shaving cuts, which enhanced his formidable aspect. De Morgan was sufficiently strong to stand up to his domineering, which many people found trying.

III

STUDENT AND PROFESSOR

When a student at Cambridge, de Morgan became conspicuous for his discursive and late reading. He was often up at 4 a.m., when the college roisterers were returning from their revels. They used to call on him to be soothed by his flute, on which he was an accomplished performer. His mother heard of his unusual habits, and remonstrated that he was said to be 'a man who reads much, but who is not likely *to do* much, because he will not conform to the instructions of those who could assist him'. Nevertheless, his progress was such that his college awarded him a scholarship in his second year.

In spite of his activity, de Morgan, like some other very industrious men, such as James Watt, Charles Darwin and Rutherford, was a voracious novel-reader. His short-sightedness discouraged him from riding or boating or field games; it also deterred him from pursuing experimental and observational science, and focused his attention on abstract studies.

His mother's persistent nagging kept religious questions continually before his mind, but helped to strengthen his attitude of non-commitment. He refused to subscribe to any creed, but appeared to sympathize most with the Unitarians. In his will, he stated that he was a Christian, but 'I have not confessed with my lips, because in my time such confession has always been the way up in the world'.

He had the same questioning attitude to all ideas, and held that a man's opinions were his own affair, and sacred; but he believed in observing ordinary social conventions. The law should be obeyed, but no effort should be spared to change bad laws.

He had the courtesy of an eighteenth-century gentleman, with the acuteness of a twentieth-century mind. No doubt he had inherited some of the social manners of his family, which had for so long taken part in ruling India. In these he was different from many of his non-conforming English friends, who came from the commercial and industrial middle class.

He distrusted educational as much as religious routine. He refused to follow the recommended courses of reading for the degree examination; consequently, though he was unanimously regarded as by far the ablest candidate, he was only Fourth Wrangler in his year. Such was the prestige of the Cambridge mathematical examination at this time, that this was regarded almost as an intellectual disaster. For the rest of the nineteenth century, most of his admirers were at pains to explain it away. De Morgan's own attitude against competitive examinations hardened steadily. He considered the Cambridge examinations as a 'writing race', and analysed in his lectures the evils of competitive examinations, with their stimulation of cramming, encouragement of facility at the expense of understanding, and the nervous strain they put on the student. In his own lectures and books he devoted more attention to the analysis and exposition of principles, and less to facility in solving problems. This aspect of his teaching resembled the Continental rather than the English tradition.

But in some ways his mathematical outlook was very English. He was anti-authoritarian. Unlike his great German contemporaries, he did not expect his students to accept revolutionary views merely because he taught them. They were to attend to principles rather than facility, but they were to be prepared to accept them only on their merits.

De Morgan's questioning attitude on religion disqualified him from becoming a master of arts and fellow of his college. He had no prospect of an academic position at Cambridge, and he had to think of a profession. He was proud of having been born in India, and desired to visit it. His mother rejected on his behalf the offer of a cadetship in the Indian service. He considered medicine, but friends advised that he was too intolerant of ignorance and folly, and had too great a 'hatred of everything low', to be a successful doctor. His mother asked him to take up law. He agreed to this, though with reluctance, for he feared he 'might find it difficult to satisfy both his clients and his conscience'.

In 1827 de Morgan entered Lincoln's Inn, and settled in London. His mathematical connections brought him in touch with the office of the Nautical Almanac; through this, he happened to meet William Frend, the noted actuary, whose academic career had been broken through religious scruples.

Frend, who was born in 1757, had been Second Wrangler in his year, and a fellow of Jesus College. Among his pupils was Malthus, with whose subsequent views he warmly disagreed. Like some other mathematicians who had no academic prospects because of their opinions, he made a living by utilizing his skill in the insurance business. He was the founder and chief actuary of the Rock Life Assurance Office. He lived in a pleasant house with wooded grounds in Stoke Newington, which had formerly belonged to Daniel Defoe. He entertained a wide circle of friends, which included Blake, Coleridge, Lamb, Wordsworth, Brougham, Campbell and others. He was a vigorous and courageous supporter of unpopular opinions which he believed to be true.

De Morgan visited the house soon after he had settled in London. He met there Frend's daughter Sophia, whom he was to marry ten years later. She was nineteen when they first met, and has recorded the family's surprise on learning that he was then only twenty-one, because he looked so much older. His serious appearance belied his nature, for he entertained his hosts with fun, fairy tales and ghost stories, and taught Sophia a new figure in cat's cradle. She recorded that his person was 'very like what he continued through life', though paler, probably owing to his excessive reading at Cambridge. He had also 'a slight pleasure in saying things which startled formal religionists', but Sophia convinced herself that he didn't really mean it.

When de Morgan arrived in London in 1827, he found himself in the midst of the discussions on the foundation of a new university in the metropolis. Frend was one of the promoters of the movement. The idea was old, but the conditions did not become propitious for its foundation until the first quarter of the nineteenth century. Bellot says that the proposal, which had fallen on deaf ears in previous centuries, was listened to at this time 'because, meanwhile, a social revolution had created a demand, which in the old seats of higher learning could not be satisfied. The growth of physical science with all its consequences, upon the one hand, and the emergence, upon the other, of a new class, differing in its social standing, its religious opinions, and its economic interests, from that which had dominated the life of the nation during the earlier half of the eighteenth century, led men to reconsider their conception of education as well as their conception of law, of politics, and of economics. This history of the foundation of the University of London is thus but a paragraph in the story of that change in the intellectual, social, political, and economic structure of public life, which came about between the American revolution and the Reform Bill. Men felt, as Priestley put it, that "a different and a better furniture of mind [was] requisite to be brought into the business of life".'

In this situation, many men put forth appropriate suggestions: Thomas Campbell the poet was one, who in 1820 had been struck by the liberal atmosphere in the new university at Bonn, where Protestant, Catholic and Jewish students benefited together. Campbell was without executive ability, and the first person to give him practical aid was the Jewish banker Isaac Lyon Goldsmid, who introduced him to Brougham. Sophia de Morgan could remember that Brougham dined with her father to discuss the scheme when she was about twelve years old. Brougham's leadership converted the proposal into a reality.

The Jewish and Dissenting businessmen who provided most of the finance for the new institution desired it to be conducted according to the business principles with which they were familiar. It was therefore launched as a joint stock company. The most important ideological feature in its constitution was the absence of any religious qualification for staff and students. It was to be devoted to education in Classics, Mathematics, Physical Science and Medicine; religion was not mentioned.

When sufficient financial support had been collected, building was started, and Leonard Horner, the brother of Francis Horner, Brougham's friend, was appointed Warden. The appointment of a professoriate was started. The chemistry chair was offered to Faraday, who refused it. The mathematics chair was offered to John Herschel, and to Babbage, but neither of them accepted. When it became open, de Morgan saw in it a chance of escape from the law, and the pursuit of his interest. He became a candidate; he was twenty-one, and much the youngest, but was elected. In a letter to John Herschel, in which he refers to the circumstances of his appointment, de Morgan said there were fifty candidates. His wife said there were thirty-two, and according to the minutes quoted by Bellot there were twenty. De Morgan attributed his appointment to Brougham and Warburton, as the only electors who would have had the courage to appoint so young a man.

The new institution could not afford to pay its professors much. During the whole period of his professorship, de Morgan's salary was never as much as £500 a year, and sometimes it was less than £300. The low salary was one of the causes why he wrote so much. He also increased his income by practising as an actuarial consultant, following his father-in-law's connection with insurance business. He became the leading actuarial expert, and was consulted by various companies on problems of particular difficulty.

De Morgan worked incessantly. He hated the country and seaside, and refused to accompany his family on vacations. In 1834 he wrote to his future father-in-law, saying that he was not surprised on returning to town to find that he was not there, as he took 'pleasure in the wilderness'. For his own part, he 'did not exceed by a single day' the estimate of the time he could 'bear the viridity of extra-urban scenery'. While his health was 'recovering from the effects of the raw atmosphere' he had been breathing, he took the opportunity of writing this letter instead of pursuing more serious work. 'This is no joke, I assure you;

whenever I return from the country I am knocked down for some days.' He had been to visit his Cambridge mathematical friend Neate, now a country clergyman. He lived in a place six miles from any town in 'a lone house he calls his rectory . . . How people live in such lone houses I know not. Conceive me reduced to clip hedges to pass away the time till dinner . . .' He went on to Cambridge, where Sheepshanks drove him to Madingley, 'a place I never saw in my life before, so you may judge how far my walks extended as an undergraduate. Came home as tired as a city mouse of hedgerows and cottages . . . If the locomotives ever come to go so quick that one tree shall not be distinguishable from another, then, and not before, do I become a traveller. Mr Stephenson (engineer) says he shall never be satisfied till two hours take us from London to Liverpool. Blessings on his heart, but either he or, better still, one of the minority who can be spared, shall *try it first* . . .'

When he had a stroke in 1868 one of his friends suggested it had been brought on by overwork. De Morgan replied: 'rid your mind of the idea. I have never been *hard* working, but I have been very very *continuously* at work. I have never *sought* relaxation. And why? Because it would have killed me. Amusement is real hard work to me. To relax is to forage about the books with no particular object, and not bound to go on with anything . . .'

De Morgan's family regretted his abandonment of law. They imagined he had brilliant prospects at the bar, but he wrote: 'I am very glad that I can sleep without the chance of dreaming that I see an "Indenture of Five Parts", or some such matter, held up between me and the *Mécanique Céleste*, knowing all the time that the dream must come true.'

He said that with his Introductory Lecture, he began to teach himself to better purpose than he had been taught, 'as does every man who is not a fool, let his former teachers be what they may'.

The new institution soon ran into fundamental difficulties. Its Deed of Settlement vested power in the proprietors. The professors were not, as such, members of the university. There were no faculties nor academic senate. Its business was conducted by a large Council, who could dismiss professors as paid employees at discretion, subject to an appeal to the proprietors. The Council had early found it necessary to have a permanent secretary to carry out its decisions, and the post had been offered to Leonard Horner, the elder brother of Francis. Leonard Horner had founded a technical school in Edinburgh, which grew into the Heriot-Watt College and ultimately a university in its own right.

He had been active in the family business of linen manufacture; an energetic and capable man, well-informed but not a scholar. He had the Scottish notion of a Principal of a University, a person of great authority and power, and he conceived the secretaryship in those terms. He objected to the title, and to the offered salary of £500, so the title was changed to Warden, and the salary raised to £1,200 a year. He stipulated that he should be the only medium of communication between the Council and the professors whom it employed. Leonard Horner had the personality of a headmaster of a school, rather than a University Principal of the Scottish type. He lacked academic authority, and being a snob, tried to substitute social influence for it.

Thus the institution, besides being new and a joint stock company in which the professors were employees, had an unsuitable head, who had not originally been intended for the position. In addition to this, the students were free from many of the constraints of the older universities; they were not under religious discipline, and did not live in residential colleges. The institution had been organized on quasi-commercial lines, the students in virtue of their fees were regarded to some extent as customers. They expected, and felt they had a right to expect, that their professors should be good lecturers and teachers. The management were therefore sensitive to students' criticisms of the staff.

Some of the professors, for various reasons, were not popular with the students, in particular the professor of anatomy, G. S. Pattison. He belonged to the old school, lecturing in pink coat and riding boots, and was not interested in recent advances in medicine. The Warden sympathized with the students, and was suspected of anonymously supporting their agitation against him.

Pattison said he had been accused of not teaching 'French anatomy'; by this was meant modern anatomy. For his part, he said, he admitted he did not teach it, whatever it might be. All that he aimed at was to 'teach anatomy for the purpose of educating useful medical practitioners'.

The dispute became a public scandal, and a committee, of which T. B. Macaulay was a member, was set up to investigate the matter. It decided that Pattison should be recommended to retire.

De Morgan and several other professors were deeply disturbed by this action. He held that the University could have no future unless 'nothing but the public voice or the law of the land' could dismiss them. Professors who could be engaged and dismissed like employees could not create an effective institute of teaching and research.

7*

Shortly afterwards, the Council dismissed Pattison. De Morgan immediately sent in his resignation. In it he said that he would think it discreditable to hold a professorship in an institution where he could be dismissed without any fault of his own.

IV

INDEPENDENT CRITIC

De Morgan resigned shortly after his twenty-fifth birthday, and Horner retired from the Wardenship for which he was not fitted, subsequently achieving more success in the sphere of factory legislation.

During the next five years, de Morgan had no academic appointment. He had resigned on a matter of principle, and he spent this period, from his twenty-sixth to his thirty-first year, mainly in teaching private pupils, extensive writing, especially for the Society for the Diffusion of Useful Knowledge, and in actuarial consulting.

This break of five years in his life, just after he had become mature and entered an extremely energetic period, was of great importance. During it he consolidated both his intellectual and moral independent position. When he returned to academic life five years later, it was far stronger than it could have been if he had not passed through that period.

This, together with his ability, gave him a special authority on questions of principle in the mathematical and scientific world. He was heard with particular respect and effect in the disputes and controversies which arose in the rapid developments in the first half of the nineteenth century, following the social and industrial revolutions and the Napoleonic Wars.

Owing to his freedom from academic duties, he had more time than he had expected to devote to scientific societies. He became particularly interested in the Royal Astronomical Society. He was elected to its council in 1830, and continued as an officer for thirty years.

De Morgan regarded the scientific developments and controversies with which he was concerned as directly linked with the contemporary social and political changes. In 1866 he wrote: 'I first began to know the Scientific world in 1828. The forces were then mustering for what may be called the great battle of 1830. The great epidemic which produced the French Revolution, and what is yet the English Reform Bill, showed its effect on the scientific world.'

He became honorary secretary of the Royal Astronomical Society in 1831, the year in which he had resigned his chair and the British Association for the Advancement of Science had been founded to remedy the backwardness of British science. Owing to his attachment to town life, he was always available. Besides his influence on the conduct of the Society, he edited many volumes of Monthly Notices, wrote critical articles on difficult historical questions, such as the discovery of the planet *Neptune*, and obituary notices of outstanding quality on contemporary astronomers.

His lack of academic position in the years 1831–36 precipitated him into extensive writing. Besides his very numerous contributions to the *Penny Cyclopaedia*, he contributed to the remarkable *Quarterly Journal of Education*, conducted for five years by the Society for the Diffusion of Useful Knowledge. It contained surveys of scientific and literary education in modern Europe, taking stock of the situation after the revolutionary upheavals. It had the same sort of aims, and performed the same kind of service for the 1830's, that the numerous reports produced since the Second World War on science and education have performed for the present post-war period. The articles foreshadow many of the topics of today. There were survey articles on *Education in Russia*, in *Spain*, in *Switzerland*, in *Virginia*, in *Ireland* etc., and on the universities of various lands.

In the first volume, published in 1831, de Morgan wrote on *The Polytechnic School of Paris*, and contributed four book reviews. He concluded his analysis of the *Polytechnic*:

'We have thus given an abstract of the history and methods of the most celebrated school of instruction for engineers which has ever existed. Such an institution is the thing most wanted in this country. It matters nothing to say, that we have carried many of the arts there taught to a higher degree of perfection than the French. If the genius of our people leads them to greater excellence in this department, why not increase the disproportion still more by the help of system and education? We may and shall be surpassed in the arts in which we most pride ourselves, unless we attend to the formation of those by whose exertions our superiority is to be maintained. Neither is the argument fairly stated, when our manhood is compared with the youth of our neighbours. Before the first revolution, no country was so destitute of practical science as France, and in thirty years no country ever made the same progress. Because we are still much in advance, does it follow that we must remain so? Are we to take no means to put ourselves in motion, until the decline of our commerce convinces us that our rivals are come up with us? It will then be too late to rectify the error, since the production of a large body of well-educated men is the work of some time, and more still is necessary before their influence can be felt. It is to be expected that the extension of the higher parts of education, which is undoubtedly taking place among us, will reach those whose business it is to apply the sciences to practice. But this is not enough to give assurance, that we shall ever find among our practical men a Monge, a Malus, or a Fresnel, unless a system be adopted calculated to encourage the application of theory to professional pursuits, and to put the researches of the few to the purposes of the many, and to stimulate those whose business lies in one branch, to bring to it the assistance of the knowledge derived from the rest.'

In the second volume he contributed a long article *On Mathematical Instruction*, dealing with the question why young people find the subject boring, and what should be done to remedy this. Incidentally, he remarks that mathematics is intrinsically interesting. 'There seems to be a magic in numbers, which no one can withstand, from Leibniz, who proposed to convert the king of China to Christianity, by means of the binary arithmetic, to the mathematical master of a country school, who measures his pupils' conviction of geometrical truths by their power of re-collecting the order in which they come.'

Among many other articles, he wrote two long reviews of Peacock's *Treatise on Algebra*, which was published in 1830, and was to have such deep influence on British mathematics. In it, de Morgan discussed the processes of mathematical understanding, and the nature of symbolism, which were raised by Peacock's critical work.

He explained the three years' delay in the review of Peacock's important book as due to its views, which were 'so new and so extensive. At first sight it appeared to us something like symbols bewitched, and running about the world in search of a meaning'; a hundred years before Pirandello's characters went in search of an author.

De Morgan sustained a uniformly high critical standard over a wider range of scientific and related literary and ethical topics than any other English writer.

In 1853 Michael Foster asked him to write down his views on university education. He said he had not the slightest diffidence in opposing his opinions to the collective deliberations of his colleagues. 'Solomon said that in the multitude of councillors there was safety; safety, not wisdom.' A numerous body always compromised, and chose expediency: 'practicability is the word, freedom from present difficulty is the thing'.

'The plan of the Universities of the Middle Ages, to which in a great degree we owe both the thought and the operative ability of the last two centuries, rested on a simple principle, which stood ready for any amount of development which its own good consequences might make possible. All existing knowledge, the pursuit of which could discipline the mind for thought and action, was collected into one system, and declared to be available for the purpose of a University. And in this manner, reason, language, and observation were cultivated together. Every means was employed for forming the future man in his relation to himself, to other men, and to the external world. The worst thing, if not the only thing, that can be said against their successors in England is that they have not sufficiently allowed the development of the principle in reference to branches of knowledge which progress has converted into disciplines, and that, each in its own way, they have given undue prominence to one of the ancient disciplines.

'The sciences of observation occupied rather a subordinate place, because in the disciplinary sense they had attained but little efficacy. To which it is to be added, that the very wants of daily life, in a rude state of co-operative power, made daily life itself such a discipline of observation as we now have no idea of. Every savage has all the knowledge of his tribe in matters to be drawn from observation and applied in practice. The man of the fifteenth century, much nearer to the savage than ourselves, had a considerable share of it. The man of our day has just as little as he pleases, and no more than his individual temperament and opportunities may lead him to acquire; the temperament not being fostered by education, and the opportunities being mostly subsequent to it.

'The great point, then, in which the old Universities ended by ignoring the progress of the world around them, the great point on which it might have been the privilege of a new one to show them that the world could teach them something even on the fundamentals of education, was the neglect of the discipline of observation, of language as connected with it and of inference as immediately derived from it . . .'

V

THE INTELLECTUAL CONSCIENCE

The action of de Morgan and others over the dismissal of Pattison contributed to the revision of the original constitution of the London University. In 1836, the University was re-established as a degree-granting body, and the teaching institution re-incorporated as University College, London. The status of the professors and the machinery of administration were improved.

In the same year, J. G. P. White, who had succeeded de Morgan as professor of mathematics, was drowned in an accident. De Morgan offered to perform the duties until a new professor was found. The College duly offered him his old chair, and de Morgan, after taking the advice of the eminent lawyer Sir Harris Nicholas on the new status of the professors, accepted it. Charles Babbage secured the advice of the same lawyer on the legal position concerning his calculating machine.

Thereafter, de Morgan continued as professor for thirty more years, until he again resigned on a question of principle. In 1866, the Senate recommended to the council that James Martineau should be appointed to the chair of philosophy. He was considered philosophically the best qualified of the applicants, but he was also a noted Unitarian preacher. The Council rejected the Senate's recommendation by the casting vote of the chairman.

De Morgan took the view, shared by others, that Martineau had been rejected on account of his religious opinions. He considered that the Council had abandoned the religious impartiality which had been of such fundamental importance in the founding of the institution.

The rejection of Martineau was in fact a sign of the increasing conventionality of the institution, which was necessary if it was to compete with the ancient universities on their own ground.

De Morgan had spent his whole life resisting expediency and he was not prepared to acquiesce in it at the end. As he wrote to a friend: 'To myself, who never will have anything to do either with religious exclusion or with atheism, the proceeding was a call to resign, which I immediately obeyed. I knew it to be an abandonment of the principle of the College done in the worst way; a pretence of fearing heterodoxy, with the fear on the minds of the leaders of nothing but theism.'

Two years later he suffered the stroke, which he considered was mainly due to the shock of the College's abandonment, as he saw it, of its principles. There were, however, other causes of his illness. His friends thought it was due in part to a lifetime of overwork, which he strenuously denied. In 1867 his talented mathematical son George, who with his friend A. C. Ranyard were the first proposers and secretaries of the London Mathematical Society, died. His third son also was seriously ill, and in 1870 his daughter Helen died. After this he sank gradually, and on 18 March 1871 he passed away.

De Morgan had been showing increasing lack of resilience under strain for several years before the final blow of the Martineau affair. His students had been finding him irritable and his lectures more difficult. In 1861 he retired from all official positions in the Royal Astronomical Society, which for thirty years had been one of his keenest interests and pleasures. The Society had departed from its custom of appointing its President on the recommendation of its council and had passed over their candidate, and preferred a wealthy amateur. De Morgan thereupon retired. As will be seen, he nevertheless came to the conclusion that a man-of-affairs who knew about science might be preferable to a professional for the Presidency of the Royal Society. He had refused to be a candidate for the Royal Society, even after the reform of the 1840's.

The reforms had produced a new difficulty for him. They restricted the number of annual elections to fifteen, which made election in fact a competitive examination. The growing number of candidates meant that 'the time is clearly coming when many of those who ought to be welcomed will be excluded for life, or else shelved at last when past work, with a scientific peerage. Coupled with this attempt to create a kind of order of knighthood is an absurdity so glaring that it should always be kept before the general eye. This distinction, this mark set by science upon successful investigation, is of necessity a class-distinction . . .'

De Morgan said he was not hostile to the Royal Society. He had served on one of its committees when invited, and had refereed papers for it. He had 'always had a high opinion of the Society upon its whole history. A person used to historical inquiry learns to look at wholes; the Universities of Oxford and Cambridge, the College of Physicians, &c. are taken in all their duration. But those who are not historians—I mean not possessed of the habit of history—hold a mass of opinions about current things which lead them into all kinds of confusion when they try to look back'.

De Morgan's distrust of any kind of identification with the establishment led him to refuse honorary degrees. When Brougham became Lord Rector of the University of Edinburgh, he asked de Morgan whether he would assent to his proposal that the University should confer on him an honorary doctorate, but even this he refused. He said that he 'did not feel like an LL.D.'.

VI

MATHEMATICS AND LOGIC

As Sir Frederick Pollock had observed, Whewell was a 'very, *very* considerable man', but 'not a great man'. He had vast learning, but not the insight of genius. He could step half of the way, but not the whole way, towards the future. He was a conservative, not a radical reformer. On the one hand, he sympathized with the new mathematical and logical criticism; on the other, he could not detach himself from the ancient Cambridge dominating devotion to mathematics.

While the reform of Cambridge mathematics and science was being intensely debated in the second quarter of the nineteenth century, Whewell published, in 1835, his *Thoughts on the Study of Mathematics as a part of a Liberal Education*. This was reviewed in the following year by Sir William Hamilton (not the great mathematician William Rowan Hamilton of Dublin), who was professor of logic and metaphysics at Edinburgh. Sir William was one of the most learned men of the age, in nearly everything, though he was without formal skill in mathematics. He was extremely annoyed with Whewell's thesis that mathematics is better than logic as a medium of liberal education. Keeping his anger on a firm rein, Hamilton began modestly by saying that he 'only contended that they [the mathematics] ought not to be made the *principal*, far less the *exclusive* object of encouragement. We speak not now of *professional*, but of *liberal* education; not of that, which makes the mind an instrument for the improvement of science, but of this, which makes science an instrument for the improvement of the mind.'

Of all intellectual pursuits, mathematics, whose utility as an intellectual exercise, when carried beyond a moderate extent, had been most peremptorily denied by the greatest number of competent judges. He proceeded to enumerate them. Aristotle had observed 'that not youths only, but mere boys easily become mathematicians, while yet incapable of practical or speculative philosophy'. 'No one, almost', said Cicero, 'seems to have intently applied himself to this science, who did not attain in it any proficiency he pleased.' Roger Bacon had noted that 'very modest scholars are competent to mathematical learning, although unable to attain to any knowledge of the other sciences'.

D'Alembert had remarked that the mathematics 'only dry up and dull the minds already prepared for this operation by nature'. Descartes wrote in 1636 that 'he was anxious not to lose any more of his time in the barren operations of geometry and arithmetic', studies which did not lead to anything important.

Berkeley doubted 'whether tedious calculations in algebra and fluxions be the likeliest method to improve the mind', while among extensive quotations from Pascal, he included: 'Mathematicians who are mere mathematicians, have thus their understanding correct, provided always that every thing be well explained to them by definition and principle, otherwise they are false and insupportable.'

To metaphysical intellects like those of Descartes and Leibniz, 'mathematical discovery shows almost as an easy game. Both were illustrious inventors, almost as soon as serious students of the science.' When Descartes published his great philosophical work at the age of forty-two, he expressly said that he had given up mathematics seventeen years before. 'Yet so far was the puerile play of the philosopher in advance of the veteran study of the mathematicians, that it is only about four years, since Fourier practically demonstrated how a great principle of Descartes previously unappreciated, affords the best and the most rapid method for the analysis of numerical equations.'

Hamilton contended that 'the merit of a mathematical invention is, in fact, measured by the amount of thought which it supersedes. It is the highest compliment to the ingenuity of a Pascal, a Leibnitz, and a Babbage, in their invention of the arithmetic machine, that there would not be required in those who use it more than the dexterity of a turnspit. The algebraic analysis is not an instrument so perfect; it still requires a modicum of mind to work it . . .'

Further support for his views on the limitations of mathematics was to be found in Clarendon, Le Clerc, Buddens, Barbeyrac, Warburton, Basedow, Walpole, Gibbon, Kirwan and Madame de Staël: 'Nothing', said this lady, 'is less applicable to life than a mathematical argument.'

That 'marvellous Prince of Mirandola' observed that mathematical science does not bestow wisdom; and it was for that reason that the ancients made it the discipline of boys. Leibniz's learned friend, the Queen of Prussia, was not blind to the evil influence of mathematics on his philosophy.

Fathers of the Church were against it. St Austin said mathematics 'lead away from God'. St Jerome said they were not sciences of piety. St Ambrose said that 'to cultivate astronomy and geometry is to abandon the cause of salvation, and to follow that of error'.

Equally severe criticisms had been made by those eminent modern German authorities Bernhardi, von Weitler and Klumpp. Goethe had noted that he had 'long been aware that the cultivation afforded by the mathematics is, in the highest degree, one-sided and contracted . . .'

Hamilton was particularly fortified by the opinions of his colleague Dugald Stewart, who had been both a professor of mathematics, and a professor of philosophy. Stewart had observed that 'while mathematical studies exercise the faculty of reasoning, or deduction, they give no employment to the other powers of the understanding concerned in the investigation of truth'. Stewart said that he had 'never met with a mere mathematician who was not credulous to a fault'. Hamilton added that Pythagoras, Plato, Cardan, Descartes, Malebranche and Leibniz were not more distinguished for their philosophical genius than for their philosophical credulity.

Finally, with regard to credulity, 'It is enough to say, that astrology was the least visionary of Kepler's beliefs; and that Napier and Newton sought and found their fancies in the Apocalypse'.

Hamilton said he could not conclude his article without strongly expressing his sincere respect for the 'venerable school' of Cambridge University, in which he had endeavoured to expose a modern abuse. 'With all its defects, there is even now, in the spirit of the place, what, were its mighty means all as well directed as some already are, would raise it in every faculty, in every department, to the highest rank among the European universities.'

At the time Cambridge stood 'alone in making mathematical science the principal object of the whole liberal education it affords . . . thus restricting to the narrowest proficiency all places of distinction and emolument in university and college, to which such honours constitute a claim;—thus also leaving the immense majority of its alumni without incitement; and the most arduous and important studies void of encouragement and reward . . .' Ten years later, when the Prince Consort became Chancellor of the University of Cambridge, he led the movement for reform virtually in these words.

Hamilton said that some parts of the reform of Cambridge were difficult and must be accomplished only from without, while others, such as the institution of two more graduate honours examinations, for philosophy and for the arts, could be established from within. His forecast ultimately proved to be substantially correct.

Ten years later, Sir William was still smouldering at Whewell's impertinence in arguing that mathematics was better than logic as a medium of university education. There was, in fact, a good deal in what he had said, as the Prince Consort and his adviser Sir Robert Peel had discovered, in their collisions with Whewell over the reform of the University of Cambridge.

Hence when de Morgan at this time published his 'numerically definite syllogism', by which he successfully introduced notions of quantity into logic, Sir William at once concluded that it was another illegitimate incursion of mathematics into culture. Indeed, it was far worse. It appeared to him that de Morgan had stolen his idea of 'the quantification of the predicate', and he was confirmed in this because de Morgan had previously written to him for information on the history of logic. In his eyes, the obstinate stupidity of the teacher, Whewell, was followed by the cupidity of his pupil.

Sir William plunged headlong into abuse of de Morgan, as he had of Whewell. But de Morgan was a more formidable intellectual opponent. Hamilton wrote to de Morgan that 'To me, it is manifest, that for the principle of the doctrine you are wholly indebted to my information; and I cannot but think that if you (through recognizing always my priority) give forth that doctrine as a speculation of your own, you will be guilty,—pardon the plain speaking—both of an injurious breach of confidence towards me and of fair dealing towards the public . . .'

De Morgan replied that "There is nothing so pardonable as plain speaking; in the present instance I owe to it the opportunity of strangling this imputation in its cradle.'

Sir William had not before been pitted against a mathematician of de Morgan's character, insight, and range of learning. De Morgan was absolutely uncompromising on the question of his intellectual honour, and relentlessly analysed Hamilton's assertion, until he had conclusively proved that he did not understand the mathematical points at issue. Hamilton's 'qualification of the predicate' was a verbalistic notion, which did not involve any mathematical principle.

De Morgan showed that there were even gaps in Hamilton's

knowledge in the history of logic. He was not aware of, or had not understood, the attention that the Bernoulli's, and other mathematicians had given to logic. He forced Hamilton to admit that he had not plagiarized him. Even then, Hamilton tried to imply that de Morgan had plagiarized him unconsciously. He suggested that de Morgan's behaviour was the result of a typical example of mathematicians' credulity and aptitude for self-deception.

He embellished a letter to de Morgan 'on his claim to an independent re-discovery of a new principle in the theory of syllogism' with the quotation from Ben Jonson: 'The Wish is father to the Thought', and from Prior: 'Caught by your own delusive art, *You fancy first, and then assert*'. He went on: 'Though I had myself written, and collected the consentient testimony of others, on the evil effects of a too exclusive study of mathematics, as enervating the intellect; still I did not, at first, accord to you the indulgence, to which mathematicians are, in equity, entitled, when, leaving the level railroad of their own, they venture to commit themselves to the pathless plains, to the hills and valleys, the rocks and quagmires, of the other sciences. I was wrong in not considering, that a blind credulity (or a blind scepticism) is, out of demonstration, the sin which most easily besets a mathematician.'

Hamilton had been making enquiries among his Edinburgh friends about de Morgan, and had learned something of him since his first incautious onslaught. 'I do not, indeed,' he now wrote, 'consider you as a *mere* mathematician; but it would be unfair to omit your principal pursuit among the causes which may account for your illusion.'

At length Hamilton asked that his original accusatory letter should be withdrawn. 'I request your permission to withdraw that letter—to hold it unconditionally *pro non scripto* . . .'

De Morgan would not accept that. 'I understand a man when he says he has changed his opinion, or that he will not or cannot maintain what he formerly said he could maintain; but I do not understand holding what was written as not having been written . . .' He printed a *Statement* on the correspondence in which he said:

'If any one should be surprised at my printing this statement, on account of the smallness of the pretext for the things alleged against me, I have only to tell him that I am as well aware of the insignificance of that pretext as he is, and that the cogent necessity, as I believe it to be, for taking immediate notice of it, arises

from the unquestioned literary celebrity and private worth of a
gentleman who was rash enough to tax me with conduct which,
could his words be made good, ought to drive me from the society
of honest men . . .'

De Morgan fully appreciated Hamilton's great abilities, and
wrote a sympathetic obituary notice of him, which surprised
many who did not understand the qualities of these remarkable
antagonists.

The controversies on the respective merits of mathematics and
logic as media of education, and between de Morgan and Sir
William Hamilton on the application of mathematics to logic,
were sufficiently interesting in themselves, but they also had
great consequences. The first made an important contribution
to the reform of Cambridge mathematics, which has enabled it
to play such a distinguished role in modern science; and the
latter was the direct cause of one of the outstanding developments
in modern mathematics, the creation of systematic mathematical
logic.

VII

GEORGE BOOLE

The influence of Peacock and the Cambridge critics of the principles of mathematics spread beyond their own circle. Foremost
among the unattached mathematicians who responded to their
stimulus, both directly and through de Morgan, was George
Boole. He was nine years younger than de Morgan, being born
in 1815, the year of Waterloo. He was the son of a small shop-
keeper in Lincolnshire. His father had been interested in mathematics and optical instruments, and had given him his first
mathematical instruction.

The family did not prosper, so Boole found it necessary to
support his parents. He ran a school in order to make a living,
and was unable to go to a university. Instead of being taught,
he had to make do with reading the original works of the masters,
such as Laplace and Lagrange. He went straight to the frontiers
of mathematical knowledge by himself, and began almost at
once to make discoveries.

He corresponded with the Cambridge mathematicians, who
encouraged him. Peacock and his pupils had investigated the
logic of the symbols in algebra. Boole asked himself whether the
operators, that is, the signs representing such operations as
addition and multiplication, also obeyed a logic of their own, and

found that they did. This was the first of his important discoveries to be immediately appreciated. He was, however, deeply engaged in research in other branches of mathematics and did not pursue mathematical logic further at the time. Among the greatest of his discoveries was algebraical invariants. He perceived that they were implied in a work of Lagrange, which Lagrange himself had not noticed. An invariant is a relation between the symbols of an algebraical expression, which remains unchanged when the expression itself is transformed. Hence, if the varying algebraical expression describes some changing feature of the physical world, the relation between its symbols, which remains constant, may correspond to something in the physical world which also remains constant, in spite of the changing feature. Thus the algebra of invariants is the natural technique for describing the constancies which remain under the changing appearances of natural phenomena.

Einstein found in the algebra of invariants the essential mathematical technique that he required to work out the theory of relativity. With it, he was able to describe aspects of the universe which remain constant, from whatever perspective it is viewed.

Boole introduced himself to de Morgan in 1842, with a letter on his *Differential and Integral Calculus*, which, as has already been mentioned, was published by the Society for the Diffusion of Useful Knowledge. This organization proved to be a medium for momentous intellectual connections, besides assisting the further education of the working and middle classes.

De Morgan and Boole had deep intellectual and temperamental sympathies, and became firm friends. Boole's attention was drawn back to mathematical logic by Sir William Hamilton's attack on his friend and encourager. He was one of the few who fully understood the points at issue, and saw that de Morgan was in the right. This stimulated him to work out his own ideas on the subject, as a support for de Morgan. He published these in 1848, in a pamphlet with the title *The Mathematical Analysis of Logic*. De Morgan appreciated its masterly quality. Boole was still engaged in the drudgery of school-teaching, without the leisure for sustained research. In 1849, the chair of mathematics in the recently founded Queen's University College at Cork became vacant. De Morgan, who had connections with the head of the college, Sir Robert Kane, helped him to secure the chair.

At Cork, Boole had for the first time adequate conditions for mathematical research. He extended his investigations in mathematical logic, and in 1854 published his *Laws of Thought, on*

which are founded the Mathematical Theories of Logic and Prob-
ability. Boole said that the design of his treatise was 'to investigate the fundamental laws of those operations of the mind by
which reasoning is performed; to give expression to them in the
language of the Calculus, and upon this foundation to establish
the Science of Logic and construct its method; . . .' He proceeded
in this magnificent style to demonstrate that logical argument
could be reduced to a form of algebraical calculation. Thus the
resources of mathematical technique could be utilized for solving
logical problems which were too subtle or complicated to be
handled by verbal logic.

Though Boole had been stimulated by de Morgan to develop
his ideas on mathematical logic, these were wider and deeper
than de Morgan's own formalist views. Boole had a command
both of symbolic and physical thinking, more like a theoretical
physicist than a pure mathematician. He was as much concerned
with interpretation as with logical consistency. He said that 'The
conditions of valid reasoning by the aid of symbols, are: *First*,
that a fixed interpretation be assigned to the symbols employed
in the expression of the data; and that the laws of the combination of those symbols be correctly determined from that
interpretation; *Second*, that the formal processes of solution or
demonstration be conducted throughout in obedience to all the
laws determined above, without regard to the question of the
particular results obtained; *Third*, that the final result be inter-
pretable in form, and that it be actually interpreted in accor-
dance with that system of interpretation which has been
employed in the expression of the data.'

Boole died in 1864 at the age of forty-nine, from pneumonia
contracted through insisting on keeping a lecture engagement,
in spite of being wet through.

The ideas of Boole and de Morgan on mathematical logic were
at first little understood and much criticized. De Morgan undertook to reply to one of these criticisms in an article which lay in
proof for a long time; in the meanwhile, Boole met his unexpected
death. When the article was published, it read as if Boole was
still alive, so de Morgan added a note on his 'old friend Mr Boole'.

'The system of logic alluded to in the last number of this
series is but one of many proofs of genius and patience combined.
I might legitimately have entered it among my *paradoxes*, or
things counter to general opinion: but is is a paradox which, like
that of Copernicus, excited admiration from its first appearance.
That the symbolic processes of algebra, invented as tools of

numerical calculation, should be competent to express every act of thought, and to furnish the grammar and dictionary of an all-containing system of logic, would not have been believed until it was proved. When Hobbes, in the time of the Commonwealth, published his "Computation or Logique", he had a remote glimpse of some of the points which are placed in the light of day by Mr Boole. The unity of the forms of thought in all the applications of reason, however remotely separated, will one day be matter of notoriety and common wonder: and Boole's name will be remembered in connexion with one of the most inportamt steps towards the attainment of this knowledge.'

De Morgan's influence on Boole has been one of the most fruitful events in modern mathematics.

VIII

SCIENCE AND RANK

De Morgan participated in the vigorous discussions in the second quarter of the nineteenth century on the character and role of the Royal Society, and the place of science in contemporary life. In 1842 he pointed out that the crucial question with regard to the Royal Society was whether it was to be conceived as a public or a private body.

The Society was 'the focus of aristocratic science, and scientific aristocracy'. Now, a scientific body, like any other, was 'either a public body, with public responsibilities, or an association of private persons. In the first case, its conduct must be judged in the same manner as that of the Government, the House of Commons, or any other . . .' public body.

If the Royal Society was regarded as a public body, then his opinion was that 'on the whole, it has not done its duties'. From the time of Newton down to the time of writing, there was much evidence that private interests, partisanship, 'acquiescence where there should have been resistance', lukewarmness where there should have been activity, and neglect where there should have been enquiry. There had not been more of each of these than had been exhibited by the various governments of the country during the same period, but 'it would be an odd defence of successive generations of scientific men, to say that they were no worse, or even something better, than Treasuries, Admiralties, and other political boards'.

It would be enough to justify the retort that 'such science was not entitled to any higher consideration than a mere mechanical trade'. But if the Society were regarded as a private body, then it was impossible to deny that the good that it had done had 'enormously preponderated' over the harm. This was to such an extent 'that (looking upon the whole as the effort of irresponsible individuals to supply the place of a government which cared nothing for the promotion of philosophy) their success has been wonderful'.

One of the causes of the current unsatisfactory situation was the dismissal in the previous century of Pringle as President of the Society by George III. This led to the election of Banks, during whose forty-two years of presidency the mathematical sciences lacked stimulus and encouragement, and 'those habits of conduct were formed which led to the subsequent controversy about the *decline of science*'. It was worth recalling that even in this period, the first of William Herschel's papers, leading to the greatest advance in astronomy since Newton, was published two years after Banks's accession, and the last, two years before his death.

De Morgan observed that Babbage's work on the *Decline of Science in England*, which had dealt with the situation, had 'carried the greater part of the press with it'. But 'speaking to Mr Babbage himself, we should have told him, that we agreed with him as to the amount of science, but denied that its *differential coefficient*, relatively to the time, was, as he asserted, negative . . .'

De Morgan considered that the poll in the famous contest for the presidency of the Society in 1830, when the Duke of Sussex defeated John Herschel by only eight votes, showed that the aristocratic influence was not so strong as had been imagined.

The *Court Journal* had said a few days before that 'the friends of astronomy and mathematics, who are anxious to raise one of their number to the chair of the society, forget that they are 30 to 640 in that society, and that any attempt to represent the general interests of science, through the elevation of a young man who has written some clever papers on astronomical and mathematical subjects, to the highest office of a society which contains ten bishops, seventy-four clergymen, sixty-three peers of the realm, a large proportion of superior officers of the army and navy, sixty-three professors of law, one hundred medical men, including those of the first talent, and a whole host of chemists, naturalists, and botanists besides must prove unsuccessful.'

The Duke was indeed successful in the election, even if only just. He was also, however, a successful president. Reflection on the Duke's presidency contributed to the formation of de

Morgan's opinion that 'a Peel or a Melbourne, a person of no lack of gentlemanly information but not versed in scientific matters' would be a very suitable president. (Adam Sedgwick, an ardent reformer, had suggested in 1827 that John Herschel would be a good candidate, on hearing that there was a move to propose Peel, then a Tory, and Home Secretary. Sedgwick already described Herschel as 'by far the first man of science in London'.)

De Morgan thought there was a good deal to be said for 'a Minister of Science and Literature'. If there were such a minister, then when the Whigs were in, 'the Whigs would somehow turn out to be the real benefactors of science', and when the Tories were in, the Tories.

If scientists were to be given honours on account of their scientific distinction, then the greatest should be given peerages, with land or money to support their position. 'Newton was certainly more useful to the country than the winner of a great battle.' But it was idle to demand such honours for scientists, until 'the public values knowledge as much as it does wealth, political importance, or military fame'.

The proper way to proceed was 'to raise science in the estimation of the public', or 'to raise the public to a proper appreciation of science'. The lack of estimation of science was due in some degree to scientific men. 'They have never taken part as a body in any of the attempts to promote education, or in any other way to elevate the intellectual character of the community.'

He thought that scientists should become busy in spreading that knowledge it was their main business to advance. It was to their own interest, more than to any others, that all orders of society should understand and appreciate what they were doing, so that they could gain public understanding and support. The time might then come when it was the general feeling that 'he who has given the human race more power, whether over their own minds or the material universe', should receive the highest honours.

Enough had been heard of the rights of man, the rights of property, the rights of industry, the rights of the crown, and the rights of the church. But the *rights of wealth* and the *rights of rank* were 'not phrases in our language. Why so? Because both wealth and rank know how to attain more than their rights, without talking about the matter. Both of these trust to the *voluntary principle* . . .'

If these two rights could be reduced to their proper proportion, it would be due to the 'action of honest sense upon men's minds'. In this, scientists should have a part, and their participation would be a consequence 'of some sort of new meaning' attached to the notion of '*the duties of science*'.

The presidency of the Duke of Sussex, in spite of the nature of the support by which it was obtained, and against all the probabilities, had turned out well. Speaking as an outsider, 'not knowing anything ourselves of the Society', he had the impression that it was never better than during the ten years of his presidency. The Duke of Sussex was therefore, in de Morgan's eyes, an exceptionally good president. This was because, in his opinion, his wide culture and experience of affairs more than made up for the limitations of his scientific knowledge.

After the Duke's resignation, the presidency was offered to, and declined by Herschel, and was filled by the Marquess of Northampton, who was active in the British Association and elsewhere. De Morgan approved of this. He observed that Newton had done little research after becoming president, and would probably not have written the *Principia* if he had been president when he first turned his mind to it. If Herschel had accepted, would he have been able to complete his account of his astronomical observations of the Southern Hemisphere at the Cape of Good Hope?

De Morgan thought that the Society should continue, if it were wise, to choose presidents of rank and influence, with as much science as could be got. He believed that men-of-affairs with scientific knowledge would govern science more wisely than eminent specialists who gave up research to undertake affairs. He sensed the dangers of restriction to purely professional values in dealing with science.

IX

HISTORIAN OF SCIENCE

De Morgan did not write any single large treatise on the history of science, but hundreds of articles on diverse topics in and on science. He was a critic of a type rare in England, but less rare abroad, whose status as an assessor of science or art is equal to those who excel in technical contributions.

The creation of a broader and deeper understanding of science is as important as discovering new phenomena. He brought to the actual assessment of the history of science technical ability in mathematics and logic, a knowledge of many languages, very wide and exact reading, ethical sensitivity, and humour; a combination unparalleled among English writers.

A striking illustration of his work is seen in his review of Sir David Brewster's *Memoirs of the Life, Writings and Discoveries of Sir Isaac Newton.* Brewster had made important optical discoveries. He had been an able professor, and had taken a leading part in the stimulation of science in Britain in the first half of the nineteenth century. He had executive ability and was a vigorous writer. He had many excellent qualifications for writing on Newton. He was the first biographer who had had complete access to the huge collection of Newton papers belonging to the Earl of Portsmouth. Brewster's biography reflected the author's abilities and authority.

Towards the end of his review de Morgan said that 'we cannot express the pleasure with which we have read his work'. He fully appreciated its information and readability. The new biography was 'the only life of Newton written on a scale commensurate with Newton's fame. It had been composed when the author had already passed the age of seventy. He hoped that he would be enjoying 'the additional fame which he has so well earned' when he reached the age of 'full fourscore'. The keen 'scientific sensibilities', which had caused him to protest against what he conceived to be the general neglect of science by the ruling powers, should make him 'fully feel that he has linked his own name to that of his first object of human reverence for as long as our century shall retain a place in literary history'.

De Morgan then made an analysis of Brewster's conception of biography, and the way he had carried it out. He had regarded himself as Newton's advocate, but nevertheless an advocate. When sins against Newton were to be punished, the accents of Juvenal were heard, but when Newton was to be reprimanded, the 'nice and delicate' accents of Horace. 'When a century or two shall have passed, we predict it will be said of our day that the time was not come when both sides of the social character of Newton could be trusted to his followers in experimental science. Though biography be no longer an act of worship, it is not yet a solemn and impartial judgment: we are in the intermediate stage, in which advocacy is the aim, and in which the biographer, when a thought more candid than usual, avows that he is to *do his best* for his client. We accept the book as we find it: we expect an *ex parte* statement, and we have it.'

Brewster's reverent attitude made it difficult to conceive Newton as a person. When Newton was a boy, he had fights at school, and rubbed an obnoxious boy's nose against a wall. Brewster described this as having been done by 'Sir Isaac'.

'Should we survive "Sir David",' wrote de Morgan, 'we shall *Brewster* him.'

There was no evidence that Newton was more than 'a clever and somewhat self-willed lad, rather late at school, with his heart in the keeping of a young lady who lived in the house where he had boarded'. He did not appear to have been more than a good student until after his graduation.

Sir David had recounted the well-known story that Newton bought a copy of Euclid at Cambridge, and threw it aside as a trifling book because the conclusions were so self-evident. He then read Descartes. but regretted later that he had not given more attention to Euclid. This had been taken as evidence of Newton's precocity, and his early lack of thorough knowledge of Euclid. But, says de Morgan, 'what Newton has written belies it. We put faith in the *Principia*, which is the work of an inordinate Euclidian, constantly attempting to clothe in the forms of ancient geometry methods of proceeding which would more easily have been presented by help of algebra. Shall we ever be told that Bacon complained of the baldness of his own style, and wished he had obtained command over metaphor? Shall we learn that Cobbett lamented his constant flow of Gallicism and west-end slang, and regretted that his English had not been more Saxon?'

In fact, the consideration of *style* in interpreting the history of science is just as important as in literature.

De Morgan became more severe on Brewster's handling of the history of the invention of the calculus by Newton and Leibniz. Newton gave a fair account of their respective contributions in the first edition of the *Principia*, but became increasingly ungenerous with the passage of years. He ended with propelling the Royal Society, under its name and authority, but under his secret supervision, to publish papers aiming at discrediting Leibniz's contribution. De Morgan indicated that expert mathematical knowledge was required to appreciate many of the papers involved. 'And we have no delicacy in saying that they ought to come under the eyes of persons familiar with the higher parts of mathematics, which Sir D. Brewster neither is, nor pretends to be.' More than a century later, the interpretation of Newton's papers is still hindered by the same difficulty.

Brewster's interpretation of Newton's conduct in religious and social affairs gave an incorrect impression of his character. De Morgan showed that Brewster omitted information when he specifically stated that his account was complete. 'We are far

from charging him with any unfair intention: we know the effect
of liars, and nothing disgusts us more that the readiness with
which suppressions and misrepresentations are set down to
deliberate intention of foul play.'

Brewster in an earlier short life of Newton had stoutly defended
the position that he was an orthodox Christian. The papers he
now published showed that he was incontrovertibly heterodox.
Brewster merely left it to be implied that he no longer disputed
Newton's heterodoxy.

De Morgan then dealt in detail with Brewster's handling of
the problem of Newton's half-niece, Catherine Barton. She was
one of the outstanding beauties and wits of the age, and had been
brought up and educated by Newton. According to the biographer of Charles Montague, Earl of Halifax, and Newton's
patron, she became 'Superintendent' of Montague's 'domestick
Affairs'. Montague left her generous legacies, including Bushy
House, today the office of the National Physical Laboratory.
She subsequently married Conduit and presided brilliantly over
her famous uncle's bachelor establishment. Brewster had blandly
stated that for a century and a half no stain had been cast on Mrs
C. Barton, and then referred to Voltaire's notorious sneer: 'I
thought in my youth that Newton made his fortune by his merit.
No such thing. Isaac Newton had a very charming niece, Madame
Conduit, who had made a conquest of the minister Halifax.
Fluxions and gravitation would have been of no use without a
pretty niece.' Brewster described this as making 'no insinuation
against the character of Miss Barton'.

The elucidation of the relations between Newton, Montague
and Catherine Barton was essential for the understanding of
Newton as a man. De Morgan's study of the evidence led him to
conclude that Catherine Barton was either Montague's mistress
or wife. De Morgan utilized his expert actuarial knowledge,
besides his historical learning and insight, in analysing the meaning of the financial provisions in Halifax's will.

Every resource had to be used in unearthing the complete
truth, which must be the best foundation for the appreciation of
Newton. It was necessary to know the truth about his jealous
and suspicious nature. 'All Newton's faults were those of a temperament which observers of the human mind know to be incapable of alteration, though strong self-control may suppress its
effects. The jealous, the suspicious nature is a part of the man's
essence, when it exists at all: it is no local sore, but a plague in
the blood. Think of this morbid feeling as the constant attendant

of the whole life, and then say, putting all Newton's known exhibition of it at their very worst, how much they will amount to,
as scattered through twenty years of controversy with his equals,
and thirty years of kingly power over those who delighted to call
themselves his inferiors.

'If we could but know the real history of a flaw in a diamond,
we might be made aware that it was a necessary result of the
combination of circumstances which determined that the product should be a diamond, and not a bit of rotten wood.'

After the publication of de Morgan's review, Brewster never
communicated with him again.

De Morgan had shown that while Brewster had written a great
biography, it was the last of an old style, not the first of a new.
In the future, the scientist was to be treated as a man, not a hero.

His review was an important action in his campaign for higher
standards in the history of science, demanding for it wider learning, greater command of mathematics and scientific technique,
and deeper insight into the conditions and motives of human
behaviour.

JAMES DEWAR

SCIENTIST INVENTORS

JAMES DEWAR
1842-1923

I

SO MUCH AND SO LITTLE

JAMES DEWAR invented the vacuum jacket for preventing heat from entering or escaping from vessels. Its exploitation in the vacuum flask of commerce, for keeping tea and other liquids hot is used by nearly everyone, and is universally known. He applied the invention in research at very low temperatures, enabling liquid air and liquid hydrogen to be prepared in quantity, and kept in vacuum vessels for long periods. The availability of these very cold liquids enabled research into the properties of substances to be carried into new regions approaching the absolute zero of temperature. More refined and sustained experiments could be made, which led to the discovery that at very low temperatures matter began to behave in ways different from any previously known. Dewar himself made some of these discoveries, in particular, that the heat properties of elements at very low temperatures vary periodically, according to their place in the periodic table of the elements. This observation, made in 1913, provided data for the theory of the atom.

The invention of the vacuum jacket also opened the possibility in the very different direction of operating at very low temperatures on an engineering scale. The development of industrial and commercial refrigeration at very low temperatures depended on it; without it, there would have been no liquid oxygen in quantity for factories and hospitals, and a thousand other purposes.

Dewar invented other devices which were of great importance in low-temperature research. He discovered that charcoal could remove the vestiges of gas left in vessels that had been exhausted by an air-pump, and thus produce a very high vacuum. He found that it was effective in removing the gas in the hollow walls of vessels made out of metal. This made it possible for metal instead of glass vessels to be used, thus facilitating operations on a large scale by making the vessels safer and easier to

227

handle. The use of charcoal for producing high vacua facilitated the manufacture of electrical products, and much of the early research on atomic physics could not have been done without it.

He introduced the use of coiled tubes for experiments at very low temperatures, which also was of great practical importance; these were more elastic than straight tubes.

When Dewar had solved the problems of producing liquid air and liquid hydrogen in quantity, he collaborated with other scientists in their application. He joined with J. A. Fleming, the inventor of the electronic valve, in investigating the effects of very low temperatures on the electrical properties of materials. He collaborated with H. Moissan, who came from Paris to work on the liquefaction and solidification of the difficult gas fluorine. Pierre Curie came to London to lecture in the Royal Institution, and they collaborated in investigating the effect of very low temperatures on radium and its products.

Besides this Dewar investigated the effects of very low temperatures on photographic action, cohesion, and many other properties of materials. He made researches in general, agricultural, and biological chemistry.

He was a member of the important Government Committee on Explosives from 1888–91, under Rayleigh. His extensive researches on explosives in collaboration with Sir Frederick Abel led to the invention of cordite, the smokeless propellant explosive adopted by the British military forces.

He was very active in work on sewage control. He and Sir William Crookes for years made daily chemical and bacterial analyses to control the quality of the London water supply.

In addition to all this, he served as an expert witness in the law courts.

He was professor of chemistry at the Royal Institution from 1877, and director of the Laboratories from 1887 until his death in 1923. During his forty-six years with the Institution, he perfected the art of experimental demonstration to lecture audiences. He devoted great ingenuity and unsurpassed manual dexterity to producing experiments which were so elegant and convincing, that verbal explanation became almost superfluous. Scientists who understood the inner significance of them were entranced by their scientific eloquence, while non-scientists found them fascinating as conjuring tricks.

Dewar's gifts were, however, accompanied by limitations as striking. He had a great deal of difficulty in getting on with

people, especially assistants and subordinates. He could do experiments more skilfully than others, and he lost his temper
with those who were less skilful. He was lacking in the art of
guidance and persuasion. He took all the credit, even when
others had done most of the work. Two of his assistants each
lost an eye in experiments on his behalf. His difficult temper
caused a smouldering discontent in his laboratory, in spite of
the volume of work coming from it. He published 257 papers,
but no assistant was ever invited to join his name to Dewar's in
the title, no matter how much he had contributed. He created no
school and left no pupils, either at Cambridge, where he held a
chair for forty-eight years, or at the Royal Institution, which
he made his headquarters.

It might have been expected that Dewar's ineptitude in personal relations would have impaired his judgment on the broader
issues of science. This was not so. In his Presidential Address to
the British Association in 1902 he made penetrating criticisms,
supported by statistics, of the British backwardness in industrial chemistry in comparison with the German, and concluded
with one of the most striking warnings on its implications for
the nation.

Dewar's foresight in this matter may have owed much to the
influence of Lyon Playfair, to whom, more than anyone, he owed
his scientific career, and to whom he remained eternally grateful.
Dewar referred to the remarks of the Prince Consort to the
British Association in 1859, which had probably been composed
with Playfair's aid. He commented that 'intelligent appreciation
of scientific work and needs is not less but more necessary in the
highest quarters today than it was forty-three years ago', when
the Prince had brought the matter before the Association.

The Prince had said that 'We may be justified, however, in
hoping that by the gradual diffusion of science and its increasing
recognition as a principal part of our national education, the
public in general, no less than the Legislature and the State will
more and more recognize the claims of science to their attention;
so that it may no longer require the begging box but speak to
the State like a favoured child to its parent, sure of his paternal
solicitude for its elements of strength and prosperity, to protect
which the clearest dictates of self-interest demand.'

Dewar pointed out that if this advice had been taken, the
country would not still be groping painfully in the dark after a
system of national education. Money would not be being wasted
on 'building imitations of foreign educational super-structures

before having put in solid foundations. We should not be hurriedly and distractedly casting about for a system of tactics after confrontation with the disciplined and co-ordinated forces of industry and science led and directed by the rulers of powerful States. Forty-three years ago we should have started fair had the Prince Consort's views prevailed. As it is, we have lost ground which it will tax even this nation's splendid reserves of individual initiatives to recover.'

After considering the implications of the statistics of chemists in Britain and Germany he said: '. . . the really appalling thing is not that the Germans have seized this or the other industry, or even that they may have seized a dozen industries. It is that the German population has reached a point of general training and specialized equipment which it will take us two generations of hard and intelligently directed educational work to attain. It is that Germany possesses a national weapon of precision which must give her an enormous initial advantage in any and every contest depending upon disciplined and methodized intellect.'

This was said twelve years before the First World War, and the same fundamental problem still confronts the nation sixty-five years later. But Dewar could not make this judgment and foresight effective. It required social and political qualities that he did not possess.

The same thing happened in the industrial development of his low-temperature discoveries. The initial industrial utilization occurred outside Britain, and particularly in Germany. Was it inevitable that he should be so lacking in some directions, while so gifted in others? Would it have been possible to make arrangements which would have made quicker national use of his low-temperature discoveries, and mitigated the effects of his limitations? Hutton has given an instance of the difficulty of co-operating with Dewar. The British Government's Scientific exhibit at the St Louis Exposition in 1904 was a replica of Dewar's Royal Institution apparatus for the liquefaction of air and hydrogen. Dewar withdrew his co-operation in the preparation of the exhibit, and refused to supply the vacuum vessels required. Others were obtained after considerable effort from Germany. The exhibit was very successful, and the American jury of awards declared it to be the finest in the whole exposition. But Dewar had severed his connection with it. In Britain the utilization of low-temperature physics fell behind.

II

SON OF A VINTNER

James Dewar was born on 20 September 1842, at Kincardine-On-Forth in Scotland. His father was a strict Presbyterian who belonged to the sect of the 'Auld Lichts', and kept the leading inn in the town. He was an original personality, as this combination might suggest. James was the youngest of his seven sons, and inherited his originality. When he was a boy, there was a good deal of musical activity in the Scottish localities. James liked music, and learned to play the flute fairly well before he was ten.

At this age he had an accident which probably determined the course of his life. He was playing on ice, when he fell through. This brought on an attack of rheumatic fever, which made him an invalid. For two years he had to go about on crutches, and he could not attend school. His lungs were weakened, and he had to give up the flute. In order that he should not miss his music too badly, his father called in the local fiddler to play to him. Fiddles were then common in Scotland, owing to the direct coastal trade with Italy, from whence they came.

Not being able to go to school, James spent a lot of time in the local carpenter's shop, where fiddles were repaired. He began to learn how to do this delicate work, and presently made fiddles on his own. He retained one labelled 'James Dewar 1854'. This was played upon at his golden wedding, and on special occasions since. Miss Penelope Howard played the Sarabande and Gigue from Bach's Partita in D minor on it, after Dr Mendelssohn's lecture on Dewar at the Royal Institution on 18 November 1966.

Dewar said that his manipulative skill, which was extraordinary, was based on this early training in manual dexterity. He had strong views on how this should be acquired. He held that it should be developed through making a real object, and not through the performance of routine exercises. In later life, Dewar came to regard his accident as fortunate, as it had led to this training, which he considered to have been the most important part of his education.

When he had sufficiently recovered, he was sent to the Dollar Academy, a well-known school not far from Kincardine. There he won a gold medal for mathematics, and a prize for natural philosophy. After leaving school he went to Edinburgh, taking his fiddle with him as a proof of his manual dexterity. He stayed with his elder brother Alexander, who had nearly completed his medical course. Alexander subsequently became assistant to the famous surgeon, Professor James Syme, father-in-law of Lister.

Dewar secured a job as some kind of servant to J. D. Forbes, the professor of natural philosophy and authority on the physics of glaciers, with whom Tyndall had much to do. He did not enter Edinburgh University as a student. He seems to have picked up physics through his employment by Forbes, probably performing the duties of a laboratory boy in Forbes's personal laboratory.

When Forbes left to become Principal of St Andrews University, Dewar was engaged as a demonstrator by Lyon Playfair, who had become professor of chemistry at Edinburgh in 1858. He now learned chemistry through assisting Playfair, who apparently sent him to attend courses of lectures, for he won various prizes for mathematics and physics in 1860–62. When Playfair retired in 1868 Dewar became assistant to his successor, Crum Brown. One of his duties was to teach practical chemistry to the medical students.

Dewar was appointed lecturer, and later professor, in the Royal Veterinary College in 1869. Four years later, he became in addition assistant chemist to the Highland and Agricultural Society of Scotland, in which C. T. R. Wilson's father had been active, and went through the country-side giving chemical advice and lectures to progressive farmers.

In 1871 he married Helen Rose Banks of Edinburgh, Lyon Playfair attending the marriage. The Dewars never had any children. Through the fifty-two years of their married life they were devoted to each other. Dewar's wife was virtually the only person to whom he deferred.

His first published research appeared in 1867; it was on the structure of certain organic substances. In it he described a mechanical device for representing the arrangement of the atoms in a molecule of benzene in seven different ways. Playfair sent a copy of the paper to Kekulé, the author of the ring-theory of benzene, and the founder of the modern theory of organic chemistry. Kekulé invited Dewar to spend the summer in his laboratory at Ghent. Dewar was twenty-five, and not a university graduate. This visit to the leading laboratory in the world in that particular field, in a foreign country, was a crucial experience for him. He not only made the acquaintance of Kekulé and the atmosphere of his institution, he also became acquainted with Kekulé's assistant Körner, who was a highly gifted chemical manipulator. Dewar's talent in the same direction made them close friends. Körner was fond of playing practical jokes, and the somewhat raw and wild young Scotsman of twenty-five found him an extremely agreeable companion.

Dewar was profoundly grateful to Playfair. He never forgot this great man's penetration, kindness, and effective help. When Playfair died in 1898, Dewar wrote to his widow: '. . . He was my Master in everything, and I owe all to him . . .' He said that the memory of him would be one of the abiding treasures of his life, and that he had been present at his marriage.

Dewar pursued researches in many different directions, on the chemistry of chlorine, on the temperature of the sun and of electric sparks; yet another direction was on the heat properties of gases. In these experiments, in the course of 1872, he invented the vacuum jacket, to prevent heat from penetrating into his calorimeters. Two years later, in 1874, in a joint paper with P. G. Tait, on a new method for obtaining very perfect vacua, he mentioned the use of charcoal made from coconut for improving the vacuum. Twenty-eight years later he returned to his use of charcoal for the improvement of vacua, and systematically investigated how it should be prepared to give the maximum activity. He discovered that at very low temperatures the activity was enormously increased.

Dewar's varied experimental researches at Edinburgh attracted notice. In 1875 he was elected to the Jacksonian chair of experimental philosophy at Cambridge.

The Reverend Richard Jackson, who founded the chair in 1782, had laid down that the professor should lecture on 'Anatomy, Animal Economy, Chemistry, Botany, Agriculture or the Materia Medica'. He was to search for a cure for 'that opprobrium medicorum called the Gout', and in order to prepare the way for such activities, he was to elucidate 'the properties of air and water, heat and cold, and what has a considerable share in the effect of all these, the powers of electricity'. In fact, he was to explore those phenomena on which 'our very existence in this world depends.' Jackson could have been well-satisfied with the incumbents of his chair, which was to be occupied by C. T. R. Wilson, E. V. Appleton, and J. D. Cockcroft, besides Dewar himself, and other eminent men, even if they were not to discover the cure for gout.

Dewar was entitled, according to the terms of his chair, to investigate anything he liked. As such a versatile experimenter he was seemingly most appropriately qualified for it, but he was not even a Scottish university man in the ordinary sense, and still less a Cambridge man.

8*

He was provided with only the most primitive laboratory space and equipment. Dewar did what he could under these conditions. He pursued spectroscopical research on the phenomena of dissociation, a term St Claire Deville had introduced to describe the reversible interaction between the atoms which make up a molecule, according to the temperature and other conditions. With rise of temperature the atoms broke apart, and when it was reduced they came together again. The phenomenon was fundamental in chemical change, and formed an important part of chemistry.

The astrophysicist J. N. Lockyer had invoked it in order to explain the condition of the gases on the sun, as revealed by their spectra. Dewar persuaded Liveing, the professor of chemistry at Cambridge, to collaborate in laboratory researches to test Lockyer's views, which he believed were not founded on sound experimental evidence. Thus he was characteristically at once involved in scientific controversy.

When he came to Cambridge, he was still a young man of thirty-three, scarcely old enough for natural patience to have become trained, even if he had possessed it. He expressed dissatisfaction with his working conditions bluntly, and soon a quarrelsome atmosphere arose around him. Only Professor Liveing and the Master of Peterhouse, Dr Porter, of which college Dewar was a professorial fellow, sympathetically understood him.

Dewar flatly said what ought to be done, but took no steps to persuade people to do it. He antagonized opposition, both intelligent and stupid. Fortunately, the Fullerian professorship of chemistry at the Royal Institution became vacant, and in 1877 he was elected to it. Thus he had two professorships, one at Cambridge and the other in London, both of which he held to the end of his life. It was virtually impossible that he could have simultaneously performed the duties of both chairs equally well. In 1887 he became director in the Royal Institution in succession to Tyndall; Dewar's heart and mind were entirely in the Royal Institution.

Just after he became Fullerian professor a major advance was made in France on one of Faraday's classical researches. In 1823, while Faraday was still Davy's laboratory assistant, he noticed that if one end of a closed glass tube containing chlorine gas was heated, droplets were deposited at the cold end. He found that these were liquid chlorine. The combined effects of pressure and temperature had liquefied the chlorine gas.

At various times during the next twenty-two years, Faraday

improved this technique by placing the cold end of the tube in cooling mixtures, and with it he succeeded in liquefying many gases. But oxygen, nitrogen and hydrogen resisted all efforts to liquefy them in this way. People began to believe that they were incapable of being liquefied, and referred to them as permanent gases.

The belief that the so-called permanent gases could not be liquefied was a psychological obstacle that hindered the search for the technical solution of how it might be done. The first solution arose through an accident. The French scientist Louis Cailletet was making experiments on liquefying gas by high pressure. Acetylene happened to be the one he was working with. His apparatus sprang a leak. He noticed that droplets appeared for a moment in the glass tube from which the gas was escaping. He perceived that the gas had been liquefied through the cooling effect caused by the rapid expansion of the escaping gas.

Cailletet arranged an experiment on the same principle with oxygen and succeeded in obtaining droplets of liquid oxygen; a very important discovery which he announced at a meeting of the French Academy of Sciences on Christmas Eve in 1877. At this meeting Jamin pointed out that now that the possibility of liquefying oxygen had been demonstrated, the next step was to obtain liquid oxygen in sufficient quantity to see whether it possessed the usual properties of liquids.

Dewar was greatly excited by the news of Cailletet's discovery in one of the fields of Faraday's classical researches. It was appropriate that it should be taken up immediately in the Royal Institution. He hastened to secure a Cailletet apparatus from Paris, with funds provided by Warren de la Rue. He demonstrated the production of droplets of liquid oxygen with his customary skill. He then started on his own development of low temperature technique and research. It was complicated and difficult, and six years passed before he made a distinct advance.

III

LIQUEFYING HYDROGEN

Cailletet successfully liquefied nitrogen by the same methods as he had used for oxygen, but he was unable to meet Jamin's demand for a quantity of liquid oxygen which could be kept boiling steadily for a considerable time. This was necessary for practical as well as theoretical reasons, to facilitate demonstrations, and to be able to try the effects of liquid air on other substances and phenomena. It was first achieved by S. F. Wroblewski in Cracow. Just before being appointed professor of physics there, he had seen experiments by Cailletet in Paris in 1882. He bought a Cailletet apparatus for Cracow, in order to engage in this line of research.

When he took up his post in the physics department he found that in the chemistry department a young chemist, K. S. Olszewski, of about his own age, had been working for a long time on the liquefaction of gases, but with poor facilities. They decided to collaborate in experiments with the new apparatus, and in 1883 succeeded in producing liquid oxygen in some quantity. These methods of liquefying oxygen and nitrogen were not, however, successful when applied to hydrogen, which evidently liquefied, if at all, at a much lower temperature.

It was known that the amount of heat needed to make a given mass of liquid change into gas was proportional to the temperature. If liquid oxygen, which boiled at a temperature, measured on the absolute scale, four times lower than that at which water boiled, then one could conclude that about four times less heat would be required to turn the liquid into gaseous oxygen than would be required to turn water into steam. It was certain that hydrogen boiled at a temperature very much lower still, if it could be obtained as a liquid at all; hence the amount of heat needed to change it from a liquid into a gas must be very much less even than that needed to turn liquid oxygen into gas.

This raised a very serious technical problem. If hydrogen were to be liquefied, then the transmission of very little heat through its containing vessel would be sufficient to convert it into gas. No vessel with the degree of imperviousness to heat required to keep liquid hydrogen, it if was obtainable, was known.

Dewar attacked this problem, developing the vacuum jacket he had invented twenty-one years earlier, and by 1893 he had found and perfected the solution. He demonstrated his vacuum flask, with the hollow double walls from which the air had been exhausted, so that the transmission of heat by convection was eliminated, and he had silvered the inside of the walls, so that transmission of heat by radiation was reduced.

The making of the vessels involved very skilful glass-blowing, and subsequent heat treatment in order to remove the strains that cause brittleness; he produced vessels of several different designs. It was evident that he had successfully carried out a great deal of very difficult technical research. No fundamental advance has yet been made on Dewar's original vessels.

He was now able to keep liquid hydrogen, if he could obtain it. He attacked the other main aspects of the problem: the construction of a cooling apparatus which could achieve a sufficiently low temperature to liquefy hydrogen. The early methods of expansion did not promise success, so he worked on the utilization of the Joule-Thomson effect. Molecules of gas attract each other slightly. Consequently, when a gas expands, work is done in overcoming this force, so that a slight fall in temperature occurs. The effect is fundamentally different from the cooling that occurs when the gas as a whole is expanded.

In 1896 he demonstrated that hydrogen could be reduced to a very low temperature by making use of this effect, and also of the heat exchange, a device invented by Siemens in 1857. He showed that a jet of the very cold hydrogen would freeze liquid oxygen solid into a blue plate, and he pointed out that his experiments had made him certain that it was possible to liquefy hydrogen. This work evidently involved a great deal of complicated development research. A few months before it was published, Hampson in England, and a few days later, Linde in Germany, took out patents for utilizing the Joule-Thomson effect.

Dewar went on with his research, publishing many papers on the effects of low temperatures on many kinds of materials and phenomena, and working towards the extremely difficult task of liquefying hydrogen. At last, in 1898, he succeeded. The machine which he constructed was of advanced and finished engineering design, a triumph of scientific engineering. It belonged to the modern era of experimental science, which has moved beyond the old science laboratory derived from the workshop of the artisan, and makes use of the resources of industrial engineering.

Dewar obtained about twenty cubic centimetres of liquid hydrogen from his apparatus in about five minutes. Its properties were extraordinary; its density was only one-fourteenth that of water. Dewar wished to measure the temperature of liquefaction exactly, but he found that his electrical thermometer would not, as he thought, work properly. In fact, the temperature was so low that the material of the thermometer was beginning to depart from the laws of classical physics, and obey those of the quantum theory, which had not yet been discovered. Nevertheless, Dewar deduced from various other measurements that the temperature must be about twenty degrees above absolute zero, which was correct.

A few days after Dewar's announcement of these splendid

achievements, Hampson complained that Dewar had made no acknowledgment of his prior patent of the cooling process, and said that he had visited Dewar's assistant Lennox at the Royal Institution in 1894. He implied that Dewar owed his success in liquefying both air and hydrogen to information he had given to Lennox. Angry exchanges ensued. It was not clear why Hampson had seen Lennox and not Dewar in 1894; nor was it clear why Dewar had mentioned Linde but not Hampson in a paper in 1896, which nevertheless showed that he was aware of Hampson's work.

The dispute did not damp Dewar's ardour. He went on to solidify liquid hydrogen, which proved to be even more difficult than expected, owing to the operation of quantum properties as yet unknown. Even better heat shielding was necessary, and he achieved this by shielding the whole vacuum vessel with liquid air. Solid hydrogen turned out to be a transparent solid, not a metal as some had forecast.

Dewar had started with the expectation that hydrogen would be the last gas to be liquefied. While he was engaged in developing low-temperature technique, the presence on earth of the inert gas helium was discovered. The existence of helium in the sun had been discovered by Janssen and Lockyer in 1868, but it was not found on earth until 1895, when Sir William Ramsay was following up the great discovery with Rayleigh, of the existence of inert gases.

Dewar thought that the hydrogen he had liquefied was a mixture containing some helium, and that he had liquefied both. In fact, there was no liquid helium in his product, so he found that, after all, there was yet another gas to be liquefied, and all the signs were that this would be much more difficult than the liquefaction of hydrogen.

He started on the task with intense effort, but he was hindered by small supplies of helium gas. Considerable quantities were required in order to keep the refrigerating cycle in a Joule-Thomson apparatus going for a sufficient time. He had not enough of the gas, and unfortunately he was not on speaking terms with Ramsey, who was at University College, only a short distance away. At the meeting in 1895, after Dewar had spoken of his hopes of liquefying hydrogen, Ramsay had got up and said that he had just heard that Olszewski in Cracow had obtained liquid hydrogen in quantity. Olszewski subsequently denied that he had ever obtained it in this form.

Consequently, Dewar was not prepared to communicate with

his fellow-Scot, so he proceeded with supplies of helium which were neither sufficient in purity nor quantity. He and Lennox built a large machine for separating pure helium, but it was not successful. They constructed a large Joule-Thomson machine for liquefying helium. Dewar did not make it entirely of metal, as he wanted to be able to see what was happening inside. Dr Mendelssohn has expressed the opinion that this was probably a mistake. Then a laboratory boy accidentally turned a tap, and the helium that Dewar did possess escaped into the atmosphere.

Dewar struggled on hopefully, but in 1908 the news arrived that Kamerlingh Onnes at Leiden had successfully liquefied helium. Dewar had lost the lead in very low temperature research. He quarrelled with Lennox, and lost interest in this branch of physics.

Presently he quarrelled with Sir William Crookes, his last remaining scientific friend. He grew older and still more difficult. Some tried to exert pressure on him to retire, which he resented bitterly. He devoted his last years to investigations of soap and other thin films, a pregnant line of research, and was still experimenting in the last year of his life. Finally, he died, on 27 March 1923, in his eighty-first year.

Dewar was elected to the Royal Society in 1877. He was awarded the Copley Medal in 1916. Numerous other scientific honours were bestowed on him, from many countries. He was knighted in 1904. He could not justifiably complain that he was not adequately esteemed.

IV

'WHY DID HE SUCCEED HERE, NOT IN CAMBRIDGE?'

H. E. Armstrong in his valedictory address at the Royal Institution on Dewar raised this question. He prefaced his address with Johnson's warning that 'we cannot trust the characters of history unless they are drawn by those who know their persons'. He said that he had wittingly sought to understand him, for no other man had been so attractive to him, or had appeared so worthy of study. But he had found him very reticent. He was normally so fiery that the inner man was invisible. 'Only now and then, especially when he was unwell and lying on the sofa' did he seem to express his true nature. Armstrong considered him primarily an artist in science, an inventor and performer of elegant experiments, who equally appreciated artistic skill in other fields, such as carving and music. His house at Cambridge and his rooms in the Royal Institution were packed with choice objects.

The musical interest of his youth continued through his life. He encouraged and helped young artists, and purchased large numbers of tickets to ensure that they should enjoy good attendances. He was fond of writing verse, and was well-read. Armstrong held that as an artist Dewar was close to the primitive in man. He ascribed to this a kind of belief in ghosts, which Dewar seemed to possess. Apparently he used to wander in the middle of the night along the famous passages in the Royal Institution, communing with the ghosts of Davy and Faraday. Perhaps this should not be taken too literally, but be regarded as a manifestation of a strong Celtic imagination. After all, no scientist of any feeling can walk where they walked, and stand where they stood, without becoming aware of an exalted message from the past, which might be interpreted figuratively as a voice intimating the possibility of human greatness.

Armstrong said that Dewar had led a Bohemian life in Edinburgh, presumably meaning that he found friends in musical and artistic circles, and hinting that he departed to some extent from contemporary conventions. In London he had a varied acquaintance outside science. Sir Henry Irving was one of his friends. Dewar worked as hard as Irving in rehearsing for his public performances, and had the spirit of an actor, making his experiments so as to produce the maximum impression on the audience. He had very beautiful fingers, which were fascinating to watch, as they flitted skilfully over the apparatus. Most of his demonstrations were based on his own original researches. They brought the spectator to the frontier of knowledge, which he could almost feel was being made before his eyes. They attracted very distinguished audiences, drawn from many professions; this brought strength to the Institution.

Armstrong suggested that as an artistic solo performer of genius, Dewar was necessarily precluded from being successful in such a place as Cambridge, with an ancient and strong academic system. Dewar could not perform within such a system. Nor was he suited to student audiences. He was a performer, not a teacher helping tyros through examinations. He needed audiences with varied and extensive experience to appreciate what he had to give.

In contrast, the Royal Institution presented the opportunities of a splendid studio for the artist. In it he could exercise his bent and his imagination, and the skill of his fingers which had been developed so well by the fiddle-making in his youth. He passionately desired to construct things with his fingers, accurately and with finish.

He had a shrewd grasp of the theory of his experiments, but he was not creative in the field of theory. He had not had sufficient systematic training in the application of mathematics to physics, and probably did not have any special talent in that direction, though with his strong and energetic mind he could read up anything sufficiently well for his purposes.

Armstrong believed that 'the art of discovery as a systematic pursuit, is only gradually learnt', and it came 'more from the suggestion of opportunity than from inspiration'. The suggestion of opportunity that had particularly fired Dewar was the Cailletet experiment of 1877, of which he was in the position to take advantage, because he had come into the atmosphere and facilities of the Royal Institution just a few months before.

The varied social life Dewar enjoyed outside science was in remarkable contrast with the vendetta state of his life within science. He got on quite well with a variety of eminent persons in government, administration and the arts, while his relations with his laboratory assistants were as close to the nadir of behaviour as his experiments were to the absolute zero.

In addition to artistic temperament, he seemed to exhibit signs of a social inferiority complex. Being received as an equal by men of social and political influence reassured him, and enabled him to behave more normally. But the presence of laboratory assistants was an eternal reminder that he also had started life as a laboratory boy. This instantly made him unsure of himself, and bad-tempered. Dewar belonged to the type of lab. boys of genius and never escaped from the memory of it. Even his incomparable predecessor Faraday did not. Faraday coped with the situation by restricting his social life. He refused the presidency of the Royal Society, and avoided social situations that might have made him feel uneasy.

Dewar's behaviour to his assistants emphasized to himself the social distance that there now was between him and them. Faraday solved the social problem of relations with technical assistants by never having one; it was a remarkable feature of his career.

Dewar's attitude to Cambridge was reflected in his views on the supersession of the British chemical industry by the German. He believed that the ancient university system destroyed originality. The only scientists who could rescue the British chemical industry were to be found among those who had been trained outside it. 'The men who escape this mental barrenness are men who were somehow or other taught to think long before they went to university'; that is, men like himself, who had learned to think and work while making fiddles in the carpenter's shop in Kincardine. These were the only men in England who could hold their own with the chemists of Bayer & Co.

The chemists of Bayer & Co. were in fact quite the opposite of this. Nevertheless, Dewar revealed what was in his own mind. He went on to say that the British 'have to train the population from the first to think correctly and logically, to deal at first hand with facts, and to evolve each one for himself, the solution of a problem put before him, instead of learning by rote the solution given by somebody else'.

He was in a way recommending that the whole population should aspire to be Dewars. If his advice had been taken, British life would no doubt have manifested a certain scientific liveliness, and also a general contentiousness with few parallels in history. One may extend Armstrong's question to cover certain aspects of Dewar's career at the Royal Institution. Why did he also fail in these?

Acquisitiveness was another feature of Dewar's personality. It arose from several motives. In one aspect, it was an extreme form of Scottish carefulness. In another, it was expressed in his collection of works of art, which were an acquisition of examples of quality.

It was not surprising that a man with such varied experimental activities should have been brusque and hard to get on with. The difficulty was increased by his particular gifts. He could do the actual experiments better than anyone else. He was not good at explaining himself verbally. His method of leading was to seize apparatus and show how, not to guide, advise and persuade his assistants and subordinates.

His acquisitiveness was manifested also in his failure to invite his assistants to join their names with his in appropriate places. His personal participation in even the details of every research contributed to this behaviour. The physical participation in everything increased his tendency to believe that he had done everything in experiments in which he was assisted. He acted as if he believed that experiments he had initiated belonged to him as permanent personal property.

A consideration of Dewar's work and life suggests that the accident in his boyhood, while having fortunate effects in some ways, as Dewar himself believed, also contributed much to the difficulties associated with him. It crippled his body for at least two years, and to some extent it crippled his personality for life. A social order that desired to make more efficient use of his kind of genius should pay attention to the implications of accidents like his in youth. It should avoid appointing this type of scientist to chairs in the ancient universities, which in his case largely sterilized one of the professorships for nearly half a century. Another conclusion is that it is desirable to ensure that the kind of research is suitable to the institution in which it is pursued.

Dewar's later low-temperature work involved engineering research and construction which was unsuited to the traditions and facilities of the Royal Institution. He was terribly cast down by being overtaken in the liquefaction of helium, though he need not have been if he could have taken a more detached view of the situation. By 1908 he was sixty-six years old; it was only natural that he should have been overtaken at that age by a younger man. Heike Kamerlingh Onnes was then fifty-five, and had just brought all his powers and facilities to their peak.

Onnes had built the first research laboratory in the world where the technique of modern industry was consciously utilized to solve problems in abstract science. He had equipped his laboratory with workshops which contained the best tools modern industry had to offer, and he built as part of the laboratory a technical school in which technical assistants could be systematically taught and trained in just those skills that were required in low-temperature physics. In this way, he prepared for the solution of those problems in physics that required attack on the engineering scale in a professional engineering manner. Scientists who were merely amateur engineers were no longer sufficient. Dewar, in spite of his natural engineering sense, belonged to an earlier craft stage of development, and was out of date.

Dewar was in the end unable to help himself because he was not sufficient of an engineer, and for the same reason, his great work had virtually no immediate influence in British industry. There was no proper medium of understanding between his science on the one hand, and British industry on the other.

The extreme form of every aspect of Dewar's life and work helps to bring out these various points in the proper management of science on the one hand, and engineering on the other, and of the collaboration between them.

OSBORNE REYNOLDS
1842–1912

I

THE INVENTOR OF STREAMLINE

WHEN modern science began to take its characteristic form in the seventeenth century, the relations between scientists and craftsmen were close. Such men as Galileo and Boyle systematically studied the activities of craftsmen in arsenals and smithies, to ascertain facts about the properties of matter which had been learned from tradition and experience. This close collaboration of scientists and craftsmen enabled them to meet the demands of the Industrial Revolution in the latter half of the eighteenth century, especially in the invention and development of steam power, and in industrial chemistry.

By the beginning of the nineteenth century the scientists and craftsmen started to drift apart again. They were separated by the drive for profit, which subordinated both science and craft to finance. The sons of successful industrialists were sent to Oxford or Cambridge, where they acquired a view of science, if they were interested in it at all, which held that it was essentially a pure intellectual discipline without connections with trade, and exalted above it.

Scientists in the growing new industry became employees, and were paid salaries that were often lower than the wages of craftsmen; the new class of industrial scientists consequently started with low social regard. The gap between science, as represented by them, and ownership grew wider. The men who combined scientific inventiveness with commercial acumen and achieved fame and riches were exceptional. They became celebrated, but the firms which they created, after these had been inherited by their sons and grandsons, generally relegated scientists to a low position in their organization.

In the middle of the nineteenth century, far-seeing men perceived that the comparative decline of the position of science in industry was in fundamental conflict with the increasing dependence of industry on science. Efforts were therefore made to improve the position of industrial science by raising the standards of scientific and engineering education, both among the masses and in the universities. The latter began, fitfully, to try to teach engineering as a profession intellectually respectable, suitable for a gentleman, and useful to industry.

The first British university to embark on this task was Glasgow. A chair of engineering was founded there in 1840, to which M. J. McQuorn Rankine was appointed. One might say that the steam engine was effectively invented in Glasgow by James Watt, and there made academically respectable by McQuorn Rankine. After Glasgow, Belfast was the next British university to establish a chair of engineering. Its first occupant was James Thomson, noted for the invention of tidal calculating machines and other work. He was the elder brother of William Thomson, Lord Kelvin.

In the first half of the nineteenth century Manchester had become accustomed to believe that what she thought today, the world would think tomorrow. Some of her proudest citizens became embarrassed when they realized that Glasgow had been before them in engineering education. With the founding of Owens College in 1868, an effort was made to make higher education in Manchester more appropriate to modern needs, and the reputation of the city. The founders appointed highly talented professorial staff. The former house of Cobden, the chief leader of Manchester political thought, was converted into lecture rooms for the professors, who included W. S. Jevons, the logician and political economist; Bryce, the lawyer who became an authority on the United States, and British ambassador at Washington; Balfour Stewart, the physicist; H. E. Roscoe, the chemist; and shortly afterwards, Schorlemmer, the organic chemist and friend of Friedrich Engels. The famous engineers William Fairbairn and Joseph Whitworth were among those who subscribed for an engineering department.

They and the governing body had the perspicacity and courage to choose Osborne Reynolds, then twenty-six years old, as the first professor of engineering. These remarkable appointments provided striking evidence that Manchester was still at the height of its social and intellectual vigour. It has been said that the spirit of an institution is established in the first ten years of its existence; the history of Manchester University bears this out.

The wisdom of the governing body's engineering appointment was not, however, immediately obvious to many of the local industrialists who had enthusiastically supported the proposal for a chair of engineering. They had envisaged a professor with long practical experience, who would provide them with engineers trained to suit their traditional requirements, and who would solve the problems arising in daily practice.

The young professor necessarily had had little experience of engineering practice. He did not conceive his task as assisting and multiplying the conventional type of engineer, the sensible man with long experience and a smattering of theory. He aimed at teaching the understanding of the science involved in engineering, and extending this science where it was not already known. McQuorn Rankine, for whom he had a profound regard, had already carried this far in connection with the science of steam, towards the understanding and improvement of that major invention, the steam engine. As this engine is a heat engine, the theory of heat, or thermodynamics, was the science primarily involved.

Reynolds was concerned more with the scientific principles underlying machines and devices involving the flow, rather than changes in heat and temperature, of fluids. He invented and developed experimental methods for investigating fluid motion, upon which modern aerodynamics and hydraulics are based. The design of jet aircraft, of giant steam turbines, of huge water power and control works depends on principles which he elucidated, and expressed in a form that could be used in practice. He was the first to conceive and demonstrate clearly the difference between streamline and turbulent motion.

The notion of streamline is of the essence of the modern world. In 1968, the centenary of Reynolds's appointment at Manchester, his ideas and attitudes were at the centre of practice. This would have seemed inconceivable and incomprehensible to the practical men who were disappointed by his appointment in 1868. At that time, he seemed to them the very opposite of a significant engineer. His personality appeared even more impractical than his engineering ideas and interests. He seemed to have difficulty in thinking along conventional lines. As he grew older, he found increasing difficulty in finding the right word for expressing his thoughts. He tended more and more to find the opposite of the correct word, and finally he became aphasic. He was virtually unable to express his thoughts, and in 1905 had to retire prematurely.

Reynolds was paradoxical on principle. He was most ingenious in finding arguments in support of ideas that appealed to him because, for example, they were those of a colleague or friend whom he liked. He held that when a scientist of established reputation has the whole scientific world against him, it is quite certain that he is right.

His belief in the power of the contrary entered even into the education of his children. Schuster, who was for many years his colleague, has described how he called on Reynolds at his house, and found him playing with his little son. He was bringing him up to do the opposite of what he was asked to do. When Reynolds said 'come here!', the small boy, to his intense delight, went away. He regarded this as a training in independence of opinion and spirit. Schuster said that the incident impressed him deeply. It would seem that Reynolds was trying to instill in his son his own processes of thought. Whether these processes were suitable for his son, or for any person other than himself, Reynolds does not appear to have paused to consider.

In ordinary conversation Reynolds was inclined to make cynical remarks. He adhered to his own opinions, which he formed for himself on every topic. He was uncompromising, and sometimes a little hasty in imputing selfish motives to his opponents. He was indeed the very opposite of the modern personnel manager's dream. And yet, he is now one of the heroes of modern engineering. He may well prove to be the greatest scientific engineer of the nineteenth century. The understanding of this contradiction is fundamentally necessary for the successful future of modern technological society, which is at odds with its heroes. Who has to change, the heroes, or modern society?

At Manchester, Reynolds was in the forefront of those who were creating the new engineering science, which deepened the understanding of the inventions and processes brought into existence by the demands of the Industrial Revolution, and opened the way to advance beyond them. If he had been born in the eighteenth century, he might never have been heard of. Like his ancestors, he might have passed his life as an eccentric clergyman, living in the country-side and cultivating scientific amd mechanical hobbies. Or his ingenious mind and simplicity of heart might have been exploited by one of those astute eighteenth-century industrialists, such as Arkwright.

The creation of the chair of engineering at Manchester, and his appointment to it, may be regarded as among the most inspired acts of science policy in the nineteenth century. They provided the conditions in which a significant genius was able to make a contribution to society consonant with his powers.

II

GENIUS REQUIRES THE APPROPRIATE SOCIAL OPPORTUNITY

Osborne Reynolds's great-grandfather, grandfather and father were successively rectors of Debach-with-Boulge, Suffolk. He came of an established clerical family, which had for a considerable time been able to secure higher education for its members. His father, the Rev. Osborne Reynolds, went to Cambridge, where he was Thirteenth Wrangler in 1837, the year in which the great mathematicians George Green and J. J. Sylvester graduated. The Rev. Osborne Reynolds was elected a fellow of Queens' College at Cambridge. He subsequently became Principal of the Belfast Collegiate School, and then Headmaster of Dedham Grammar School in Essex, before following his father as Rector of Debach.

Osborne Reynolds was born at Belfast on 23 August 1842, when his father was principal there. While the family was at Dedham, he was personally educated by his father. At the age of nineteen, in 1861, he was sent to an engineering workshop at Stony Stratford, to learn how to be a working mechanic, as quickly as possible and as far as time would permit, before proceeding to Cambridge to read mathematics. In modern jargon, he was put through a crash programme to acquire the elements of workshop skills before going to the university.

Reynolds said in his application for the chair at Manchester that from his earliest recollection he had had 'an irresistible liking for mechanics'. In his boyhood he had had the advantage of his father's guidance, who also was a lover of mechanics, and 'a man of no mean attainments in mathematics and their application to physics'.

After he had spent a year in the workshop, and had sufficiently mastered the details, his attention was drawn to various mechanical phenomena. He discovered that a knowledge of mathematics was necessary to explain them, so it was suddenly decided that he should go to Cambridge to read mathematics, before going into the office of a civil engineer. He hastily learned some Greek in a few weeks, to pass the entrance examination. He went to the same college as his father: Queens'. His mathematical studies were successful, for he graduated as Seventh Wrangler in 1867, and was elected a fellow of Queens' College.

He entered the office of the civil engineer, Mr John Lawson, in London. But he was there for only a very short time, as he applied for the new engineering chair at Manchester and was successful, in 1868. He may have been influenced by the tradition of the engineering chairs at Belfast and Glasgow. His father was no doubt well-acquainted with developments at Belfast University. The father of James and William Thomson had been professor of mathematics at the Belfast Royal Academical Institution, and became professor of mathematics at Glasgow University. The Thomsons, like Reynolds, had been carefully grounded in mathematics by their father.

It seems evident that there was a strain of mechanical and scientific talent in the Reynolds family, which did not find its appropriate opportunity for expression until the social change in the middle of the nineteenth century. This produced the new higher engineering education, in which it was possible for men like Osborne Reynolds to find scope for their genius.

Reynolds was outspoken in his admiration for McQuorn Rankine. Like him, he had a wide range of interests, direct intuitions, and the ability and determination to work out difficult and complicated problems. He agreed with Rankine's view that engineering education should be based on a scientific training. He worked out a course for his students which was remarkable for its thoroughness and completeness. He held with uncompromising conviction that all engineering was one, and the same fundamental training was required for all branches of engineering, whatever speciality the engineer might later pursue.

Reynolds suffered a personal misfortune, as well as the usual difficulties in creating a new professorial department, the second of its kind in England. He had married in 1868, the year of his appointment, and then, in the following year, his wife died. Their son died at the age of eleven. This probably made his peculiarities of thought more pronounced. He did not marry again until 1881. By his second wife, Anne Charlotte, daughter of the rector of Otley in Suffolk, he was to have three sons and a daughter. It may not be entirely unrelated to his second marriage that he began to publish the most brilliant of his many researches in 1883.

Students found his course severe, and his lectures often perplexing and difficult to follow. One of his most famous pupils was J. J. Thomson, who graduated in engineering at Manchester, before going to Cambridge to study mathematics and physics. He described how Reynolds would rush into the lecture room, his mind full of other things, and pick up a textbook which he opened at random, in order to focus his attention, and find something to lecture on. His eyes would light on a formula, and he would at once say: 'That's wrong', and write it on the blackboard. Then he would set out to show that it was wrong, by deriving it from first principles. After many false starts, corrections and rubbings-out, he would announce towards the end of the hour that the formula was, after all, correct.

J.J. said that the spectacle, which was that of a first-rate mind coping with a problem from first principles, in which nothing was taken for granted and common, and uncommon, mistakes were made and then corrected, was highly educative for those students who could appreciate it, but the less-talented found it frustrating.

His method of writing accounts of his researches, as published in his papers, resembled his lecturing style. He always searched for a simple idea that would explain mechanical phenomena, rather than derive a general theory from the simultaneous action of several different causes. When he had found the simple idea, he then wrote out, not a simple explanation of the phenomenon he had been investigating, but a description of the complicated path by which he had arrived at the simple idea. He devoted a lot of space to dealing with the points that had given him trouble, and little to those which had not. But often the points that had troubled him were obvious to the reader, while those obvious to him were not. However, when he occasionally gave popular lectures on the important discoveries in his difficult papers, he was often very lucid and stimulating.

He did not read widely in the current journals. Whenever he heard of a new idea, he immediately thought it out for himself, often arriving at a wider and deeper view of its implications. He invented his own terminology, and even gave his own special meaning to conventional terms. He affected to despise mathematics, but did not hesitate to use it with power when necessary. He regarded intuitive grasp of mechanical and physical principles involved in phenomena as of by far the greater importance.

Reynolds hated advertisement. He was aware of the value of his work, and was prepared to leave its assessment to the future. He was extremely generous to pupils and collaborators with suggestions and help. Schuster has described how, when Crookes had invented his radiometer in 1873, discussion arose on the explanation of its action. The vanes attached to a vertical axle in a bulb from which the air has been exhausted revolve when a beam of the sun's rays falls on them. There was no immediate agreement on the explanation of this phenomenon.

Reynolds suspected at first that the forces causing the rotation were internal, arising from the evaporation of condensed moisture by the thermal rays in the sun's beam, though he soon adopted the theory now accepted. Schuster suggested to Reynolds that the question whether the rotation was caused by internal or external forces could be solved by investigating the reaction of the containing vessel from the revolving vanes.

About two years later, after Schuster had returned from an expedition, Reynolds came into his laboratory one evening, and said that he had set up the experiment with a radiometer which he had suggested. He wanted him to come and do the experiment, and do it now. Schuster returned with him. They suspended the radiometer with an attached mirror, and as the light fell on the blackened surfaces of the vanes, the vessel swung round. When the vanes settled down to a steady rotation, the vessel slowly returned to its position of rest. Though Reynolds had made all the experimental preparations, he would not hear of a joint publication of the result, which subsequently appeared in the *Philosophical Transactions* of the Royal Society.

Reynolds pursued his experimental researches for twenty years with very modest resources, making many of his experiments at home. He was profoundly interested in the Manchester scientific tradition, of which Dalton and Joule were the most famous exponents. He had a leading part in promoting memorials of them in Manchester. Joule was still active when Reynolds came to Manchester. Like Dalton, Joule was a leading figure in the Manchester Literary and Philosophical Society, the sixth oldest scientific society in the world. Reynolds served as secretary of the Society from 1874–83, and as President for 1888–89.

He wrote a memorial volume on Joule for the Society. It was published in 1892, and is one of the finest biographies of a scientist in the English language. Reynolds addressed himself to the interpretation of the significance of Joule's researches, and their relation to the conditions and demands of the times, as well as the accounts of the facts of his life and work. Joule performed many of his experiments at home, so Reynolds was following a habit well known in Manchester.

In 1888, however, the opening of the Whitworth Engineering Laboratory in the University enabled him to make experiments on a larger scale. Joule had made classical measurements of the Mechanical Equivalent of Heat between 1843 and 1878, by essentially craft methods, in experiments carried out in his home. His results depended on the accuracy of a single thermometer in each experiment. Reynolds had had triple expansion steam engines and hydraulic brakes installed for experimental purposes.

One of the exercises with the hydraulic brakes was the comparison of the great heat generated in them with the amount of work absorbed. He presently realized that the apparatus would enable him to determine by experiments on an unprecedented, and engineering scale, the mechanical equivalent of heat, with a new order of accuracy. His apparatus enabled him to measure the amount of work required to raise a pound of water from freezing point to boiling point.

The object of measurement was absolutely definite, and did not depend on any temperature scale, and as the amount of water used in the brakes was very large, the margin of error was thereby greatly reduced. Water at freezing point was fed into the brakes, where friction raised it to boiling point. It was then run into a tank on a weighing machine, which measured its quantity accurately and absolutely. The work done to raise the quantity of water from freezing to boiling point was measured by the couple or forces on the shaft being braked, multiplied by the number of revolutions.

Reynolds described these experiments in the Bakerian Lecture to the Royal Society in 1897. They were a notable example of the evolution of experimental determination of an absolute constant of nature from the domestic laboratory to the engineering scale.

III

THERE ARE ALWAYS PROBLEMS AT HAND

Twenty years passed before Osborne Reynolds's opportunities for making experiments on an engineering scale were facilitated by the provision of an adequate engineering laboratory. Meanwhile, he studied problems at hand, on which he made valuable progress. His first published paper was on the mechanics of a device familiar in shooting booths on fair-grounds, in which a small ball is kept in the air by a vertical jet of water. He was not dependent on complicated apparatus, though he made good use of it when he could obtain it.

In this respect he resembled Rutherford, who once said to a student dissatisfied with what he considered were inadequate experimental facilities: 'Why, I could do research at the North Pole.' In fact, Reynolds did turn to rain, snow and hailstones in his early days at Manchester, when he had no adequate engineering laboratory. He published a notable research in 1876, in

which he elucidated the conditions which determine whether
the condensation in a cloud will lead to the production of rain,
snow or hail. He demonstrated that hailstones were formed by
the aggregation of small frozen particles. This was due to the
larger frozen particles falling more rapidly, thus colliding with,
and catching smaller particles. He succeeded in producing artificial hailstones by blowing plaster of Paris powder into a jet
of steam. He found that they had the shape and structure to be
expected from his theory. Nearly a hundred years later, in 1966,
these experiments were still being cited with great admiration
by investigators of the physics of clouds.

In his earlier years he made many other researches on what
J. J. Thomson has called outdoor physics, no doubt because he
had not yet obtained the larger engineering research apparatus
which he desired. He sought for explanations of the properties
of the solar corona, the aurora, and comets' tails in terms of
electrical and evaporative processes. He made an artificial corona
around a brass ball, which resembled the solar corona, by means
of an electrical discharge from the ball when suspended in a
vessel from which the air could be partially exhausted.

This kind of research, both experimental and theoretical, now
occupies a conspicuous place in modern space research, in which
the phenomena of interplanetary space are interpreted in terms
of the combined action of electrical and fluid forces.

He showed that the inductive action of the sun might be the
cause of the electrification of clouds, producing thunderstorms.
He showed by experiment that the probable cause of the splitting
of trees struck by lightning was the sudden conversion of water
in the sap into steam. He also investigated the destruction of
sound by fog, and why fog-horns appear less loud against than
with the wind, and why there are areas were they may not be
heard at all.

Reynolds's interest in the physical properties of liquids led
him to experimental researches on cohesion. The theory of
surface tension, based on molecular forces, indicates that liquids
should be capable of supporting high tensions. It is not, however,
very easy to devise experiments in which liquids are submitted
to tensions. Reynolds showed that a column of mercury more
than two metres long could be suspended in a vertical tube, that
is, a column nearly four times the length of the mercury column
in a barometer tube. This showed that the liquid mercury was
able to support a tension of at least three atmospheres, or forty-
two pounds to the square inch. In another experiment, by means

of a centrifugal action, he showed that water could sustain a
tension of at least twelve atmospheres, or 167 lb per square inch.

Reynolds never lost interest in 'outdoor' physics. His last
paper was on the slipperiness of ice. He commented that it is
the only solid in the natural conditions of the surface of the earth
which is perfectly slippery. He thought it notable that there had
been 'little or no curiosity as to the physical significance of this
unique property'. He thought that this was because people grew
up from infancy with the knowledge, and took it for granted.
They supposed it was slippery merely because it was ice. He said
that nature's most successful method of concealing her secrets
was to leave them exposed.

This thought expressed the essence of Reynolds's genius. He
had the ability, which he consciously cultivated, of looking at
common things after he had removed the blinkers of habit from
his eyes.

He explained that he had come to look freshly at the slipperiness of ice after his mind had been occupied with the problem
of lubrication. He had become interested in experiments by
Beauchamp Tower, who assisted Rayleigh in hydrodynamical
researches in 1875–76, on the lubrication of the bearings of
machinery. Tower had shown that the surfaces between the
bearing and the shaft are separated by a thin film of oil under
pressure. Reynolds perceived that the film might be thick enough
for the theory of hydrodynamics to be applied to the motion in it.

Preliminary experiments showed that the bearing must be
distinctly wider in diameter than the shaft, which does not revolve with its axis coinciding exactly with that of the bearing.
The rotation is eccentric to an extent determined by the load,
the speed of revolution, and the viscosity of the oil. The surface
of the shaft and the bearing do not approach each other most
closely in the line in which the load acts, but to a side of this line.

As Reynolds had perceived, the standard equations of hydrodynamics applied to the movements in the film, and his application of them showed that the oil film was stable, in spite of the
enormous pressure on it. In turbines, the fluid presses the turbine wheel horizontally, parallel to the shaft, as well as causing
it to rotate. A special bearing to take this horizontal pressure is
therefore necessary, both in steam turbines and in water turbines
used in liners and warships.

On the basis of Reynolds's results, Michell and Kingsbury
invented the thrust bearings which have made practicable the
use of large turbines driven by steam or by water. Kingsbury, an

American engineer of Pittsburgh, endowed the Osborne Reynolds Fellowship in Engineering at Manchester University in 1919, as 'some recognition of the debt he owed to Reynolds' researches in lubrication'.

But to return to the slipperiness of ice; while the process of lubrication was in his thoughts, he happened to be using a hot soldering iron. He accidentally pushed it against a block of solder, along which it slipped, without friction. 'It was a perfectly casual accident, but under the circumstances it caused me a sense of mental shock, as I instantly recognized the analogy to the action of a skate on ice.' The pressure of the hot iron on the block was sufficient to melt the surface of the solder. The liquid layer then lubricated the surfaces between the iron and the block. He said that the shock was the result of the reflection that he had never before thought of why ice is slippery.

Another of Reynolds's direct observations of significant phenomena was his famous explanation of the familiar observation that when the foot is put down on firm sea sand from which the tide has recently receded, and is consequently still moist, the sand around the footstep becomes lighter and drier, while the sand under the footstep becomes darker and wetter. He showed that this was due to the different volume of granular substances, such as quantities of small balls or grains of sand, depending on the way the particles were arranged in the structure.

He filled a thin rubber sack with fine shot. When placed on a table, it settled almost in the form of a pile of shot. But when the interstices of the particles were filled with water, and the mouth of the sack was tied tightly, the sack suddenly began to behave as a solid body, taking the form it had just before its mouth was tied.

Reynolds saw in the phenomena of the different volumes of the different arrangements of the same number of spherical particles in contact a clue to the structure of matter and the mechanics of the universe. He devoted his last year to working out this idea in his *Sub-mechanics of the Universe*, an obscure and difficult work written when aphasia was already overtaking him. Profound judges, such as Horace Lamb, have felt that this last work of Reynolds contains deep ideas which he did not succeed in making wholly explicit, and that its full understanding will require the attention of another genius whose mind worked in the same way as his. Eddington was one of those who tried to understand his last work, and who, like Reynolds, also left a last work of a similarly impressive though obscure kind.

IV

FROM THE MECHANICS OF NATURE TO THE
PRINCIPLES OF MACHINES

Reynolds began to investigate the properties of large machines and the products of engineering construction, as opportunity offered. In the early 1870's, shortly after going to Manchester, he was attracted by a problem of the British Navy, which was then experiencing much trouble caused by the racing of screw propellers in high-speed ships. Among other effects, holes appeared in the metal blades, known as cavitation. He investigated the phenomena theoretically, and also with experiments on scale models.

He showed that if the propeller was not sufficiently deep in the water, air was drawn in by it, which interfered with the movement of the blades. He investigated the effect on the resistance to the ship of running the propellers at different depths. He examined the action on the propeller of the different layers of water moving at different speeds in the ship's wake, and he studied the effect of the propeller on the ship's steering.

Besides these particular investigations, he worked out the fundamental mechanical conditions which enable the results obtained from experiments with models to be applied to full-scale ships. Among other properties, the model should have the same shape underwater as the full-scale ship, and its centre of gravity should be in the same place in the centre of the ship.

For the model to give corresponding information on the performance of the ship at a given speed, it must move at a much lower speed. Conversely, the behaviour of the ship will correspond to that of the model at a much lower speed. The relation between the speed of the model and the speed of the ship for corresponding information is given by the ratio between the square roots of their lengths. If the model is four feet long and the ship is four hundred feet long, then if the ship's behaviour at 20 knots is to be investigated, the model must be propelled by $\frac{2}{20}$, or one-tenth the speed, that is, two knots. Reynolds's results were confirmed by large-scale experiments under the auspices of a British Association Committee, and by tests carried out on H.M.S. *Minotaur* and H.M.S. *Defence* by the Admiralty.

He subsequently carried out research on life-boats, following a series of disasters off the Lancashire coast. He elucidated the

OSBORNE REYNOLDS
holding a model for illustrating the effects of packing spherical
particles

conditions under which models of such boats could be effectively used for improving their design, and making their performance in heavy seas safer. He explained that if the models are of the same form, then their behaviour in a rough sea would correspond to that of the life-boats, if the height and length of the waves to which they are subjected are on the same scale as the models, and the speed of the wind to which they are subjected, in comparison with that of the wind on the life-boats, is as the square root of the ratio of the scale. Thus the behaviour of a model four feet long, buffeted by waves two feet high and by a wind of twenty miles an hour would correspond to that of a life-boat thirty-six feet long, buffeted by waves twenty-four feet high and a wind of eighty miles an hour.

Reynolds provided the knowledge for a substantial improvement in the means for saving life at sea. His investigations of wave motion led to a theoretical discovery which assumed even greater importance.

In 1877 he published a paper on the Group Velocity of Waves, in which he added to the results obtained by G. G. Stokes on this fundamental phenomenon. As a ship ploughs through the water a wave slants back from its bow for some distance and then fades away. Another wave then appears parallel to the first, and a third parallel to the second, and so on. The waves form a group, whose velocity is less than one half of that of an individual wave. Reynolds pointed out that the energy of the train of waves moves at the same speed as the group velocity. This phenomenon is of basic importance not only in the properties of wave motions in familiar fluids, such as water, but in the properties of all matter, which according to modern physical theories possesses among its characteristics certain wave properties.

Reynolds became interested in the application of screws in pumps, and in 1875 took out a major patent for improvements in centrifugal pumps and turbines. It incorporated the idea of a succession of stages, in which each stage took some of the energy out of steam entering the machine at high pressure. He introduced guide vanes round the impeller to increase the efficiency of the extraction of kinetic energy from the steam.

He built and operated the first pump of this type in the Engineering Laboratories at Manchester. It was the forerunner of the turbine pumps since made in vast numbers. He introduced the idea of rotating guide vanes, which are now universally used for regulating the flow in water turbines.

His patent covered multi-stage turbines driven by vapours,

9

gases and liquids. In it he said that 'the novelty of my invention consists in repeating the action and again causing the fluid to traverse one or more additional sets of moving passages alternating with fixed passages. In both cases, that is in obtaining motive power and raising and forcing fluids, instead of alternate sets of fixed and moving passages all the passages may be in motion; but in that case the alternate sets of passages must move in opposite directions. It is not necessary that the several sets of moving passages should be connected with, or move round the same shaft.'

Reynolds anticipated both the multi-stage Parsons turbine, and the Ljungstrom turbine with opposite rotation of the moving elements. He made and operated a small experimental multi-stage axial flow steam turbine. It ran at 12,000 revolutions per minute. As the turbine wheel was only six inches in diameter, the clearances between the turbine blades and the casing were large in comparison with the wheel diameter. Consequently, the leakage of steam past the blades without doing work was large. Reynolds concluded that his turbine could not be made sufficiently economical to compete with the reciprocating steam engine, and become a practical source of power. He did not perceive that if his turbine were made on a bigger scale it would become more efficient, for the clearances would remain the same, so that the volume of steam leaking through them would be much less in comparison with that doing work on the blades.

It is remarkable that the great master of scale effects should not have noticed this. Perhaps it was because his inventions were so little inspired by the motive of commercial gain, even if he took the trouble to patent them. He may have done this to establish his priority in ideas rather than ownership. Parsons' contribution was to see that the axial steam turbine could be made efficient, and organize its manufacture, use, and sale. In spite of being the son of a peer, Parsons could take his jacket off, and offer to fight recalcitrant workmen. With Reynolds such a thing would have been inconceivable. Reynolds made an immense contribution to engineering science, but he was not an industrial engineer. The difference between the types of Reynolds and Parsons strikingly illustrates the difference between scientific engineering invention, and the developmental engineering research often necessary to make such invention useful.

Reynolds also worked on the theory of the nozzle afterwards used by De Laval, in which the velocity of the steam is increased by expansion through an expanding nozzle. He pointed out that the speed of the steam in the narrow neck of the nozzle was the same as that of sound waves in steam in the same condition.

Reynolds's researches on the behaviour of mixtures of steam and air on the cold surfaces of condensers were scarcely less important and far-sighted. He showed that the size of the surfaces required in a condenser for a steam engine increases very rapidly with the increase in the amount of air mixed with the steam. Thus the reduction of the amount of air present is of great practical importance, especially in the large modern steam turbines. In 1874 he published a paper in which he analysed theoretically the action at the heating surface of a boiler, by which heat is transferred to the water or working medium. He confirmed his result by experiment. During the last half-century it has become the foundation for the scientific design of heating and cooling surfaces, working with liquids and gases in motion.

Reynolds provided much of the engineering science which has made possible the varieties of modern turbines, turbine pumps and compressors. The design of pumps, steam turbines for power stations, and jet engines depends more, perhaps, on his contributions than on those of any other man.

V

FROM THE PRINCIPLES OF MACHINES TO THE CONTROL OF NATURE

Reynolds's researches on the motion of objects through water, and the flow of water past obstacles and through pipes led to several of his most important discoveries. The high resistance of flat plates to motion through water when they are pushed with one of their faces across the line of motion is familiar from common experience. The resistance is due to the creation of vortices or eddies behind the plates, which bring a large amount of water into motion and absorb a large amount of energy. Reynolds gave the first visual demonstration of these vortices in a lecture at the Royal Institution in 1877, by introducing jets of solution of a coloured dye in front of the moving plate. The streaks of dye were whirled into the vortices and revealed their structure and movements. He subsequently made much use of this technique for revealing the motions of fluids. He showed that a vortex once formed may travel through a fluid for long distances with small loss of energy.

His most famous papers on fluid motion were published in 1883–84, on 'the two manners of motion of water' and 'on the law

of resistance in parallel channels'. The first manner of motion
was when the particles of the fluid followed perfectly defined
and orderly paths, and the second when they moved in eddying
and virtually chaotic paths. The first came to be called 'streamline motion', and the second was named by Kelvin 'turbulent'.

Reynolds investigated experimentally the flow of water in
pipes, and the conditions which determine whether it would be
smooth or 'streamline', or whether it would be chaotic or 'turbulent'. His experiments confirmed his deductions from dimen-
sional theory that there is a 'critical velocity', depending on the
ratio of the viscosity of the fluid to the diameter of the pipe, at
which streamline changes into turbulent flow. In his experiments
he used coloured dye solutions for revealing the motions. These
produced coloured streaks, which he illuminated by the light
from an electric spark.

Reynolds compared the two kinds of motion with those of
soldiers who were respectively disciplined and undisciplined.
Soldiers move in orderly fashion under discipline. Particles of
fluids move in streamline when a corresponding condition exists.
This is a certain degree of viscosity in the fluid. If the discipline
or the viscosity is too weak, the motion becomes disorderly and
chaotic.

Also in analogy with troops, a heavy fluid is more likely to
become disordered than a light one, just as heavily equipped
troops cannot manœuvre as easily as those lightly equipped.

His results immediately reconciled earlier experiments in the
subject, which had appeared to lead to contradictory conclusions.
It became clear that this was because some had experimented
with flow below, while others with flow above, the critical velocity. Reynolds deduced a formula for calculating the critical
velocity, from the principle that viscosity tends to stability, while
inertial forces tend to instability. The change in the kind of
motion would therefore depend on a relation between them.

He deduced this relation in terms of the viscosity and velocity
of the fluid, and the diameter of the pipe. It defines similarity of
motion not only in pipes with parallel sides but in flow past bodies
of similar shape. It is known as the 'Reynolds number'. With it,
it became possible to work out the respective conditions in which
the flow around a full-scale aircraft, and around a small-scale
model of it, are the same. Thus it enabled the problems of aircraft design to be accurately investigated by experiments on
small models.

This greatly reduced the cost of aircraft research, and greatly increased its safety. In fact, without the 'Reynolds number' there would be no modern aircraft, and together with his other inventions, no modern steam and water turbines to drive big ships and power stations.

When the Cavendish professorship of experimental physics became vacant in 1884, Reynolds, like G. F. Fitzgerald, W. Garnett, R. T. Glazebrook and A. Schuster, was a candidate for it, but J. J. Thomson, who had been one of his pupils, was preferred to him and the others. It was perhaps as well, for if Reynolds had gone to the Cavendish professorship, he might have been diverted from engineering, in which his genius was comparable with that of J. J. Thomson's in physics. Reynolds's creative powers were not discouraged by Cambridge's choice. He was in the midst of his greatest researches, and they continued unabated.

Another of Reynolds's explanations of natural phenomena arose out of this research, the calming of rough seas when oil is poured on them. The wind which whips up the waves produces a stable form of motion. The water inside the waves moves steadily and is free from eddies. When oil is poured on the surface it spreads in a thin film which offers a slight resistance to its extension or contraction. The force is very small, but is sufficient to alter the movement of the water inside the waves. It has an effect of the same kind as the presentation of a solid wall, which makes the movement of the water inside the waves unstable, and subject to eddies. Thus the energy of the wind now goes into the creation of eddies underneath the surface, rather than the increasing of the height of the waves. Consequently, the surface of the sea becomes calmer, and the disturbance is buried underneath. Reynolds said that there was nothing in mechanics more striking than this phenomenon. 'A film of oil so thin that we have no means of illustrating its thickness, is yet able entirely to prevent an action which involves forces among the strongest we can conceive.'

Since Reynolds made these observations, the measurement of the thickness of thin oil films on water was perfected by Rayleigh, Langmuir and others, giving quantitative values to the forces which he saw qualitatively so clearly in his mind.

His investigation of the conditions which establish similarity of flow in pipes and tunnels of different sizes led him to a research of fundamental significance for the construction of water-power plants, harbours, and other major civil engineering projects.

In 1887 he read a paper to the British Association on how the conditions for the regulation of rivers and estuaries could be investigated by experiments on small-scale models. The construction of the Manchester Ship Canal, and the harbour works in the Mersey for Liverpool raised these questions in a very close and immediate, practical form.

The idea of using small-scale models for solving the problems of modifying rivers to make them more useful for transport and other purposes was not new. It had been used with some success by Fargue in France in 1875. He had not, however, reduced the method to a scientific system. By empirical judgment he had fixed the relations between the scales in the vertical and horizontal directions, and the volume and period of flow of water through the model.

In 1885 Reynolds constructed two tidal models of the upper estuary of the Mersey. He investigated the effect of six thousand artificial tides in one of the models. His first aim, apparently, was to discover how the water circulated in the estuary, and what eddies it formed. He noticed, however, that a flat bed of sand on the bottom of the model was gradually carved into shapes which resembled those of the sandbanks and channels seen in the natural estuary. He commented that 'the causes of these' could be seen in the model. This inspired the idea that it would be possible to forecast the effects of works before they had been built. He said that 'this method of experimenting seems to afford a ready means of investigating and determining beforehand the effects of any proposed estuary or harbour works; a means which, after what I have seen, I should feel it madness to neglect before entering upon any costly undertaking'.

Reynolds showed that the technique could give reliable results, and put it on an adequate scientific basis. He made models geometrically similar to the rivers to be investigated, and calculated the exact time that flow should continue to give accurate forecasts of what would happen on the large scale. He controlled the design of the model and the conduct of the experiment according to the general principles of dynamical similarity.

On behalf of the British Association he made an extensive research on the actions of currents and waves on the beds and foreshores of estuaries. He showed how the effects of groynes and walls on the formation of banks and the prevention of erosion could be forecast.

Reynolds's pupil and subsequent successor, A. H. Gibson, who carried forward his great researches on hydraulic engineering, gave a striking illustration of Reynolds's intuition which, added to his theoretical and experimental ability, made his genius so fruitful. Fifty years after Reynolds's classic experiments Gibson constructed a tidal model of the Severn Estuary, to investigate the problems of designing and building a Severn barrage, and the effects it would have on the Severn and its ports. He found that sand with fine grains of a certain average size gave the best experimental results. If the sand was substantially finer or coarser, the results were not so good. Reynolds in his original experiments had intuitively chosen fine Calais sand, with grains of just about the same size.

The great developments of modern drainage and power plants, irrigation schemes and harbour constructions, which have changed the aspect of large areas in many countries, increasing the supply of power and the control over rivers and the sea, affecting the lives of millions of people, are based especially on Reynolds's scientific engineering investigations. Today, all advanced countries have large hydraulic research laboratories for designing major new constructions, such as harbours for trade, and multiple purpose power and irrigation plants, in Asia, Africa, Australia and Europe.

Whenever one of these great works is seen and inspected, it is to be remembered that the solution of the problems of its design owes more to Osborne Reynolds than any other man.

After his premature retirement in 1905, he went to live at St Decuman's in Somerset. His aphasia, or speechlessness, grew worse, and on 21 February 1912, he died.

Reynolds was elected a Fellow of the Royal Society in 1877. In 1888 the Society awarded him a Royal Medal. In 1968 the University of Manchester held a celebration of the centenary of his appointment as professor and the founding of his department. At it, eminent engineers and scientists reviewed his inventions and discoveries, and their ever-growing influence on the great works of today and of the future.

CHARLES BABBAGE
1791–1871

I

THE SPIRIT OF A FUTURE AGE

BABBAGE was the most effective initiator of the reform of British science at the beginning of the nineteenth century, to adapt it to the needs of the new industrial age. His achievement in this direction was due to his creative originality and intellectual force. He was in advance of most of his scientific contemporaries in recognizing the importance of political action with regard to science.

In his youth he had been delicate, and tormented with shyness. When he overcame his shyness he became explosively assertive. He attempted to carry out what he regarded as his political duty on behalf of science. His personality was not, however, suited to political action. By about the age of forty he had broached his main ideas, and accumulated so many opponents and barriers that he could not advance further.

Lyon Playfair, who possessed high political qualities, knew Babbage in the latter half of his life. He found his information and conversation fascinating, but he said that Babbage 'always considered himself a badly treated man, and this feeling at last produced an egotism which restricted the number of his friends'. During a journey with the Prince Consort, Playfair 'strongly urged the desirability of the Crown bestowing honours on men of science. I pointed out that while the Army, Navy and Civil Service received titles and decorations in profusion, the Crown bestowed few on men of learning. The consequence was that they ceased to look on the Crown as the fountain of honour, and created titles for themselves, so that such letters as F.R.S. become more esteemed than those like K.C.B. This separation of the Crown from learning was not wise in the interests of Monarchy.'

The Prince readily agreed, and asked Playfair what he would recommend. He suggested that 'one or two of undoubted position were made privy councillors, mentioning Faraday and

Babbage as two men entitled to this honour'. He was commissioned to ascertain whether they would like to be appointed to
the Privy Council.

Playfair happened to sound Babbage first, 'who was delighted
with the suggestion, but made it a condition that he alone should
be appointed, as a reparation for all the neglect of the Government towards his inventions'. The condition 'was naturally
disagreeable to the Prince Consort, and no further steps were
taken to open the Privy Council to men of science'. Playfair
interpreted Babbage's behaviour as purely personal, in implying
that 'Even the association of such a distinguished man as
Faraday would take away from the recognition which was due
to him.'

How was it that in the scientific world of Young and Faraday,
it was Babbage who was most effective in promoting the movement for bringing science and social life into more fertile combination? And why should the latter part of his life have disintegrated in bitterness and ridicule?

Babbage asked his friend and executor Harry Wilmot Buxton
to write his biography. Buxton worked on this with great pains,
and completed more than two thousand neatly written pages of
manuscript. The unpublished work is in the Museum of the
History of Science at Oxford. Most of it is devoted to descriptions of the development and construction of the machines, but
among other points of interest, light is thrown on the origin of
Babbage's attitude to science. How did he arrive at such an
unusual mixture of subjects, such as pure mathematics and the
economy of manufactures? Why was he so determined in pressing the importance of the latter? Buxton says that he was an
enthusiastic admirer of Francis Bacon, and regarded him as the
founder of the modern philosophical outlook. 'He was an earnest
disciple of his philosophy, and like his great master, he directed
all his speculations to some practical end, calculated to mitigate
the labour of life and secure the general happiness of mankind.'

Babbage held that Socrates, Plato and Aristotle had had a
retrograde influence. 'Had Plato condescended to speculate upon,
or even encourage those engaged in the invention of machinery,
instead of condemning such labours as unworthy of a philosopher, our predecessors might have long since anticipated many
of the results which have been realized in our time, and indeed,
the application of machinery to mathematical operations might
have long since been recorded as a fact of history.' Buxton says
further that 'much that still lies buried in the womb of time might

9*

have been long since brought to light, and astronomy and navigation, with other arts of civilized life have acquired a degree of advancement and excellence which is still wanting'.

Babbage's philosophy impelled him in the direction of novel combinations of sciences, to be developed and applied for the benefit of mankind. He described himself as 'a reformer both in science and in politics'. He insisted on combining science and politics, just as much as pure mathematics and industrial processes, and research and institutional management, which other people believed should be kept apart.

He twice stood for Parliament while he was Lucasion professor of mathematics at Cambridge, as a Liberal candidate for Finsbury, in 1832 and 1834, on the policy that he would promote the interests of the industrious and intelligent classes. He had already invented his first calculating machine, and industrial operational research. In 1832 he came third with 2,311; the first and second gained respectively 4,278 and 2,848. By 1834 his reputation with the electors had been undermined, partly by the spreading of the rumour that he had misappropriated Government funds supplied for the construction of his machine, and he was at the bottom of the poll with 379.

He worked hard for William Cavendish, the future seventh Duke of Devonshire, in the General Elections of 1829 and 1832, as candidate for Cambridge University. Cavendish had been Second Wrangler and First Smith's Prizeman when Babbage was one of the examiners. After the fiasco of the second Finsbury contest, Babbage retired from the front-line of politics.

During the eighteenth century industrialism had overtaken the old mercantile order. By the beginning of the nineteenth, the existing scientific institutions had become out of date. The Royal Society, in the form shaped by Newton in physics and Banks in biology, no longer suited contemporary science, which was being orientated to the needs of an industrial state.

Banks died in 1820, after ruling the Royal Society in the manner of an autocratic improving landlord for nearly forty-two years. He had had a leading part in inspiring the foundation of the British dominion in Australia, and had had the whole world scoured for cultivable plants for the benefit of British agriculture and the empire at large.

His system of management of the Royal Society was frustrating to the kind of scientific development which was now required. His successor, Humphry Davy, who tried to assume Banks's social mantle and manner, was conscious of the need for change towards the development of the industrial sciences of chemistry and physics. The lag of scientific organization behind the new needs of science made the scientific world as a whole appear to him to be in a state of decline. Shortly before he died in 1829, he had considered writing a book on the subject.

Davy was unable to carry this out owing to ill-health, and he was also inhibited by social ambition from frankly criticizing the old order. He had arrived in London as a young man of humble and provincial origin, while Banks was still in supreme authority. He was deeply impressed by him and aspired to his position. No one foresaw the new industrial development more vividly than Davy, but he had been born too early not to be overawed by the surviving grandeurs of the old order.

Another man was needed to break its social as well as its scientific domination. Davy was born in 1778. Babbage, born thirteen years later, was less involved in the declining order. Unlike Davy, the son of a Cornish landlady, he belonged to a wealthy banking family engaged in the financing of the new industrial age. He could look landlords like Banks coolly in the eye, from the secure basis of the growing wealth and social power of his class and its intellectual equipment of Adam Smith's political economy. Babbage's extraordinary confidence arose from his class background as well as his temperament.

The overtaking of the old scientific leadership by the new scientists gave an impression that science as a whole, as represented by the old leadership, was falling back.

Babbage's trenchant criticism raised determined opposition, which made serious difficulties for him. Though he belonged to a rich banking family, he had chosen to devote himself to science instead of going into the family business. He was financially dependent on his father, and in awe of him. He was anxious to produce successful results quickly in order to satisfy him, by demonstrating the value of science for commerce and industry. He wished to avoid involving him in expense on his experiments. He also had a rapidly growing family; his wife bore him eight children in thirteen years. He tried hard to secure a well-paid appointment to gain financial and filial independence, but his scientific controversies and novel ideas hindered his candidatures. He grew increasingly fractious.

Miss Maboth Moseley has commented on the degree of personal strain under which he lived at this period, which helps to explain his later almost unbalanced behaviour. Until 1826–27, up to the age of thirty-five, he bore the strain, though only with effort. Then suddenly, his father died, his wife died in childbirth, and two of his children died. He had a nervous breakdown.

He inherited £100,000 from his father, which relieved him from financial anxieties, but the shock of his personal losses left a permanent mark on his personality. Before that stage was reached he had promoted reforms and ideas which were among the most important of the age.

The traditional leaders of opinion regarded him at first as a genius, later as a crank, and finally as somewhat deranged. The eminent patent lawyer, Lord Moulton, in an address in 1904 on *Invention*, instanced Babbage as the kind of inventor who failed because he was always having new and better ideas before any of his inventions was completed. He described how he had once been taken to see his workshop. 'In the ante-chamber I recognized parts of the well-known calculating machine that, many years before, he had brought to the stage of actual working, and I asked him as to its completion. 'Oh, I have done no more at that', was his reply. 'Before finishing it I conceived the idea of my analytical machine which was so much better that it would have taken more to complete the first machine than to make the new one.' We then came to the analytical machine, parts of which were lying about, and he explained to me its principles and mode of working. 'Have you got it finished?' I asked. 'No,' he said, 'for I have come on to a new idea which throws it so completely in the shade that it would be mere waste of time to work further on it.' And he then explained to me this new idea that was to revolutionize even the world of advanced thought in which he lived.'

Moulton said that in his secret heart he considered the inventors who left their inventions unfinished were 'an almost unmitigated nuisance. They accomplish nothing themselves and they detract from the merit of those who by greater perseverance and more patient labour have succeeded where they have failed. Their inventions attain posthumously a short-lived forensic glory by being paraded as anticipations of some later invention which has proved itself to be worth defending.'

T. H. Huxley was wiser in his opinion: 'I knew Mr Babbage, and am quite sure that he was not the man to say anything on the topic of calculating machines which he could not justify . . .'

In fact, further on in his address Moulton said that what was wanted was 'union of invention with a system of practical development'. He said that this was the source of the American lead in mechanical invention. 'Men possessing inventive genius of a high order are maintained as part of a business organization for the express purpose of making inventions which when made, are duly tested, and if found of practical value are exploited on a large scale, the inventor reaping thereby his reward.'

Moulton's skill in patent cases was unequalled, but outside legalities his judgment was limited by his social philosophy. He placed responsibility for the completion of invention on the individual, according to the orthodox *laissez-faire* attitude of his day. Yet he knew that the 'union of invention with a system of practical development' was necessary. It was this contradictory attitude which contributed to the British technological decline. Responsibility for the advance of science rests jointly on the individual and on society. In Babbage's case, the main responsibility was with the latter. It was the business of government and society to see that his inventions were completed.

As Babbage's inventions did not produce results during his lifetime, he was ridiculed. In his last years he was known as an angry old man who chased organ-grinders that disturbed his quiet. In the second half of the twentieth century Babbage is being mentioned in the same breath as Shakespeare and Newton as the most significant of Englishmen. He invented the computer and foresaw its implications.

II

EARLY LIFE

Charles Babbage was born on 26 December 1791, near Teignmouth in Devon. His father Benjamin Babbage, a native of Totnes, was the manager of the noted progressive banking firm of Praed, Mackworth and Babbage. The poet and political satirist Winthrop Mackworth Praed belonged to the family of his father's partners.

Babbage was deeply attached to his mother, who before her marriage was Betsy Plumley Teape, also of Totnes. He wrote in 1851 that one of the strongest reasons for desiring public recognition of his work was 'to gladden the declining years of her who with more than prophetic inspiration, foresaw as woman only can, the distant fame of her beloved offspring'.

She had watched with maternal care over the dangers of his childhood, trained his infant mind, mildly checked the rash vigour of his youth, and 'remained ever the faithful and respected counsellor of his riper age'.

If she had not survived, there might still have been 'another

parent whose less enthusiastic temperament had ever repressed
those fond anticipations of maternal affection, but who now in
the ripeness of his honoured age, might be compelled, with
faltering accents, to admit that the voice of the country confirmed
the prediction of the mother'.

Some of Babbage's difficult temperament was due to rebellion
against paternal repression. When he was an infant he was sickly,
and thought to be weak in mind as well as body. He was too
delicate to be disciplined, and developed habits of idleness and
infantile pleasures which he never completely overcame, though
he grew robust. He survived several brothers.

As he did not flourish in his parents' London house, he was
sent to live near Exeter with a clergyman who kept a school. This
master was instructed to look after his health, and not press
knowledge on him. Babbage became well again, but idle and
addicted to fantasies. He frightened other boys by pretending to
produce ghosts and practise magic.

After he had recovered his health in Devonshire, he was sent
to a private school near London, which had thirty pupils. Babbage seems to have owed much to this school. It had a small but
excellent library, in which he found 'Ward's Young Mathematician's Guide' to Algebra. He had always been 'partial' to
arithmetic, and this work fired his enthusiasm for the higher
mathematics. He regularly got up at three o'clock in the morning to pursue the new interest.

Sleeping in the same room as Babbage was Frederick Marryat,
the future Captain Marryat, who also desired to join the early
morning algebra sessions. Babbage refused him on the ground
that he did not think his interest was serious. Marryat thereupon
fixed his bed so that Babbage would have difficulty in getting up
without waking him. After a long battle of wits, Marryat won.
In course of time, more boys joined the sessions, and presently
took to playing with fireworks instead of algebra. This led to
the discovery and suppression of their early morning activities.

After leaving school, Babbage was placed under a clergyman
near Cambridge, and then under a classics tutor at Totnes, to
prepare him to enter the university. While there, he became
interested in the idea of a universal language, and made some
progress in devising one. He did not hear of John Wilkins's work
on this subject until he was at Cambridge.

His father consulted one of the Cambridge college tutors for
advice on how he should pursue his career. The only advice he
could get was that his son should not purchase his wine in Cam-

bridge; which advice, said Babbage, 'was quite sound, but very limited'.

He spent all his leisure reading such mathematical books as he found by accident; in particular, Woodhouse's *Principles of Analytical Calculation*, from which he learned Leibniz's notation for the calculus, and the treatises on Fluxions of Maclaurin and Simpson. He also read Lagrange's *Théories des Fonctions*. He used with equal facility 'the dots of Newton, the d's of Leibniz, or the dashes of Lagrange'.

He looked forward to Cambridge with intense delight, expecting that the difficulties which he had not been able to overcome by himself would be swiftly resolved. He imagined forming chess and mathematical clubs among his future friends.

On his way through London to Cambridge in 1811, he sought a copy of Lacroix's *Differential and Integral Calculus*, the most modern treatise of the day. French books were very difficult to procure during the Napoleonic wars, and Babbage was shocked to find that a copy would cost seven guineas. After much consideration, he bought the book, went to his college, Trinity, met his tutor, and found lodgings. Then he spent most of the night poring over Lacroix.

A few days later he went to his tutor with one of his mathematical difficulties. He was told that it would not come in his examination, and he need not bother about it. He went with another difficulty to one of the lecturers, and received a similar answer. A third effort to be enlightened left him with the impression that the person he consulted was ignorant of the matter, though he took some pains to disguise his ignorance.

Thus, wrote Babbage, he 'acquired a distaste for the routine of the studies of the place, and devoured the papers of Euler and other mathematicians', which he found in the library.

At the time, Cambridge was agitated by a controversy whether the Bible should be published merely as it stood, or with notes to make it intelligible. The walls of the town were covered with posters, supporting one side or the other. On a day during this period, his friend Slegg was suddenly called away from a mathematical discussion in which they were engaged. While he was waiting for Slegg to return, and his mind was still full of mathematical considerations, his gaze happened to fall on the posters. The idea of writing a parody on them, making propaganda for mathematics instead of Bible study, occurred to him.

He drew up a poster in the same style, suggesting that a society should be formed for translating Lacroix's *Differential and*

Integral Calculus, and holding 'periodical meetings for the pro-
pagation of d's', and 'consigned to perdition all who supported
the heresy of dots'. When Slegg returned Babbage put the
parody in his hands. Slegg thought it very funny, and suggested
showing it to his friend Bromhead, later a mathematician of note.

Bromhead enjoyed the joke, but said that the idea of forming
such a society ought to be taken seriously. It was agreed that a
meeting should be called at Bromhead's lodgings to discuss it.
Among those who attended were J. F. W. Herschel, G. Peacock,
and D'Arblay (the son of Fanny Burney, Mme D'Arblay). They
constituted themselves 'The Analytical Society', hired a meeting
room, and read and discussed papers.

They were ridiculed by the dons, but refused to be put down,
so 'it was darkly hinted that we were young infidels'. Babbage,
Herschel and Peacock became close friends, and made a pact to
'do their best to leave the world wiser than they found it'. They
decided to publish a volume of Transactions. This was carried
out by Herschel and Babbage, and the latter proposed that its
title should be: 'The Principles of pure D-ism in opposition to
the Dot-age of the University'. Herschel dealt with mathematical
analysis, and Babbage with the calculus of functions.

Extensive reading had shown that the adoption of the Leib-
nizian notation was essential for the progress of mathematics in
England. But it was 'hopeless for any young and unknown author
to attempt to introduce the notation' directly, so members of the
Analytical Society decided to translate Lacroix's *Elementary
Treatise on the Differential and Integral Calculus*. The first part,
170 pages long, was on the differential calculus, and was translated by Babbage; the second, running to 269 pages, by Peacock
and Herschel. An appendix of 104 pages on *Differences and
Series* was contributed by Herschel, and a collection of *Notes* by
Peacock and Herschel. This work was published at Cambridge
in 1816.

Herschel had been influenced by Robert Woodhouse, a Cambridge mathematician who since 1803 had been publishing able
works, in which Continental notations were recommended.
Woodhouse had an acute critical mind, and drew attention to
logical difficulties in the Continental methods, which reduced
the effectiveness of his works as propaganda for them. Consequently, the reform was carried out by the talented students,
who advocated the Continental methods and new mathematical
subjects enthusiastically, without reservations.

Peacock, Herschel and Babbage published a collection of

examples in the new mathematics, together with solutions. Peacock dealt with the applications of the calculus, Herschel with those of the calculus of finite differences, and Babbage with the solution of functional equations. This provided the teachers of mathematics in Cambridge with ready-made material, which greatly facilitated the reforms.

English mathematics was brought up to date by students doing their teachers' work for them. Meanwhile, the students had to take their examinations. Babbage refused to compete for honours. He moved from Trinity to Peterhouse, and graduated in 1814 with a pass degree. Herschel came out First Wrangler in 1813, with Peacock Second.

Babbage's refusal to submit himself to the honours examination of 1813 has usually been attributed to vanity; he could not bear the thought of being beaten by Herschel and Peacock. At this date the examination still retained some of the peculiarities inherited from the past. The questions were not set in a printed paper, but announced verbally by the examiner, one by one, each question after the first not being announced until one of the candidates had called out that he had 'Done' the previous question. Joseph Romilly, who was Fourth Wrangler in 1813 when Herschel and Peacock were First and Second, recounted many years later how he had been irritated by Peacock's continually bawling 'Done, done', after each question was announced; yet Peacock had not come out First. Printed examination papers, from which the candidate could choose which questions, and in what order, he wished to tackle, were not introduced until fourteen years later. The old system put a premium on readiness and composure, and it would not be hard to understand that a mathematician might find a contest of this kind distasteful.

Herschel was a very gifted man, who had grown up in the atmosphere of his father's greatness. His scientific interests had been fostered by most inspiring connections, and careful tuition. When young, Herschel had found Eton too barbarous. He was promptly brought home, and provided with a good tutor. He accomplished excellent work in pure mathematics, chemistry, the logic of scientific method, and observational astronomy. He was in the forefront of most of the progressive scientific activities of his time.

Herschel was socially charming. He was as easy to get on with as Babbage was difficult, but he lacked Babbage's dominating concentration. He spent his life completing his father's work, and helping others, including Babbage, to realize theirs.

Though Babbage had agonizing attacks of shyness, he had an extensive social life. He was in the habit of entertaining twelve friends to breakfast in his rooms at Trinity every Sunday after chapel. He kept a 'beautiful light, London-built boat', and sailed miles into the fens, taking 'two or three strong fellows' with him to row the boat back if the wind was contrary.

He was interested in chemistry, and attended Smithson Tennant's lectures. Having a spare room in his lodgings, he fitted it up as a laboratory, in which he and Herschel collaborated.

Babbage had the advantages of the well-to-do son of a banker. His means enabled him to pursue his own aims with cussedness as well as independence.

In his *Memoirs* Babbage says that his friend Thomas Robinson reminded him later in life that he had first thought of the invention of a calculating machine in 1812 or 1813, before he had graduated. 'One evening I was sitting in the rooms of the Analytical Society, at Cambridge, my head leaning forward on the table in a kind of dreamy mood, with a Table of Logarithms lying open before me. Another member, coming into the room, and seeing me half asleep, called out, "Well, Babbage, what are you dreaming about?" to which I replied, "I am thinking that all these tables (pointing to the logarithms) might be calculated by machinery".'

Babbage did not say in his Memoirs that *he* recollected this occasion. In his unpublished papers he left a different account, quoted by Buxton. According to a note made in the 1830's, he said that about 1820–21, his friend Herschel brought with him some calculations made by two professional computers for the Royal Astronomical Society. They started on the laborious task of checking them. The 'discordances were so numerous that I exclaimed "I wish to God these calculations had been executed by steam", to which he replied: "It is quite possible".' Babbage then pursued the idea.

Babbage gave yet another account of the origin of his calculating machine. The way in which he dealt with this matter suggests that he was conscious of some degree of indebtedness. Herschel may have given him some impulse and strengthened his confidence to persevere. No exact conclusions can be drawn, but it is certain that Babbage's own contribution was overwhelmingly greater than any other.

He graduated, and married, in 1814. His wife Georgiana was a sister of Wolnyche Whitmore, M.P. for Bridgnorth in Shropshire. In 1815 he settled in London at No. 5 Devonshire Street,

Portland Place. He pursued his researches and the production of a family with passionate intensity. After his wife died prematurely in 1826, he never lived at 5 Devonshire Street again, nor did he ever again show intimate interest in any other woman. He left his mother at Devonshire Street to look after her grandchildren, while he went to live at No. 1 Dorset Street, Manchester Square, which had formerly been occupied by Wollaston.

When his sole daughter died in her teens he was still more deeply bereft. Altogether, five of his children died, and only three sons survived. These do not seem to have seen much of him until they were old enough to enjoy his workshops and help in experiments; his youngest son never seems to have overcome awe of him.

Babbage made an early visit to Paris in the company of John Herschel, where he met Laplace, Poisson, Fourier and Biot. Biot's son subsequently translated his *Economy of Manufactures and Machinery* into French. In 1815 Babbage had seen Napoleon on the *Bellerophon*, through a telescope off Torbay, near his Devonshire home. He later became acquainted with many members of the Bonaparte family. When Louis Napoleon was imprisoned at Ham in 1843 he wrote to Faraday, saying that his best occupation there was studying his works, and he asked him to give his regards to Babbage.

Babbage's most important foreign tour arose from his nervous breakdown after his wife's death. He set out in 1827 to recover his health. In the course of his journeyings he became acquainted with Alexander von Humboldt, and through this accidentally found himself involved in the first great international meeting of scientists, in Berlin in 1828. This stimulated him to further action on the national and international organization of science, and inspired him to take a leading part in the foundation of the British Association for the Advancement of Science.

III

HIS FIRST CALCULATING MACHINE

The French Revolutionary governments rationalized French society, and as part of this process rationalized the methods of measurement by introducing the metric system. This made it necessary to carry out the huge task of recalculating the standard mathematical tables used in practice, on the basis of the new system.

The French mathematician M. Prony, who lectured at the

Ecole Polytechnique on the method of differences, was entrusted with the preparation of the new tables. In the course of reading Adam Smith's description in the *Wealth of Nations* of the manufacture of pins by the division of labour, it occurred to him that the same principle could be applied in calculating by the method of differences. This consisted of analysing a calculation into a system of additions and subtractions, so that even the most complicated formula could be evaluated by the performance of the simplest arithmetical processes.

After a short holiday in the country, he returned to Paris with a plan for the *manufacture* of logarithms. He recruited half a dozen of the most eminent French mathematicians to suggest the most suitable basic mathematical formulae. He then obtained a team of seven or eight capable mathematicians to reduce this evaluation to a series of elementary steps that could be carried out by unskilled calculators.

A third team of sixty to eighty persons, nearly all of whom knew little more arithmetic than simple addition and subtraction, were engaged to carry out the final computations. The tables so calculated filled seventeen folio volumes, and were produced with hitherto unexampled speed.

Babbage reflected that it ought to be possible to perform the simple operations carried out by the third team of unskilled persons by machinery, just as the industrialists at the beginning of the Industrial Revolution had discovered how to mechanize the simple processes into which manufacture had been analysed by the application of the principle of the division of labour. If manufacture could be mechanized, so could calculation.

While he was speculating about this possibility, he was involved in practical problems of making astronomical instruments, in particular, making accurate measuring scales. Thus he was thinking of the theoretical problem of how calculations might be made, and the workshop problems of making scientific instruments, at the same time. Babbage says that he discussed these two subjects in 1819 with Wollaston, who told him that his plan for marking the divisions on instruments had been proposed long before by a French scientist, but that he ought to persevere with his idea of a calculating machine.

Babbage now began to think out in detail the design of a calculating machine operating according to the Method of Differences. He called it a *Difference Engine*.

It had to perform two distinct arithmetical processes; it must be able to add digit to digit, and carry tens to the next digit. To be of practical use, the machine must be able to perform these operations much faster than they can be done by a man. This was one of the points in which the earlier calculating machines of Pascal and Leibniz were inadequate. Babbage succeeded in making substantial advances in speed only through years of research and experiment.

Another important feature was that the machine must produce reliable results. It was therefore desirable that it should print the results, so that errors arising from copying by human operators could be eliminated.

Babbage ultimately worked out several different methods of doing this. In one, the machine gave the answer in movable type. In another, type around the edges of wheels was pressed onto a mould, so that the result was automatically registered on a stereotype, from which any number of printed copies could be taken. He devised a third method, by which the result of the computation was punched onto a copper plate. He invented a punch which could move along three directions at right angles for this purpose. It was in fact a general shaping machine, which he later found very useful for many other purposes.

Babbage constructed his first small working model between 1820 and June 1822. He sent a description of it to Davy, as President of the Royal Society. It 'produced figures at the rate of 44 a minute, and performed with rapidity and precision all those calculations for which it was designed'.

He gave a list of tables which it could be used to compute, and said that his 'statements may perhaps be viewed as something more than Utopian'. Knowing from his own experience 'the difficulty of convincing those who are but little skilled in mathematical knowledge, of the possibility of making a machine which shall perform calculations, I was naturally anxious, in introducing it to the public, to appeal to the testimony of one so distinguished in the records of British science'.

Being convinced of the great utility of such machines, he had diverted his attention from pure mathematics, 'which possesses charms of a higher' order, to the development of the model, which had now been carried to the stage 'where success is no longer doubtful'. The expense of perfecting it would however be considerable, and probably not be repaid for a long period of time. He therefore felt unwilling to commence this undertaking, 'as altogether foreign' to his 'habits and pursuits'.

Davy saw and admired the machine, and the Royal Society appointed a committee to consider Babbage's proposals. Besides

Davy, it included Brunel (the father of Isambard Kingdom Brunel), John Herschel, Wollaston, Young, and others. The committee reported that 'they consider Mr Babbage as highly deserving of public encouragement in the prosecution of his arduous undertaking'. Its report was sent to the Treasury.

In 1823 Babbage had an interview with the Chancellor of the Exchequer, to ascertain whether the Government wished him to construct a large difference engine which would print its results. Babbage returned from the interview under the impression that the Government wished him to construct such a machine at its expense, because of its value in calculating tables for nautical purposes; but no minute of the interview was made, and it appeared later that no clear expression of official desire was on record.

Meanwhile, a sum of £1,500 was sent to Babbage by the Treasury 'to enable him to bring his invention to perfection, in the manner recommended'. Babbage believed that he would be able to complete it in two or three years.

From this point, misunderstandings about Babbage's machines grew steadily. As Alexander Strange subsequently remarked, they arose in the first place from the absence of a Minister of Science whose department was technically qualified to understand and aid such a development. Moreover, scientists of the highest personal distinction showed lack of judgment and insight in this matter. Young let it be known that though he had acquiesced in the report of the Royal Society committee of which he was a member, and not doubting that such a machine could be made, 'he conceived that it would be far more useful to invest the probable cost of constructing such a calculating machine as was proposed, in the funds, and applying the dividends to paying calculators'.

The difference engine which Babbage began to design and construct, as he thought, for the Government, was based on his model, but was much larger. It had twenty places of figures, and six orders of differences, which greatly increased the scope of the machine. But it also greatly increased the complexity of design and the number of parts. Instead of completing a simple difference engine quickly, he plunged into the intricacies and novelties of improved design. As he struggled with each feature, new ideas in principles of calculation, methods of designing machinery, and workshop techniques for making metal parts to new standards of accuracy, took shape in his mind.

He invented a mechanical notation which assisted him to de-

sign new machinery in his head, and interpret complicated drawings quickly without confusion. He said that 'it has given us a
new demonstrative science, namely, that of proving that any
given machine can or cannot exist; and if it can exist, that it will
accomplish its desired object'.

Babbage thought he ought to have been given one of the two
new Royal Medals awarded in 1826. According to the terms of
the awards, they were to be given for work done in the previous
year, but the Royal Society gave them to Dalton and Ivory, who
had done splendid work, but respectively twenty and three
years before. Babbage called the awards a 'fraud', and regarded
them as one of the examples of mismanagement by the Royal
Society.

One of his most arduous problems was the design of a mechanism which would carry the tens swiftly. 'Multitudes of contrivances were designed, and almost endless drawings made, for
the purpose of economizing the time and simplifying the mechanism of carriage.' Babbage said that the mechanical means he
finally adopted for this purpose bore 'some slight analogy to
the operation of the faculty of memory'.

After years of labour on the mechanization of the carrying
motion, he said that 'it occurred to me that it might be possible
to teach mechanism to accomplish another mental process,
namely—to foresee. This idea occurred to me in October, 1834.
It cost me much thought, but the principle was arrived at in a
short time. As soon as that was attained, the next step was to
teach the mechanism which could foresee to act upon that foresight. This was not difficult . . .'

Babbage's imagination, and very words, took wing into the
second half of the twentieth century, so it is not surprising that
he failed to meet the needs of the first half of the nineteenth.

He found that the mechanical difficulties and the expense of
completing the difference engine would be much greater than
he had anticipated. He drew freely on his own fortune, and
damaged his health by overwork. He went abroad in 1828 to
recuperate. His friends became busy in Whitehall, and got in
touch with the Prime Minister, the Duke of Wellington, to
secure more support. The Duke consulted the Royal Society,
which most strongly recommended the completion of the
machine.

His friends also got busy in Cambridge, and secured for him the
Lucasian chair of mathematics, which had been held by Isaac
Newton. Babbage heard of this while he was still in Rome, and

immediately drafted a letter declining it. English friends persuaded him not to refuse the chair, so he accepted.

After Babbage had returned to England, he demonstrated the
model to the Duke, and shortly afterwards he began to receive
further government aid. Babbage was provided with a fire-proof
building to contain his engine and drawings, and the workshops
for completing it. Payments to the engineer-in-charge, however,
fell into arrears, owing to the slowness with which government
funds were paid, so he departed, taking the special tools with
him, which he was legally entitled to do. Babbage was deprived
for the time of his own drawings.

With construction halted, and bereft of his drawings, Babbage's
genius was undeterred. He revolved the problems of the machine
in the loneliness of his imagination, and suddenly the greatest
idea of his life sprang into being. A *'principle of an entirely new
kind* occurred to him, the power of which over the most complicated arithmetical operations seemed nearly unbounded'. With
it, a machine could be constructed that could solve the problems
of mathematical analysis, which he would therefore call an
Analytical Engine.

He had thought of the principle of the modern computer. He
saw that to utilize it, thousands of parts would be required, compared with hundreds in the simple difference engine. This made
further simplification of the mechanisms absolutely essential,
otherwise, machines operating on the new principle would be
impracticable. If such improved mechanisms could be devised,
the machine operating on the new principle would calculate
much more quickly than the old difference engine.

Babbage became absorbed in the idea of the new machine,
and sought instructions from the Government whether he should
complete the difference engine, or investigate the possibilities
of his idea for a new kind of calculating machine. Exchanges
between ministers and Babbage continued, while the situation
became more confused.

At last, after work on the difference engine had been suspended
for eight years, Babbage was informed by the Chancellor of the
Exchequer in Peel's administration, that the Prime Minister
and himself 'both regret the necessity of abandoning the completion of a Machine on which so much scientific ingenuity and
labour have been bestowed'. The expense which would have
been necessary to render it satisfactory either to Babbage himself,
or make it generally useful, appeared to be far more than they
felt justified in incurring. They withdrew all Government rights

in the 'machine as a present constructed', and placed it entirely at his disposal in order that they might 'to a degree assist' his 'future exertions in the cause of science'.

Babbage declined to accept the machine; finally, he saw Peel himself. He reported afterwards that he was unable to explain his plans to him satisfactorily .This was because of the state of Peel's information on the subject, and the view he took of Babbage's services and position.

The incident provided a classical example of the failure of relations between politician and scientist. Both were men of exceptional ability, and their misunderstanding was due to lack of an adequate organization for handling scientific matters, not to lack of intelligence on their respective sides.

When work on the difference engine ceased, the Government had already spent £17,000 on it, and Babbage more than £20,000 from his own fortune. While the eight years of exchanges about the difference engine proceeded, Babbage got on with the elaboration of plans for his new machine. He thought out the mechanical devices that would be needed, and had the necessary drawings prepared. All this was done at his own expense.

Babbage's efforts to proceed with the development of his calculating machines brought him into contact with the realities of the relations between science and industry, and science and government. It was characteristic of his genius that he did not observe them passively, but investigated and strove to improve them.

This he did through his books on *The Decline of Science in England*, and *The Economy of Machinery and Manufactures*.

IV

THE DECLINE OF SCIENCE IN ENGLAND

Many of the creative scientists in England at the beginning of the nineteenth century felt with passionate concern that British science was in a state of decline. They found that new branches of science were not advancing as fast as they should, and they looked around for the causes of retardation.

Babbage became their most incisive spokesman, because of his intellectual identification with one of their main groups, his insight into the trend of the age, and his powers of expression. These qualities were made more effective by his financial independence and his exceptional detachment from the social considerations usually known as tact. He said things which other young men of comparable ability did not like to mention in public.

As a student Babbage, with Herschel and Peacock, had seen the hindrance of the old Cambridge tradition to the cultivation of the new mathematics, and had joined in steps to improve the situation. As a young scientist his first contact with the scientific world was through the Royal Society, as the traditional sponsor of new scientific ideas. He found it was virtually without practical power, and immediately concluded that its condition was one of the causes of the bad state of British science. He and his friends tried to effect improvements, but found themselves outmanœuvred and defeated by the officers.

Having failed to work from within, Babbage decided to try to work from without. He wrote his *Reflections on the Decline of Science in England*, which was published in 1830. He said that he hoped 'it will ultimately do some service to science, and without that belief I would not have undertaken so thankless a task. That it is too true not to make enemies, is an opinion in which I concur with several of my friends.'

The decline in quality was connected with the absence of proper refereeing of papers submitted for publication. Babbage quoted at length John Herschel's strictures on the English journals of chemistry. Unlike the French *Annales de Chimie*, these contained 'crude and undigested scientific matter'. The French societies had committees which thoroughly read and discussed papers, and this, 'perhaps more than anything had contributed to the high scientific tone of the French *savans*'.

The excellent scientific journals conducted by the German scientists Poggendorff and Schweigger presented the progress of science throughout Europe. Anything interesting was noticed and circulated by them, including British discoveries. It was encouraging for British scientists to know that their work was instantly reported, and 'repeated, verified and commented on', in Germany and also in Italy. 'Here, whole branches of continental discovery are unstudied, and indeed almost unknown, even by name. It is in vain to conceal the melancholy truth. We are fast dropping behind. In mathematics we have long since drawn the rein, and given over a hopeless race . . .'

One could not expect complete administrative efficiency from unpaid officers of scientific societies, who often did a great deal of 'quiet and unostentatious' labour, which enables societies to be carried on. But Presidents of Societies, who enjoy high prestige by virtue of their position, should be 'answerable to the Society' for the way in which they conduct their office.

The control of the Royal Society had fallen into the hands of a clique, and no longer rested with the members as a whole. 'If such an Institution can be of use to science in the present day, the attention of its members may be excited to take steps for its restoration.'

The English, particularly in 'the more difficult and abstract sciences', were much below other nations, even small ones. 'That a country, eminently distinguished for its mechanical and manufacturing ingenuity, should be indifferent to the progress of inquiries which form the highest departments of that knowledge on whose more elementary truths its wealth and rank depend, is a fact which is well deserving the attention of those who shall inquire into the causes that influence the progress of nations.'

The tracing of 'the gradual decline of mathematical, and with it, of the highest departments of physical science, from the days of Newton to the present', had to be left to the historian. But action to improve the situation could not wait until the historian's investigations had been completed. It was necessary to deal at once with the more obvious of the factors causing the decline. One of these was the contemporary system of education. Babbage discussed this question under the heading of the Reciprocal Influence of Science and Education. He referred only to education in the public schools and universities, treating it thereby as a preserve of the upper classes.

The young men from the public schools were 'ignorant almost of the elements of every branch of useful knowledge', while the universities, which were originally founded for instructing priests, were given almost entirely to 'classical and mathematical pursuits'. During the last fifteen years much had been done to improve the system, but it ought to be extended to 'nearly the whole of the aristocracy of the country', that is, the ruling class ought to be educated in modern mathematics and science.

A university degree should be a pledge to the public that its possessors have a certain amount of knowledge, covering the newer sciences as well as the old. It is necessary 'to keep pace with the wants of society'. This would dispose of young gentlemen's excuse for not working, that 'classics and mathematics, are not adapted either to his taste, or to the wants of his after life'.

The lack of scientific education in the upper classes was reflected in Parliament. 'The discussions in the Houses of Lords or Commons, which arise on the occurrence of any subjects connected with science, sufficiently prove this fact.'

After Education, Babbage discussed the Inducements to Individuals to cultivate Science.

There was the Professional Impulse. Men entered professions to make a living, and their profession set aims for ambition and standards for performance. In England, however, the pursuit of science did not 'constitute a distinct profession', (Whewell had not yet coined the word 'scientist') so men of science were deprived of the impulses and helps which come from being members of a profession.

One effect of this was that the public, and even men of 'sound sense and discernment' were unable to distinguish between those with low and those with high acquirements. This applied 'with peculiar force to all the more difficult applications of mathematics', and tended to check the energies of those who only looked within England for reputation.

Owing to the lack of a recognized scientific profession, important positions requiring considerable scientific knowledge for their proper performance were frequently filled by amateurs, or by persons whose main efforts had been in other fields, for instance in medicine or law.

In England, law offered the greatest prize for talent. But it engrossed the attention more than any other profession, and was 'least benefitted by a knowledge of science'. This was one of the causes why 'it so very rarely happens that men in public situations are at all conversant even with the commonest branches of scientific knowledge'. There was scarcely any example of such a person acquiring a scientific reputation through work of his own. This was particularly true with regard to mathematics, 'which, from its extreme difficulty, and the overwhelming attention which it demands, can only be pursued with success by those whose leisure is undisturbed by other claims'.

With regard to *National Encouragement* for science, its smallness was excused by the principles of *laissez-faire*. According to these, the public which profit from a new invention are much better judges of its merit than the State, and the reward to an inventor from the sale of the fruits of his invention to the public is far greater than any award that could be granted to him by the State.

Babbage was in a difficulty here, for he was the son of a banker and an orthodox believer in the political economy of capitalism. 'It must be admitted that, as general principles, these are correct . . .' But there are exceptions. 'All abstract truth is entirely excluded from reward under this system.' Only the application of science to common life can be rewarded in this way. He instanced Stevinus's discovery of the hydrostatic paradox, which remained only an abstract principle until Bramah combined it with a pump to produce the hydraulic press. Even Bramah's invention did not come into general use until his patent had expired, so that others were encouraged to make further improvements.

The interval that separated the discovery of latent heat and its application to the steam engine was short, 'but it required the efforts of two minds; and both were of the highest order': Black and Watt.

Continuing the discussion, Babbage's genius penetrated far into the future. 'In mathematical science, more than in all others, it happens that truths which are at one period the most abstract, and apparently the most remote from all useful application, become in the next age the bases of profound physical enquiries, and in the succeeding one, perhaps, by proper simplification and reduction to tables, furnish their ready and daily aid to the artist and the sailor.'

If it was important to the country that abstract principles should be applied to practical use, then it was clear that those who were capable of doing it should be encouraged. 'Unless there exist peculiar institutions for the support of such inquirers or unless the Government directly interfere, the contriver of a thaumatrope [that is, a moving picture apparatus] may derive profit from his ingenuity, whilst he who unravels the laws of light and vision, on which multitudes of phenomena depend, shall descend unrewarded to the tomb.'

He questioned whether it was good policy for a country to allow such a genius as Dalton's to 'be employed in the drudgery of elementary instruction' of children. He ought to have been properly looked after long ago. Babbage indicated in 1838 what the application of his calculating machines to Dalton's numerical atomic theory implied. 'The whole of chemistry, and with it crystallography, would become a branch of mathematical analysis, which like astronomy, taking its constants from observation, would enable us to predict the character of any new compound, and possibly indicate the source from which its formation might be anticipated.'

He thought that such achievements as Dalton's were too extraordinary to be frequent, and if they were to be encouraged at all, it would have to be by 'some direct interference of the Government'. Babbage proposed that Dalton should be presented at

Court, and this was accomplished through Brougham, then Lord Chancellor.

The organization of support for science presented difficulties. The ruling class 'might not possess sufficient knowledge either to judge themselves, or know upon whose judgment to rely'.

He recommended consideration of the French encouragement of science. Laplace, Carnot and Chaptal had been given important positions in the State. Eminent French scientists generally enjoyed better salaries than British. Prussia especially gave encouragement to science. What were the prospects for the talented young British scientist? 'There are no situations in the state, there is no position in society to which hope can point, to cheer him in his laborious path.' It was almost impossible to pursue abstract science without a fortune, and at the same time giving proper attention to the fortune, if one had one.

Babbage then examined the state of the learned societies in England, to see how it bore on the conditions of science. The need for division of labour had led to the formation of new societies for botany, geology, astronomy and other branches of science. This development had generally been opposed by the Royal Society, and the new societies deplored 'with filial regret, the second childhood of their common parent'.

Babbage said that he would have been glad to have remained silent if remonstrances had been listened to, but as this had not happened, he would now endeavour, by the force of plain and perhaps painful truths, 'to direct public opinion' to the need for the reform of the Royal Society.

He recommended publicity in the management of its affairs, printed statements, and occasional discussions at general meetings; in fact, the methods which had been adopted in the contemporary business world. He objected to the custom by which the President of the Royal Society nominated the members of the Council, and disapproved of the holding of many offices by one person. He drew attention to waste in the expenditure of the Society's funds, and irrelevant considerations in the award of medals.

He said that recognition and reward were of profound importance to science. 'The products of genius are the actual creations of the individual.' They should possess the rights of property in the highest degree. 'If the institution of our country, and the opinions of society, support us fully in the absolute disposal of our fields, of which we can, by the laws of nature, be only the transitory possessors, who shall justly restrict our discretion in the disposal of those richer possessions, the products of intellectual exertion?'

Monopolies under the name of patents had been devised to assist those who chose to exploit their discoveries. 'Honorary rewards and medals have been the feeble expressions of the sentiments of mankind towards those who have preferred the other course.'

Babbage later suggested that the status and influence of scientists should be increased by the establishment of an Order of Merit. He also suggested that there should be Life Peers, who would include scientists. He made the latter proposal in 1833, in connection with the reform of the House of Lords. One of the main uses of an Upper Chamber in a popular government was to give consistency to the more fluctuating opinion of the immediate representatives of the people. 'It is to the political what the fly-wheel is to the mechanical engine.' Thus 'none but persons duly qualified should have seats in the House of Lords. Peers should be elected for life:—the Peerage should *not* be hereditary'.

Babbage thought that one of the most important reforms required in the Royal Society was the limitation in the number of fellows. He quoted with approval the Royal Society minute of 1674, which contained various proposals for making the Society prosper, including 'the ejection of useless Fellows'. The Society now had 714 fellows, only 72 of whom had contributed two or more papers to the *Philosophical Transactions*.

The Society had indeed appointed a reforming committee, containing Davies Gilbert, Wollaston, Young, South, John Herschel, Beaufort, Kater and himself. It reported in 1827, and recommended that membership should be restricted to 400, with the election of 4 new members a year. The report was, however, side-tracked by the President, Davies Gilbert.

Babbage then considered some of the discreditable actions of scientists, which are not usually discussed with frankness, such as trimming observations to gain a reputation for accuracy, and the cooking of results.

He concluded with *Suggestions for the Advancement of Science in England*. His first was that fellows of the Royal Society should develop the habit of independent expression of opinion. Their tendency to acquiesce in manœuvres was to be attributed partly to 'that reserved and retiring disposition, which frequently marks the man of real knowledge, as strongly as an officious interference and flippant manner do the charlatan, or the trader in science'. It was due also to the tendency to defer too much to the President's opinion, and not to bother about anything in which their own interests were not immediately concerned. He suggested that presidents should be elected for two-yearly periods.

In Babbage's time, many medical men sought to become fellows, because it was good for their medical reputation. He thought that this tendency should be curbed.

He commented, too, on the growing influence of the Royal Institution. It had been founded for 'the cultivation of the more popular and elementary branches of scientific knowledge, and has risen, partly from the splendid discoveries of Davy, and partly from the decline of the Royal Society, to a more prominent station than it would otherwise have occupied in the science of England'. The Royal Institution interest had at the time succeeded in securing the appointment of two Secretaries to the Royal Society. 'In a short time, unless some effectual check is put to this, we shall find them nominating the President and the rest of the officers.'

With regard to the Society's publications, he thought the punctuality and regularity of the appearance of the *Philosophical Transactions* worthy of the highest praise, especially in comparison with the delays in corresponding foreign publications. They should, however, contain more on the proceedings and history of the Society. Abstracts should be published.

On the subject of the *Union of Scientific Societies*, he proposed that the various scientific societies should occupy 'one large building'. Considerable economy would result through the use of common meeting rooms, libraries, services, etc.

He attached a report on the Congress of the German Natural Philosophers, which had been held at Berlin in 1828, under the presidency of Alexander von Humboldt. He attributed the holding of the congress to the determination of the Prussians to rebuild their country after the Napoleonic wars, on the basis of knowledge as the source of power. Babbage was the sole British participant in this famous meeting, and returned intent on promoting a similar organization in England. This led to the foundation of the British Association for the Advancement of Science in 1831, of which Babbage became one of the original trustees.

Babbage's book, which contained so much insight, outspoken criticism, and creative suggestion, provoked many responses. One of the most interesting was by Faraday's friend, the Dutch physicist Gerrit Moll, of Utrecht. Moll sent his manuscript to

CHARLES BABBAGE

Faraday, who published it with a preface written in August 1831, the very month in which he had discovered electromagnetic induction.

Faraday wrote that 'without being considered as expressing an opinion on the subject either one way or the other, I am still desirous of placing my friend's reasons before the public, not merely because no one can judge correctly who has heard but one side of a question, but also as a great literary curiosity', for it was 'an extraordinary circumstance for English character to be attacked by natives and defended by foreigners'.

Moll considered that Babbage did not offer proof of the decline relative to other countries. He thought that British ignorance of foreign languages was a serious weakness, but he looked to the new University of London to provide the remedy with its plan for more attention to modern languages. Another English weakness was the high price of books, which was 'an intolerable impediment to the diffusion of knowledge'.

Moll said that the way in which mathematics was studied and used in France and in England was entirely different, and it was not so evident 'in which country mathematical science is turned to a better account'. The concentration on mathematics in France was due to the revolutionary turning away from the past. The study of the classics was largely abolished, and mathematics substituted in its stead. Every youth of ability entered on it, and considered himself capable '*de faire des x*'.

The French mathematicians were not so good at application. 'A man after studying Poisson may scarcely know a wheelbarrow from a steam engine.' There were no books in French like Robison's *Mechanical Philosophy*, which presented science in a form suitable for the new industrial engineers.

The English scientists were generally more flexible and adaptable. Wollaston, Herschel and Babbage himself were examples of men who worked 'successively and successfully' in different branches of science 'Mr Babbage, had he been a Frenchman, might have written a standard book on mechanics, but he could never have thought of inventing that wonderful calculating engine which it must be the wish of every lover of science to see him bring into use and perfection.'

If the French superiority in pure mathematics was real, it was not due to deficiency in the English genius, but to different traditions in cultivating it. Laplace and Lagrange were professors at the *Ecole Normale*, and Monge at the *Polytechnique*, and taught as such. Foreigners were astonished to see that at English

10

universities it was possible for scientific professors to dispense
altogether with the discharge of the duties of such positions.
(Babbage was Lucasian professor at Cambridge. He never lectured, and did not reside in the university.) 'This appears a
glaring abuse, which elsewhere would call for a speedy remedy.'

The status of scientists in France was much less good than
Babbage believed. When Napoleon obtained power he offered
places and high salaries to eminent scientists to bring them over
to his party, and increase the respectability of his regime. They
were really bribes to secure their 'silent vote and sanction' to his
decrees. What happened to scientists who were not abject was
illustrated by the case of Legendre. When he refused to vote for
a ministerial candidate for membership of the Institute, 'he was
deprived of a scanty pension, his all'.

Moll's view of French scientists may be compared with those
of an eminent Frenchman from a different sphere. Stendhal,
who had studied mathematics in his youth, wrote in *Vie de
Henry Brulard*:

> The Emperor then began to elevate the throne of the Bour-
> bons and was assisted by the unbounded baseness of M. de
> Laplace. It is a singular thing that poets are noble and generous
> while scientists in the proper sense of the word are servile
> and mean. What servility and meanness was not practised by
> M. Cuvier towards those in power! M. le Baron Cuvier always
> agreed with the basest policy.
>
> When the Order of the Reunion was created, I was in the
> most intimate Court circles, he came positively *weeping* for it.
> I shall report in due course the Emperor's reply. Sold by
> baseness: Bacon, Laplace, Cuvier. M. Lagrange, it seems to
> me, was less low.
>
> Secure of glory through their writings, these gentlemen
> hope the scientist will hide the statesman; money affairs as
> well as favours, they hasten to exploit for their own advantage.
> The celebrated Legendre, geometer of the first order, on re-
> ceiving the Cross of the Legion of Honour, attached it to his
> coat, looked at himself in the mirror, and jumped for joy. The
> room was low, his head hit the ceiling, and he fell down half
> knocked out. What a worthy death this would have been for
> this successor of Archimedes!
>
> What did they not stoop to in the Academy of Sciences from
> 1815 to 1830, and after, to secure decorations! It is unbeliev-
> able; I had the details from MM. de Jussieu, Edwards, Milne-

Edwards and through Baron Gerard's *salon*. I have forgotten most of the dirty things.

A diplomat is less base, in that he says openly: 'I shall do everything to get on.'

Englishmen ought to understand that the high salaries paid to some scientists under Napoleon came out of the Universitarian Retribution, 'a duty levied upon all those who receive any instruction whatsoever. No one is allowed to learn to read, write, nor can frequent any school, from the lowest to the university, without paying a duty for it.' Moll concluded that he would not pretend to determine how such things would be relished in England, and whether 'it is not better to keep "the schoolmaster abroad" than to press down instruction of every kind by taxation'. He left the last word with Brougham.

Moll in his correspondence with Faraday on the problem of the alleged decline of science, referred to the idea of 'negotiating a loan of foreign talents and of subsidizing foreigners', a topic much discussed in the second half of the twentieth century through the drift of scientists from the poorer to the richer countries.

Moll and Babbage were friends. Moll called to see the difference engine, and was deeply interested in it. Babbage was delighted with his grasp and intelligence.

V

ON THE ECONOMY OF MACHINERY

Babbage visited workshops and factories in England and on the Continent, to find engineering processes which might be of use in constructing his calculating machines. His overall view led him to apply to the various kinds of machines he saw, 'those principles of generalization', which were habitual in his mathematical studies. He began, unconsciously at first, to consider what would be the best form of a type of machine, and the most efficient way of using it. He invented for himself what is now called Operational Research. Under the heading of Contriving Machinery, he conceived the idea of planned invention, and suggested the steps an inventor should follow.

He intended to deliver lectures on the results of these investigations as the Lucasian professor of mathematics at Cambridge, but he was induced not to do so, no doubt because it did not fit in with the subject conventionally taught by the occupants of the chair of Isaac Newton. Babbage's work was as important for the coming age of automation as Newton's for the age of navigation, but Cambridge thought, which had been harnessed to the needs of the mercantile age, was unable at that time to appreciate the significance of new subjects that would be of paramount importance one and a half centuries later.

Babbage tried to express his regard for Cambridge, in spite of its not wanting to hear him on his new subject, by publishing his lectures as a book, and dedicating it to the University. He printed a fine head of another unwanted originator, Roger Bacon, under the title. There was some resemblance, both in feature and expression, between them. Babbage wrote in one of his prefaces that some of his critics had amused themselves 'with the wildness of the schemes' which he had occasionally thrown out. He had himself 'sometimes smiled along with them'. No doubt it would be wiser for present reputation to offer only profoundly meditated plans, but knowledge would not be most advanced by that course. New ideas might 'kindle the energies of other minds more favourably circumstanced for pursuing the inquiries'. He had, for example, pointed out that four-fifths of the steam power used to blow air through iron-smelting furnaces actually cooled them. It was desirable to separate the oxygen from the nitrogen, and feed it pure into the furnace. He suggested that it might be possible to do this if the two gases could be liquefied at different temperatures under great pressure, and discussed some of the technical problems that would be involved.

He proposed the use of liquid hydrogen as a way of storing power, the introduction of central power stations for the restoration of domestic manufacture, and the use of the interior heat of the earth after the exhaustion of the coal supplies. He advocated the verification of the quality of consumer goods by an independent committee, like a consumer council. He proposed conspicuous post-boxes for collecting letters, and the introduction of a parcel post. This was because 'as the post office regulations stand at present, it constantly happens that persons who have an extensive reputation for science, receive by post, from foreign countries, works, or parts of works, for which they are obliged to pay a most extravagant rate of postage'. There should be a special rate for printed matter.

He became deeply interested in the economics of publishing, after applying cost analysis to the production and selling price of his own book, and found himself in conflict with the publishing trade. He looked into the economics of publishing still more

closely, and discovered that 'some of the periodical publications
of the day ought to be regarded merely as *advertising machines*'.
He found that 'a host of ephemeral publications are written into
a transitory popularity, and by the aid of this process, the shelves
of the booksellers, as well as the pockets of the public, are dis-
encumbered'.

His researches into the causes of accidents to ships acquainted
him with the word 'snag'; he promptly went into its orign. 'Snag
is the name given in America to trees which stand nearly upright
in the stream, with their roots fixed at the bottom.' They hole boats
which inadvertently sail into them. Babbage looked into everything.

In his book he discussed how machines are used to concentrate
and regulate power, and exert forces which are too great for
human effort, and too delicate for the human touch. They are
used for extending the time of action of forces for saving time in
natural operations, and for registering operations. Babbage gave
numerous examples to illustrate the various purposes, and a long
chapter on various copying processes. He was particularly interested in copying, because of the device required in his calculating machines for printing the results.

After reviewing the mechanical principles successfully used
in industry, he drew up a plan for making systematic studies of
industrial processes. It was important to write down information
as soon as possible after examining machinery, but this could
generally not be done while actually watching the machines in
operation. It was therefore desirable to have questions drawn up
beforehand, carefully worked out in detail.

The General Inquiries should contain about thirty questions,
covering the history of the invention and its introduction into
England; origin and price of raw materials; varieties of the
manufactured article; defects; adulteration; waste of material;
tests of quality; wholesale and retail prices; cost of the machinery,
its wear and tear, where it is made and repaired; principal seats
of the industry; duties, etc.; comparison with foreign articles;
size of export trade, etc.

The sheet on Processes included such questions as: the mode
of executing it, with sketches of the machinery; number of persons required to attend the machine, whether men or women or
children; their pay and hours of work; whether work continues
night and day without stopping; piece-work or day-work; who
provides tools, master or man; degree of skill; apprenticeship;
number of operations per hour; number of failures per thousand;
master or workman charged for failures, etc.

Babbage gives advice on making the observations. For instance, if the observer stands with his watch in his hand before 'a person heading a pin, the workman will almost certainly increase his speed, and the estimate will be too large'. A better result is obtained from an average of what is considered a fair day's work. If this cannot be obtained, 'the number of operations performed in a given time may frequently be counted when the workman is quite unconscious that any person is observing him'. He mentioned that Coulomb, who had great experience in making such observations, emphasized that the results should be received with caution.

Further information could be deduced from the data, and their consistency verified, by simple calculations. It was important to draw up questions in such a way that the answers would demonstrate the reliability of the questioner, as well as the answers.

He thought the principle of work analysis of such importance that it was desirable to give an example of 'its precise and numerical application in some specific manufacture'. He chose the pin-making industry, because it was one of Adam Smith's classic examples of the division of labour. He embodied his results in two tables, one on English and the other on French pin-manufacture. He gave the times in hours for executing each of the seven main processes in making 1 lb of pins, to four places of decimals. The cost of each process per 1 lb of pins was given to the nearest halfpenny, and the price of making each part of a single pin was given in millionths of a penny.

With this precise knowledge of every stage in the manufacture, it was possible to discover the points in it which were most susceptible to improvement, and which offered the best means for increasing efficiency and profits. This is the substance of modern Operational Research as applied to manufacture.

He used his exact analysis of the manufacture of pins by hand to compare it with the performance of 'a machine for making pins, invented by an American', bringing out its advantages and disadvantages.

Babbage pointed out that 'the division of labour can be applied with equal success to mental as to mechanical operations'. In fact it is 'capable of being usefully employed in preparing the road to some of the sublimest investigations of the human mind', and he had utilized it for this purpose through his invention of the difference calculating machine.

Babbage strove his utmost to break down the false distinction between pure and applied knowledge, which does not arise naturally, but is a product of social class attitudes.

The application of exact numerical analysis of all processes, industrial and intellectual, would provide 'a body of information equally important to the workman, the capitalist, the philosopher and the statesman'. It enabled the statesman to act from knowledge, 'for without it he must trust entirely to others'.

In his discussion of the desirability of exporting machinery, which was widely doubted at the beginning of the nineteenth century, he said that this implied 'much too limited a view of the possible, and even probable, improvements in mechanics'. He forecast that the number of makers of machinery would ultimately surpass that of the number of users.

Finally, the science of calculation was advancing with giant strides. It had already succeeded in describing the gravitating masses of the universe, in expressions of its own condensed language, 'which are to the past as history', and 'to the future as prophecy'.

The same science was 'preparing its fetters for the minutest atoms that nature has created'. It had already provided a comprehensive system of light. This science of calculation 'becomes continually more necessary at each step of our progress', and 'must ultimately govern the whole of the applications of science to the arts of life'.

VI

THE COMPUTER

Babbage's later conception, containing the principles of the modern computer, was derived from an analogy between the operations of textile weaving, and the operations in computing the value of a formula. Babbage described it as 'weaving formulae'.

In the Jaquard loom, sets of cards with punched holes are used to control the threads so that warp and weft produce a predetermined design. The system is capable of weaving any design. If both warp and weft consist of white threads, the design will be a damask pattern, but if the colour of the warp threads is varied, the design will be coloured, though its form will be the same.

The machine should therefore consist of two parts:

'1st. The store in which all the variables to be operated upon, as well as all those quantities which have arisen from the result of other operations, are placed.

'2nd. The mill into which the quantities about to be operated upon are always brought.'

There were therefore 'two sets of cards, the first to direct the nature of the operations to be performed . . . the other to direct the particular variables on which those cards are required to operate'. Every set of cards can be re-used at any future time to recalculate the formula for which they were designed. Thus the machine would 'possess a library of its own'.

Babbage said that his friend, the eminent Irish mathematician MacCullagh, asked him what the machine could do if, in the midst of a calculation, it needed a figure from a table of logarithms. He said that the machine would ring a bell and stop, exhibiting a written request for the logarithm wanted. An attendant would then feed it into the machine. If the attendant happened to give it the wrong logarithm, it would stop again, and ring a louder bell.

MacCullagh asked why, if the machine could tell whether the logarithm was correct, it should not have been able to choose it correctly. A few days later, Bessel and Jacobi arrived in England. They asked Babbage exactly the same question. MacCullagh happened also to be again present, so Babbage gave the answer to all three together. He explained that it was done with the aid of another class of punched cards, which he called number cards.

Babbage thought out all the principles required in the modern computer, and even invented much of the terminology used today.

He designed a machine which, in theory, could carry out the calculations of a modern computer. He constructed parts of such a machine, but could not complete it with his own resources. Without modern electronic devices, such a machine would have been very large. It could not have been completed, except with the resources of the State, or of mankind in co-operation.

Babbage said that in the course of attempting to develop the machine he was four times confronted with what appeared to be impossibilities. The first was in the carrying processes in the addition of numbers, which involved the operations with partial analogies to memory and foresight. The second was the apparent impossibility of representing a number of indefinite size on a machine of finite size. He found that this could be evaded by associating the representation of indefinitely large numbers with the infinite in time instead of the infinite in space. The third was the ability of the machine, which so astonished Bessel, Jacobi and MacCullagh, to know when a wrong logarithm is offered to it, but not to know the right one. The fourth, that it was possible to construct the machine so that, if stopped in the middle of a calculation, and the figure wheels were altered so that the numbers were falsified, the final calculation, and all the intermediate steps in the calculation, would nevertheless be entirely free from error. It was possible to do this by means of a very simple principle. In 1840 Babbage was invited by Plana, the Italian astronomer to whom Brougham and Routh dedicated their commentary on Newton's *Principia*, to visit Turin, and discuss his machine. Plana said that from what he had heard, 'Your engine gives us the same control over the executive which we have hitherto only possessed over the legislative department.' Babbage was delighted with his 'exact prevision of its powers. Even at the present moment I could not express more clearly, and in fewer terms, its real object.' Babbage had a perfectly clear insight into the role the computer was to play in future administration.

Among the scientists who met Babbage was the young mathematician L. F. Menalrea. He was deputed to make notes of Babbage's exposition of the principles of the machine. Menalrea, who subsequently became one of Garibaldi's generals, published his account at Geneva in 1842. This was translated by Ada Byron, Countess of Lovelace, the mathematically gifted daughter of Byron, wo refers to her in Canto III of *Childe Harold*: 'Ada! sole daughter of my house and heart!' At Babbage's suggestion she expanded the paper to about three times its original length. She was twenty-seven when she accomplished this work.

Ada Byron was born in 1815. She never knew her father, who separated from her mother shortly after she was born. Her mother, Lady Noel Byron, had a masculine intellect, considerable mathematical ability, and an angularity of disposition, which caused Byron to refer to her as the 'Princess of Parallelograms'.

It seems that Ada first met Babbage when she was about fifteen. He took pleasure in encouraging her mathematical studies, and presently realized that she had a mathematical talent. De Morgan wrote in 1844 that from the beginning of his correspondence with her she showed a power of mathematical thinking that was 'utterly out of the common way'.

Mrs de Morgan went with Ada to see Babbage's machine. 'I well remember accompanying her to see Babbage's wonderful analytical engine. While other visitors gazed at the working of this beautiful instrument with the sort of expression, and I dare say the sort of feeling, that some savages are said to have shown on first seeing a looking-glass or a gun—if, indeed, they had as strong an idea of its marvellousness—Miss Byron, young as she was, understood its working, and saw the great beauty of the invention.'

Through her husband, the Earl of Lovelace, Ada became passionately interested in horse-racing and betting. Babbage was an authority on the mathematics of probability, and she drew upon his aid in making complex betting calculations. She and her husband had serious losses, which caused him to stop, but she went on in secret. She fell into the clutches of unscrupulous men, and pawned the family jewels to meet their demands. Her mother retrieved the jewels to save the family honour.

She died from cancer at the age of thirty-seven. She had appointed Babbage her executor, and it seems that he removed from her papers any that might have reflected on her reputation.

Babbage suggested that the Universe is a machine programmed by the Almighty, on the analogy with his computer. It could operate for a given time according to a certain law, and after that according to a second law for a further given time, and so on. This 'offered a striking parallel with, although at an immeasurable distance from, the successive creations of animal life, as developed by the vast epochs of geological time'.

His idea contains the essence of the modern theory of the development of organisms through the programmed development of DNA and the proteins out of which they are made.

Babbage compared a 'miracle' to the moment of change from the operation of one programme to another. He was very much pleased with this idea, which, he considered, justified the belief in the possibilities of miracles. His theological friends told him, however, that his idea was heretical.

Bowden has expressed the opinion that Babbage was too ambitious in design. As soon as he conceived a new principle, he went to the limit in trying to realize it. After discovering the principle of his computer, he thought of the biggest calculation that man would ever be called upon to make. He started by trying to design a computer which could handle a calculation of this size. His analytical engine was theoretically as versatile as the modern electronic computer, but as it would have had to be made of wheels and mechanical parts, it would have been of enormous size. It became practicable only after the discovery of the electron, which is an almost infinitely more versatile instrument than a piece of metal.

If he had made small machines they could have been brought into industrial use immediately, and the computer would have become an instrument of commerce and research a hundred years earlier. Babbage preferred to aim at perfection. Consequently, he was condemned as impractical.

But as Alexander Strange pointed out, Babbage was let down by the absence of a proper state organization of science. From the perspective of the British nation, it was not Babbage who was impractical, but the statesmen of his day, who had failed to create an adequate state scientific organization.

VII

POSTHUMOUS TRIUMPH

The rise in scientific influence of Davy and Faraday was parallel with the increase in political influence of craftsmen in the Industrial Revolution. They entered science without the university education customary for intellectual members of the old ruling classes.

Babbage entered science with the outlook of a banker and industrialist. He carried this outlook into science, as Davy and Faraday had carried theirs. He aimed at making industry scientific, and industrializing science. He repeatedly said that his great object was to discover the laws by which men make discoveries, and then hand their operation over to 'the domain of machinery'.

He succeeded in carrying his ideas so far that they passed beyond the possibilities of his own century into the latter half of the next. He found himself isolated. Virtually no one, except Alexander Strange, fully understood that he was a normal man who appeared abnormal because he was intellectually a century in front of his time.

Peel revealed the class-nature of the most serious opposition to Babbage, when he told Croker that he could not ask a House of Commons, thinly attended and in the main by country squires, to vote for grants of money for making a machine for evaluating algebraic functions.

Apart from this political consideration, which showed that the class-structure of the House of Commons was not suitable for the encouragement of science, Peel also depended on what he supposed to be the best technical advice. He, and the Chancellor of the Exchequer, Goulburn, who stopped Government support for the development of Babbage's machine, acted on highly-esteemed scientific advice.

The Government consulted George Biddell Airy, the Astronomer Royal, who was the most eminent scientist in government science, and had for years given valued advice on a wide range of topics. He had reported to Goulburn that Babbage's machine was 'worthless'. Babbage and Airy had conflicting views, which led to bitter controversies.

In the course of one of these, the astronomer Richard Sheep-shanks, the friend of Airy and de Morgan, expounded the reasons for the contrast between the influence of Babbage and of Airy in government circles. He said that Babbage had a 'quarrelsome and spiteful temper', the 'blundering pertinacity' of 'a diseased mind', and 'implacable hatred'. He knew 'nothing of character', and 'his vanity led him to wish for interviews', because he believed in his powers of personal persuasion. He was useless on committees because he was 'always striving to be original'. His enemies deemed him 'a crotchety, impractical, disappointed, cantankerous fellow'.

In contrast, 'When Mr Airy wants to carry anything into effect by Government assistance, he states clearly and briefly, why he wants it; and what is the probable expense: he also engages to direct and superintend the execution, making himself personally responsible, and giving his labour gratis. When he has obtained permission (which is very seldom refused), he arranges everything with extraordinary promptitude and fore-sight, conquers his difficulties by storm, and presents his results and his accounts in perfect order, before men like Mr Babbage or myself, would have made up our minds about the prelimi-naries. Now men in office naturally like persons of this stamp. There is no trouble, no responsibility, no delay, no inquiries in the House; the matter is done, paid for, and published, before the seekers of a grievance can find an opportunity to be heard. This mode of proceeding is better relished by busy statesmen, than recommendations from influential noblemen or fashionable ladies.'

Airy was extremely industrious, and gave much prompt and good advice. He strove to keep all scientific advising of the Government in his own hands. Unfortunately, while generally right on ordinary problems, he was apt to be wrong on major matters, such as Babbage's machine, Adams's discovery of the planet *Neptune*, and Faraday's theory of light as electrical vibrations. His friends appreciated his efficiency and helpfulness, but underestimated his lack of intuition.

For Babbage, Airy was the embodiment of reaction in science. But there may also have been additional causes of his antagonism. Airy was a friend of Sheepshanks. The hatred between Babbage and Sheepshanks was extraordinary. Babbage has generally been blamed for this, as a man impossible to get on with. However, R. S. Hutton has related an amusing story of Rutherford, very characteristic of his interest in common humanity, which may throw some light on this antagonism.

Hutton happened to call on Rutherford one evening, and found him checking off the names of fellows of the Royal Society two generations before his own. When asked what he was doing, he said that he had recently read the autobiography of Mrs H. M. Swanwick, in which she had mentioned that her mother was the natural-born daughter of a fellow of Trinity, whose bust was in Trinity Library, and had had something to do with standards of weights and measures. This had aroused Rutherford's curiosity. He had examined the busts in the library, but had been unable to identify the one referred to. This had whetted his detective instinct. He busily studied the Royal Society records, and presently discovered that the ancestor must have been the Reverend Richard Sheepshanks. In his day, it had been impossible for a man to retain his fellowship on marriage, so 'all was explained'.

Sheepshanks was the son of a wealthy Bradford wool merchant, and was a generous benefactor both to astronomy and to Trinity College. Evidently, in the days of Babbage and Sheepshanks, the lives of fellows of Trinity had their complications, which may have injected an emotional intensity into differences on technical matters not otherwise easily intelligible.

Sheepshanks had smuggled an astronomical instrument through the customs in order to save trouble. Babbage harped on this delinquency, especially in a clergyman. Perhaps he was implicitly getting at him on other grounds, too. At any rate, Sheepshanks's animadversions on Babbage need to be taken with caution.

In 1852 Babbage tried once more to secure Government finance for the construction of his machine. He was ardently supported by the Earl of Rosse, the eminent astronomer, and President of the Royal Society. Rosse, who had solved the difficult engineering problems in the construction of his great reflecting telescope, was particularly well-qualified to express opinions on scientific machinery.

Again the application was rejected. Disraeli, the Chancellor of the Exchequer, was prompted to report 'that Mr Babbage's projects appear to be so indefinitely expensive, the ultimate success so problematical, and the expenditure certainly so large and so utterly incapable of being calculated, that the Government would not be justified in taking upon itself any further liability'.

Rosse in his Anniversary Address to the Royal Society in 1854 commented: 'That the first great effort to employ the powers of calculating mechanism, in aid of the human intellect, should have been suffered in this great country to expire fruitless, because there was no tangible evidence of immediate profit, as a British subject I deeply regret, and as a Fellow my regret is accompanied with feelings of bitter disappointment.'

As for Babbage, he forecast that if 'any man shall undertake and shall succeed in really constructing an engine embodying in itself the whole of the executive department of mathematical analysis upon different principles or by simple mechanical means, I have no fear of leaving my reputation in his charge, for he alone will be fully able to appreciate the nature of my efforts and the value of their results'.

When the exigencies of the Second World War forced the development of the computer, Babbage's forecast was triumphantly vindicated.

Babbage's inventive genius was not concentrated merely in a single direction. His interest in machinery and political economy drew him into railway engineering. Isambard Kingdom Brunel consulted him on the measurement of forces in running trains. Babbage invented the dynamometer car for this purpose, with instruments for continuous simultaneous recording of up to twelve different forces. He demonstrated that vibration was reduced by the broad gauge. He invented the cow-catcher, and was present at the opening of the Liverpool and Manchester Railway, when Huskisson was killed. He proposed continuously moving causeways, and sliding trains.

He was particularly proud of inventing a lighthouse lamp with a device by which it could be covered and uncovered; in this way, the lighthouse could be made to signal its identity, so that mariners could recognize it and confirm where they were. He was asked for particulars of the invention by several governments, and shortly afterwards the Russians used the principle in signalling from Sebastopol when it was besieged in the Crimean War.

Among his other inventions were the use of mirrors for indirect sighting of gunfire; rockets for boosting projectiles; spotlights in theatres, and an ophthalmoscope.

Babbage, in spite of his fierce scientific controversies, had an active social life, even though a large part of it was extinguished by the death of his wife. He went to champagne parties in Park Lane, enjoyed the company of educated ladies, and the conversation of Hallam, Rogers, and other scholarly friends.

His sons Henry Prevost, Benjamin Herschel, and Dugald Bromhead Babbage survived him. Benjamin and Henry used to help him in his experiments. Henry was educated at University College, London, and became a major-general. He worked and wrote on his father's machines, and died in 1918 in his ninety-fourth year. Benjamin became a geologist, and worked on the survey of Western Australia.

Babbage died on 18 October 1871 in Marylebone, London. He bequeathed £1,000 to Benjamin; his machines, tools, models and drawings to Henry, and after a few bequests, equal shares of the remainder of his estate of about £40,000 to his three sons.

ORGANIZERS

WALTER MORLEY FLETCHER
1873-1933

I

A CLEAR-CUT ORGANIZER

THE British Government's reorganization of its system of scientific research, carried out in 1964, made big changes in some branches, but retained and extended that existing in others. Foremost among the latter was the Medical Research Council. Indeed, the method of organizing government research which had been developed particularly in the field of medicine was extended to the physical sciences, through the creation of the new Science Research Council, while the old organization for Scientific and Industrial Research was dissolved, and most of its laboratories incorporated in the new Ministry of Technology.

This indicated that, after some fifty years of experience, since the research organizations had been founded, it had been concluded that the form of organization of research evolved by the Medical Research Council had special merit, while that of the Department of Scientific and Industrial Research required substantial transformation.

The Medical Research Council was effectively established by its first Secretary, Walter Morley Fletcher. The outcome of the Council's work proved that the methods of organizing research which he elaborated have commanded lasting approval.

An early concrete illustration of the success of these methods was the conversion of the great discovery of insulin into a major medical remedy. The lines on which this was done were followed by the Council twenty years later in performing the same service for penicillin. The Medical Research Council supported much of the original research on vitamins, and made a large contribution to the revolution of scientific and public knowledge of nutrition.

Besides the promotion of many other important researches, it helped the universities to obtain new laboratories, such as those for biochemistry at Cambridge and pathology at Oxford, which, under the leadership of F. G. Hopkins and H. Florey respectively, became world-famous schools of their subjects. Following this tradition, the Medical Research Council has in the 1960's founded its Institute of Molecular Biology at Cambridge, regarded by many as the foremost British scientific research laboratory of the day.

There is now a list of Nobel Laureates, from Hopkins and Florey to Perutz and Crick, who have been supported or assisted by the Council, and whose discoveries have confirmed the fruitfulness of its policy and judgment.

Walter Morley Fletcher accordingly appears as an outstanding example of the significant type of organizing scientist, who can recognize talent, and secure the means through which it becomes fruitful. His life and activities will be examined in order to identify the qualities and conditions which enabled him to make such a notable contribution to the organization of scientific research.

He was a tall man of six feet two inches, who walked in a manner that at once made a decisive impression. His head was long, with a large bald brow; he had bright penetrating grey-blue eyes, set close together owing to his rather narrow face. His chin was determined and his mouth thin-lipped. Underneath his lively, intelligent expression, there was a certain grimness. Altogether, he appeared formidable, especially when he kept his natural eagerness and high self-opinion under firm control. He was apt to offer unsought advice, which some regarded as arrogant. He came to believe in the innate superiority of some men, which entitled them to rule, and he admired those who by birth and inclination were Tory in their social views. Admirers who were well qualified to judge his achievements, such as the American physiologist A. N. Richards, described him as an aristocrat in science, solely concerned with quality.

Morley Fletcher had a high potential for upsetting people; yet, in spite of this, he accomplished a major achievement in the organization of research, which involved dealing with a wide range of personalities and professions. In particular, he had to deal with the medical profession, which has a long and strong tradition of independence. He fought successfully the efforts of the doctors to bring medical research under the control of the Royal College of Physicians. Among the factors that helped him in this, besides his own ability, was the support of scientists of genius, in particular of F. Gowland Hopkins.

While fending off control by the clinicians, and that aspect of medicine represented by Harley Street, he nevertheless made use of the tradition of independence in the medical profession to strengthen and protect the independence of those engaged in medical research.

The organization he created became particularly notable for the high quality of the research workers it supported, and the agreeableness of their scientific working conditions. They were subjected to the minimum of administrative routine, which enabled Morley Fletcher's organization to spend the maximum on supporting researches, and the minimum on administration. Among other qualities, his achievement also depended on his scientific ability, which secured the respect of men of genius.

He was a keen judge and passionate admirer of talent. He had the capability and energy to provide it with appropriate support. He also had good fortune. Some of the difficulties in creating a state organization of medical research which he was least well equipped by nature to deal with, were solved for him by the pressure of historical and social circumstances arising out of the First World War.

II

NONCONFORMIST DESCENT

Walter Morley Fletcher was born in Liverpool on 21 July 1873. Both his parents were descended from generations of Nonconformists and Puritans, with their traditions of independence, energy, and attachment to principles. His grandfather David Fletcher kept a school for boys, which he conducted on enlightened lines at Denmark Hill. He had married Elizabeth, one of the two celebrated Evans sisters of Ottery St Mary in Devon. Coleridge had been among the suitors of the other. The Fletchers had two daughters and three sons. The daughters started a school for boys at Brighton, to which their little nephew Walter Morley Fletcher was later sent.

All of David Fletcher's three sons acquired intellectual interests. One of them became an engineer, and built a steam road-car, which he drove from Reading to Maidenhead as early as 1843. Alfred, the father of Walter Morley Fletcher, showed aptitude in mathematics and science. In those days, Cambridge was by far the most prominent English university in mathematical science, and it would have been natural for Alfred to have proceeded there for a higher education. But being unable as a Nonconformist to sign the Thirty-Nine Articles, which was still required of all who entered the ancient universities, he could not.

He accordingly went to the University College in London, where he was most influenced by the teaching of Augustus de Morgan in mathematics, and of A. W. Hofmann in chemistry. He was a brilliant student. He won the Gold Medal for Chemistry in 1851, Henry Roscoe being second, and Frederick Abel still lower down.

The year 1851 was very significant for Alfred Fletcher's science, but it was to prove still more so for his life. The opening of the Great Exhibition brought to London hundreds of thousands of visitors. Among these were Mr Richard Morley of Leeds and his daughter Sarah, who stayed with their friends, the Fletchers. Mr Morley was the manager of a large cloth factory, a solid Yorkshire Nonconformist. Sarah was a cousin of H. H. Asquith, the prime minister. She fell in love with Alfred, and they were married in 1854.

Alfred Fletcher entered the new aniline dye industry started by the eighteen-year-old William Henry Perkin in 1856. This crucial development marked the foundation of the modern chemical industry, with its profound social as well as scientific implications. It was, however, not easily achieved. The new scientific industry presented difficult practical as well as scientifice problems. Alfred Fletcher found himself unable to cope with the former, and was compelled to find other work. He became Chemistry Inspector of the Local Government Board in the Liverpool District, and in 1884 Chief Inspector for the country, with his headquarters in London.

Alfred Fletcher was a charming man of many gifts. He had remarkable physique besides intellectual ability, and he lived to the age of ninety-four. But he was not very practical in life as well as in business. He and his young wife immediately embarked on a large family. She had a temporary mental breakdown through over-frequent child-bearing, but recovered to live beyond the age of ninety. The Fletchers had no fewer than ten children, six of whom were strapping sons, Walter being the youngest. He came of parents with enduring physique, as well as intellectual ability.

Sarah Fletcher as a Yorkshire Morley was more practical, and had more than the usual share of the family management. Her husband's salary was small in proportion to his responsibilities, and both were worried by financial stringencies.

Alfred Fletcher's keen scientific interests were a natural encouragement to any scientific bent in his children. He took pleasure in explaining scientific matters, and he had a small laboratory in his house. His second son Herbert responded to this environment. He studied chemistry and won a scholarship at Trinity College in Cambridge. Here he came under the influence of Michael Foster. He transferred from chemistry to physiology, and prepared to study medicine. He was awarded a blue for running, and was President of the Cambridge Athletic Club. Later he became Chief Physician of St Bartholomew's Hospital.

Walter Morley Fletcher had before him the splendid example of this elder brother, whom he passionately desired to emulate. He was also much influenced by a strong-minded elder sister, who became a noted missionary in India, and probably helped to impress in him the confidence in the intellectual capacity of women, which became conspicuous in his support for women in scientific research.

As a small boy, his energy and strength were already evident, and he exhibited a passion for collecting odds and ends which rapidly developed into his own little museum. When his father moved to London in 1884, he took a large house in Gordon Square, and Walter, now aged eleven, was able to have a whole room for his museum. His father increased his collection by such items as the skull of a baby.

After attending his aunts' school in Brighton, he was sent to University College School, where Michael Foster had been a pupil forty years before. His education at this school was unusually wide and thorough. He maintained his museum, and he witnessed with passionate pride his brother Herbert winning races for Cambridge, and ensuring the defeat of Oxford.

He kept a diary which exhibited intense interest in collecting, natural history, conjuring, and general scientific reading. He attended scientific lectures and explored the Zoo and the London Museum. During the holidays he went on strenuous bicycle tours. As he became a more senior schoolboy, he began to imitate his brother Herbert's running. He worked hard at science, and conceived the project of following him as a scholar to Trinity College.

He added to his natural history collecting an energetic new interest in genealogies and family histories. He investigated the pedigrees of the Fletchers and Morleys in detail, and retained this interest. Then he took to making rubbings of church brasses. Later on, he collected old playing cards, books and furniture.

In 1891 he competed for a scholarship at Trinity College, following in his elder brother's path. He travelled to Cambridge, where his father met him at the station. In the cab they took to

drive to Trinity, his father told him he would find it very difficult
to support him if he did not get a scholarship or at the very least
a subsizarship, the lowest rank of scholarship. He shattered
Walter's nerve by querying the wisdom of his going to Cambridge at all, and said that he could secure him a job as a dentist's
apprentice, which would enable him at once to earn a living,
and put him in the way of a comfortable career.

It was not surprising that, after this lack of imaginative understanding by his father, Walter was suddenly taken ill, after his
first papers, with a severe attack of erysipelas, and could not
take any more papers. This was not the only occasion on which
he became ill in examinations; he was evidently highly strung.
He had always exhibited an intense, energetic activity, liable to
be accompanied by a stutter when he was excited. Such experiences as that in the cab between Cambridge station and
Trinity may have heightened his natural emotional tension.

Walter had, however, sufficiently impressed the Trinity examiners to be awarded a subsizarship, in spite of sitting only one
day of the examinations. His father, who could scarcely have
understood what a shock he must have given him, especially
with the talk about money, now sent him on a holiday to Turkey
for the good of his health.

Walter Morley Fletcher seemed to develop ambivalent
qualities in his personality, on the one hand a passionate interest
in his ancestral traditions, and on the other, an even more passionate desire to escape from them.

III

CONFORMIST ASCENT

Walter Morley Fletcher went up to Trinity in 1891, desperately
intent on securing a place in that majestic institution. He identified himself with every whisper of its tradition, and each stone
and beam of its structure. The College never had a more devoted
son, and in the last days of his life his eyes continually returned
to a photograph of the Great Court in May sunshine.

Like his elder brother Herbert, he attached himself to Michael
Foster's school of physiology. He worked for his science degree
with physiology as his chief subject. He was very hard up, and
kept himself for his last two years by coaching.

Fletcher became a confirmed member of the Church of England, thus relinquishing his Nonconformist tradition. He became
an ardent supporter of compulsory College chapel service.

He found friends among young Trinity gentlemen, and members of well-known families, such as the Wedgwoods. He followed his brother in athletics, and became a good hurdler. Through his athletic friends he was introduced to Montague James, then Dean of King's and Director of the Fitzwilliam Museum, and later Provost of Eton and author of ghost stories. James became one of his closest friends. They shared antiquarian hobbies, and also a certain juvenility.

Fletcher developed a passionate regard for Eton. He even tried to become a master there, fortunately without success. He sometimes astonished people in later life by giving the impression that he felt his lack of a public-school education, and in particular one at Eton, was a personal disaster. This was all the more striking, because his real education at University College School could scarcely have been better.

In 1894–95 he completed his Cambridge degree, securing a first-class in physiology. He was engaged as a coach to Robin Strutt, a nephew of A. J. Balfour, and was delighted with the acquaintance and society of that statesman and his family. In the following year, he coached the son of Lord Rothschild, and was impressed by the magnificence of the surroundings at Tring.

Fletcher grew delighted with educated high society. Some of his later critics felt that he suffered from a social inferiority complex. No doubt it was connected with the repressions of his early nonconformity. He appeared to feel that life had done him an injury in not placing him by birth in the rank of society to which he believed that he naturally belonged.

Fletcher was elected to the Coutts Trotter studentship in 1896, which gave him a clear year for research. J. N. Langley suggested an investigation of the anatomy of sympathetic nerves, which he carried out. However, Fletcher had a bias towards chemistry, which he had acquired from his father. He asked Michael Foster whether he thought that there was any future in the application of chemistry to physiology. At this enquiry, Foster rolled his large beard over his mouth with both hands, to smother his hilarity.

Reassured, Fletcher determined to pursue this line. Now it happened that the botanist F. F. Blackman had recently invented a sensitive apparatus for measuring the gases emitted and absorbed by the leaves of plants. With this apparatus, it had become possible to measure the output of carbon dioxide at frequent intervals, and trace variations in the rate of output. This permitted the measurement over a considerable period of time, not merely of the total quantity of carbon dioxide emitted, but to elucidate the mode of output.

Fletcher determined to use an apparatus of this kind for elucidating the way in which carbon dioxide and other substances were emitted in living muscle. He applied the Blackman technique for studying plant respiration to the investigation of respiration in animal tissue.

During the previous half-century, an elaborate theory of respiration in muscle had been propounded by Liebig and other eminent German chemists and physiologists. According to it, when a muscle contracted, it emitted a burst of carbon dioxide. Fletcher found that on the contrary, there was no emission of carbon dioxide unless the muscle was repeatedly stimulated.

The results in his first paper on the subject disproved an important accepted theory, and were of fundamental importance. He was able to offer this splendid work in his thesis for a fellowship of Trinity. His year was a particularly difficult one, for the College was offering only two instead of the usual four fellowships, and these were to cover the arts as well as the sciences. As a candidate for a fellowship, Fletcher was also in the very unusual position of not being a scholar of the College, owing to his misfortune in the entrance scholarship examination.

In order to safeguard his future, he decided to compete for a scholarship at St Bartholomew's Hospital, to enable him to qualify as a medical doctor. He had to take this examination in London, and some written papers in Cambridge in the Trinity fellowship examination, during the same week, travelling from one city to the other to sit for the papers.

He was successful in the hospital examination, so he knew that, whatever might happen to the Trinity fellowship, a medical career was open to him. With feelings of the deepest nauseating despondency he awaited the result of the fellowship election.

Presently he heard that he had been one of the two successful candidates, in spite of the severe competition, and his lack of standing. He was transported with joy. His classical discovery had carried him past all obstacles. There were scientists in Trinity who could justly assess what he had offered. He became a fellow of Trinity in 1897, at an inspiring period in the College's history, when J. J. Thomson, J. N. Langley, Bertrand Russell, A. N. Whitehead and others were at the height of their powers. This was a crucial factor in giving Fletcher his strong sense of quality in science.

He now settled down to his fellowship, entering into every

detail of the college life and tradition, and finding in these the satisfaction of deep emotions.

Nevertheless, at the same time, he travelled up to London three times a week to St Bartholomew's Hospital, to take his clinical training for a medical degree. This he acquired in 1900. This clinical training proved of great value to him when medical research came under his charge. It helped him in dealing with the clinicians in the difficult problems that arise in relations between clinical medicine and medical research.

He continued his researches on the chemistry of muscle, though his medical and numerous college activities prevented him from devoting more than a portion of his time to it. He made progress, but it was hardly to be expected that he would immediately obtain new results as important as his first.

He became busily engaged in College lecturing, and the direction of medical and science students, and in 1903 was appointed Senior Demonstrator in Physiology in the University.

Among the young don's many undergraduate friends was James W. Cropper, the son of a Westmorland gentleman descended from a Liverpool Quaker family of shipowners and traders. The Croppers, who claimed a relationship with John Knox, had been associated with the Macaulay family in their Liverpool days in the struggle against the slave trade. This connection was followed by one with the Macaulay's relatives, the Trevelyans, who became prominent as historians, and in Trinity College.

The Croppers had long since joined the Church of England, but they still preserved links with many of the great Quaker families, such as the Peases, Frys and Hodgkins.

James Cropper sought Fletcher's help in obtaining partners for members of the family party which he brought to a Trinity ball, the last in the nineteenth century, to be held in the Backs, the gardens beside the river behind the colleges. Fletcher became acquainted with his sisters.

He presently became engaged to Maisie Cropper, and five years later, in 1904, they were married. Fletcher now needed an adequately paid position.

In 1905 he was appointed one of the three tutors of Trinity College. As such, the moral and general welfare of about two hundred students were in his charge. The appointment was for ten years, of high standing, but very demanding. It was the kind of post which might fit a man to be a master of a college, but left not much time and energy for such exacting work as fundamental research. He did not drop research, but he was unable to complete the most famous piece in which he ever participated, until he had secured the collaboration of another scientist even more gifted in research.

A Trinity tutor had much administrative work, and it was desirable that he should be sympathetic to the varied interests of undergraduates, who might be studying in any field of art or science, or scarcely studying at all. Fletcher possessed the administrative energy and skill, and perhaps shared even too much in the interests of the young. In addition to his research and his strenuous college tutor's life, he was deeply interested in, and worked hard for, the University Pitt Club, of which he was President from 1905 until 1914. He wrote a history of this institution, which was completed by his son, and published in 1935, on the centenary of its foundation.

The club was one of many founded in the earlier decades of the nineteenth century, in honour of the younger William Pitt. These clubs rallied Conservatism, especially after the Reform Bill of 1832. The University Pitt Club at Cambridge was regarded by its early members as a means of ensuring the return to Parliament of Conservative instead of Radical members for the town of Cambridge.

In the early days the propriety of its methods was sometimes questioned. For example, in 1843 Sir Robert Peel found it necessary to write to his son, who was a member, enquiring about an accusation of bribery, expressing his confidence that he would never have been associated with anything of that kind.

In his book, Fletcher wrote that although, since 1868 at latest, the Pitt Club had 'ceased from all political activities and has elected members to its social advantage without any regard whatever to considerations of political party, the tradition has always been preserved that the Club was originally formed to unite undergraduates attached to the Conservative party by birth or inclination, and to promote the party interests'. As T. R. Elliott put it, the Pitt Club was 'an undergraduate society which selected its entry on principles that were emphatically not proletarian'.

This set of social ideas was in contrast with those of his Nonconformist ancestors, and contained in themselves contradictions which may have reflected the contradictions of nonconformity and conformity within himself. He held Tory ideas, conceived with the sharp clarity of Puritan principles, and propelled by an inexhaustible nonconformist energy.

In the decade before the outbreak of the First World War, Fletcher had become deeply identified with Trinity College, and its extensive connections in science and society. He had been joined through marriage with the gentry of Quaker descent. In addition to his own scientific research, small in quantity but high in quality, he had had experience of academic and scientific administration, and extensive contact through a wide social network with many influential elements in English society. His scientific and his social connections were both strong, and of equal weight.

IV

SOCIAL POWER AND SCIENTIFIC GENIUS

Fletcher had by his great capability and energy established his position in Cambridge. He now used his position to assist a scientist of the first order, who in turn assisted him to major achievements which he would probably not otherwise have accomplished.

The Cambridge school of physiology had been founded by Michael Foster, who had little talent for research himself, but an outstanding gift for recognizing and encouraging genius. In 1898 he invited Frederick Gowland Hopkins to come to Cambridge and undertake teaching and research in chemical physiology.

Hopkins had grown up outside the university system. He had learned his chemical techniques as a technical assistant in the private laboratory of a chemical consultant, who made analyses of urine for hospitals, and of poisons in murder trials. Hopkins applied the high skill he had acquired in analysis to highly original elucidation of chemical problems of biological significance, such as the colour of insects, and the bearing of the chemical composition of excrement on the theory of evolution.

He did not take a medical degree until he was thirty-four, and when he accepted Foster's invitation, he arrived in Cambridge at the age of thirty-seven, without any experience of the Cambridge teaching system, or indeed of any university teaching system. In order to secure an adequate income, he had to undertake the supervision of the medical students at Emmanuel College. He set about learning the courses and texts he was supposed to teach. He sat up until the early hours of the morning, swotting at the details, with his wife beside him to see that the fire did not go out.

Hopkins struggled with the teaching and supervision for years, exhausting himself, distracted from research, and depressed in spirit. In this distressing situation, Morley Fletcher gave Hopkins, twelve years his senior in age, but without his command of university teaching procedure, crucial academic support.

Hopkins said that when he went to Cambridge in 1898, he had been struck by a paper which he had read earlier in the year on the respiration of surviving frog muscle. He had looked forward to meeting the author, Walter Morley Fletcher, who, he felt sure, must possess remarkable qualities as an investigator. His results illuminated a fundamental question in biology, the relations in time between the active manifestations of life, and the processes of oxidation which supplied the energy for those manifestations.

His results disproved the obscurantist theory concerning these relations, which had inhibited both thought and experimental investigation. It had come to be believed that chemistry was too blunt an instrument for the elucidation of *active* events in living tissues. Morley Fletcher's results showed that this was untrue, and the effects of his discovery, that chemistry could indeed be effective in elucidating the activity in living tissues, was still being felt nearly half a century later.

Hopkins 'soon felt the spell of his very exceptional and magnetic personality', and hoped to tempt him into biochemistry, but he presently realized that Morley Fletcher could never 'be completely happy in the narrows of specialism'. However, in 1907 Hopkins joined Morley Fletcher in a chemical investigation that followed from his first paper, which had become classical. They made a precise investigation of the appearance and disappearance of lactic acid in muscle, a phenomenon which had been the longest known chemical event associated with changes in muscle.

Spallanzani in 1803 and Liebig in 1850 had shown that muscle could contract and relax in the absence of oxygen, and it had also been shown that lactic acid was produced by fatigued or dying muscle. Hermann in 1877 propounded a theory of these phenomena, based on a hypothetical giant molecule in muscle, which he called 'inogen'. Verworen produced a similar theory, based on another hypothetical molecule which he called 'biogen'. It was supposed that the behaviour of muscle could not be analysed beyond these hypothetical giant molecules, which were assumed to be too complex to be susceptible to current methods of chemical analysis.

With Hopkins's collaboration, Morley Fletcher was able, by 1907, to identify more precisely the roles of oxygen, carbon dioxide and lactic acid in the contraction and recovery of living muscle.

This paper is regarded by many as the beginning of modern biochemistry. It completed the revolution begun by Morley Fletcher's first paper. It showed that life is a complicated chemical symphony based on a few chemical themes, not a simple symphony based on a few unanalysable giant molecules peculiar to living processes.

The addition of Hopkins's genius to Fletcher's own heroic efforts to continue research in addition to intense tutorial and College activities had produced this fundamental result. Hopkins himself published in 1910 his famous paper demonstrating the existence of what he called *accessory food factors*, now known as vitamins.

Hopkins all this time, since his arrival in 1898, had been working away at the treadmill of unsuitable academic teaching. He now suffered a nervous breakdown, brought on also by a fall in his uncomfortable and inadequate laboratory, in which he dashed his head against an iron spiral staircase.

By this time, Morley Fletcher had been a tutor of Trinity for six years, and had become an influential member of the College. He was shocked by these events, and especially by the comments of some who believed that Hopkins, who was now forty-nine years old, was worn out and had come to the end of his research career.

Fletcher wrote a magnificent letter to the council of his college, pointing out that Trinity had not been giving the University as much financial assistance as formerly, and a recent Report indicating that a chair of biochemistry should be founded, provided the College with the opportunity of rectifying this failure. He said that perhaps all the chief problems in physiology, pathology, pharmacology, therapeutics, agriculture, embryology, and genetics were waiting upon progress in this new branch of chemistry for their solution. Cambridge had the man who was most fitted to lead this development, but his position was ludicrous, if not scandalous, for he was sterilized for research by the excessive teaching that was demanded of him, in order to secure an adequate income. He suggested that Trinity should offer him a Praelectorship and Fellowship which would provide him with the proper conditions for research, until such time as the University founded a chair of biochemistry.

Morley Fletcher personally explained to everyone prepared to listen the immense importance of this proposal, and the College finally accepted it. He immediately sent the news to Hopkins at Felixstowe, where he had gone to try to recover his health.

Hopkins replied that he was still too invalid to find adequate words to express his feelings. Nevertheless, he composed a beautiful letter, in which he described the news as astounding, and filling him with many emotions. He was glad to have received it through him, to whom he had owed so much kindness, and he saw his hand in 'this most astonishing consummation'.

The Master of Trinity, Dr Montagu Butler, received many congratulations on this splendid action which rescued the greatest biochemist of the age, and helped to ensure him thirty-seven more years of major leadership in science. Butler sent them all to Morley Fletcher as 'their proper owner, or at least custodian'.

So Morley Fletcher had used his scientific and social power on behalf of scientific genius.

V

STATE RESPONSIBILITY FOR THE PEOPLE'S HEALTH

The National Insurance Act introduced by Lloyd George in 1911 marked a turning point in British history. It provided a large section of the working population between certain ages and within a certain range of means, with some insurance against ill-health. The Act signalled the retreat of private enterprise in the realm of health, and it led immediately to the foundation of two technical services.

The first was the Tuberculosis Service, which did much to mitigate this terrible disease in Great Britain. The second was the state organization of medical research, which arose out of a clause of the Act, providing that one penny per annum for each insured person should be devoted to medical research. The original aim was that the funds so collected should be devoted to research on the prevention and cure of tuberculosis, in order to reduce the vast expenditure that was foreseen on tuberculous patients.

Largely owing to the efforts of Christopher Addison, the distinguished anatomist, doctor and statesman, who had assisted and advised Lloyd George in the drafting of the medical aspects of the Act, this aim was widened to research bearing on 'any disease to which insured persons are subject'.

WALTER MORLEY FLETCHER

The clause provided, even in the first year, the then very considerable sum of £57,000 for research. The policy for utilizing the fund had not been worked out, so in 1913 a properly con-constituted Medical Research Committee was formed to administer it. Hopkins said that the chief credit for this crucial decision was due to Lord Astor, Dr Addison himself, and the civil servant Sir Robert Morant. The eminent patent lawyer and scientist, Lord Moulton, was made chairman. A council of some forty medical men was formed to advise the Committee.

The members of the Committee were all busy men, and could give only limited time to its affairs. At first it met in Moulton's house, and conducted its business after being magnificently entertained to dinner by the Chairman. The circumstances were exceedingly pleasant, and the proceedings very informal. They soon drifted into interesting but academic discussions, in which everyone expressed his opinions, but decisions were few and vague. Most of the members began acutely to feel the need for more formality, and the services of an administrative officer.

Even those who agreed on the need were slow to agree on the type of officer required. Some thought the post should be purely secretarial, and that a trained civil servant would be most suitable; others were in favour of able personalities not necessarily possessing much knowledge of the spirit and needs of scientific research; there were even those who thought that the post might be part-time.

Hopkins and some other members of the Committee began to suffer 'real and grave discomfort' while the appointment was in suspense. It seemed as if an ideal appointment would be impossible. Looking back on the time, Hopkins said that it could now be seen that 'the future of medical research in this country was then facing a critical moment'.

In the course of anxious discussions as to who should be proposed for the post, T. R. Elliott, who had worked in physiology at Cambridge and knew Morley Fletcher well, suggested to Hopkins that he should be considered. Hopkins regretted that he had not thought of this himself, and immediately proposed him to Moulton, who was already aware of Morley Fletcher's scientific reputation. Moulton asked Hopkins to sound him.

The proposal came to Morley Fletcher at a very good moment, as his ten years' appointment as a Trinity tutor was drawing to its end. As Hopkins said, 'fate was preparing for him an opportunity for services to science, which, though indirect, were to be not less, but greater, than any individual investigator could

hope to render'. He discovered that Morley Fletcher would indeed be prepared to accept the appointment. He brought Moulton and Fletcher together in his own house, and it was then
agreed that Morley Fletcher's name should go forward.

Thus the most important figure in deciding the kind of man
who was to organize medical research in Britain was Hopkins,
and the most important circumstance was the personal relationship between them. Hopkins felt that he owed his later scientific
life, and almost his later life itself, to Morley Fletcher's support
in Trinity. He had come to appreciate his qualities both as a
scientific investigator, and a man of judgment and action.

Morley Fletcher was appointed Secretary of the Medical
Research Committee in the spring of 1914. The Committee was
attached to the National Health Insurance Commission, which
had been set up to carry out the Act. Its chairman was Sir Robert
Morant, who acquired the reputation of being one of the most
creative, forceful and dextrous of civil servants in all that service's
history. He was a tall, muscular man, who had been poor in his
youth, and had concentrated at Oxford on theology and boxing,
in both of which he excelled. After teaching in a preparatory
school he became tutor to the nephews of the King of Siam. His
immense ability and energy led him into the creation of the
educational system of that country, but they also aroused opposition, which caused him to retire to England in 1894, at the age
of thirty-one. He joined the Education Department in the
following year. He worked out the plans for the Education Act
of 1902, which involved the incorporation of many contrasting
and sometimes conflicting elements. He welded these together
by constructive organization, which he carried through by persuasion, guile and force, exercised with inexhaustible energy.

He launched the British state insurance system, and when the
Ministry of Health was founded in 1919, he became its first
Permanent Secretary. It was said of him that he found no idea
too big, and no detail too small, for his attention. He was inclined
to be unorthodox, impatient of opposition, and suspicious, but
never shrank from criticism when challenged.

Morant and Morley Fletcher were both big, very able and
self-confident men, whose psychology as well as physique had
some things in common. They understood and appreciated each
other.

When Morley Fletcher left Trinity College to be Secretary of
the Medical Research Committee, he found its policy vague, and
subject to lobbying from many quarters, good and bad. It had been

decided to found a Medical Research Institute, but there was little agreement about its form, and still less about the nature of its research activities. The situation was chaotic, and Morley Fletcher was without experience of government administration. Even his salary was not, at first, more than his income had been at Trinity. It would have been far from surprising if he had taken the first opportunity for returning to Cambridge.

Morant's presence and example encouraged him to remain, and cope with the severe difficulties of creating a medical research organization. They also confirmed him in his own inclination to create an administration according to his own ideas and under his own domination. Like Morant, he dealt personally with big ideas and small details. He preferred to have the fewest possible staff, and do as much as he could himself. His collaboration with Morant strengthened a tendency which had already become habitual during his busy Trinity tutorship.

He started his first office in Westminster with a staff of one clerk, a personal secretary and a couple of typists. The government medical research organization has ever since retained this feature of exceptionally small administrative cost, in comparison with expenditure on research.

VI

THE FIRST WORLD WAR

Morley Fletcher plunged immediately into the problem of finding a proper working relationship with the existing Lister Institute for Preventive Medicine. Within a few days he went to one of Moulton's dinners, attended by thirty-five scientists, ranging from Marconi to Sherrington. He lunched and argued for hours with Almroth Wright, and had tea and argument with Moulton. He dined with Astor, Addison and Morant at the House of Commons, met other members, and persuaded them to agree to new proposals which would ease negotiations.

Afterwards he smoked with Morant on the Terrace, where John Burns, the President of the Board of Trade, joined them. He had a fierce discussion with Burns about babies, milk, and the health of the working classes. He found that Burns spoke with the diffuseness of the half-educated, was very vain, and would be an 'infernal bore' to meet more than once. Then he and Starling and Dale dined together for further discussions on the Lister Institute.

Such was the maze of negotiations in which he had at once

become involved. It looked as if the unravelling of the administrative knots under the leisurely conditions of the period, which Moulton's dinners typified, would take many years.

Before Morley Fletcher had been in his post more than a few weeks, the situation was suddenly changed by the outbreak of the First World War. To the majority, it had been utterly unexpected, and its consequences were not foreseen. The efforts to meet its needs produced social effects that had not been sought as ends in themselves.

Morley Fletcher was particularly affected in this way. He immediately offered the help of his medical research organization to the military, to assist in the solution of their medical problems, old and new. The war created a situation where effective medical research might achieve results on a vast scale, in a form which could be quickly and profoundly appreciated.

The war also provided urgent tasks for the numerous personalities who had had so much leisure to spend on dinners and discussion, without being under any pressing need for quick results. The scores of scientists and personalities, among whom Morley Fletcher had been plunged, presently went off to undertake war duties.

He found himself left almost alone to run his new medical research organization. This was very onerous, but it gave him the opportunity of creating, with the minimum of hindrance, his own highly personal type of organization. If the pre-war conditions had continued, he might well have found the parliament of medicine, exemplified by Moulton's dinners, unmanageable and frustrating. The circumstances of the war immensely increased his administrative opportunities.

The Committee had decided to advance medical research by the foundation of central research laboratories, of which the Institute of Medical Research at Hampstead was the first; and by stimuling, and co-operating with, independent investigations in private and voluntary institutions. Hitherto, virtually all British medical research had been done in institutions of this type.

The Central Research Instititute was converted into the Hampstead Military Hospital. Its departments of bacteriology under Almroth Wright, biochemistry and pharmacology under Dale, applied physiology under Leonard Hill, and statistics under Brownlee were accommodated elsewhere, and carried out important war work in connection with inoculation, drugs, physical performance of personnel, and military medical statistics.

During the First World War trench fever, trench nephritis and *encephalitis lethargica* were clearly recognized for the first time. Morley Fletcher actively promoted their elucidation. Trench fever was investigated at the request of General Headquarters in France. In England an obscure disease appeared. Investigations promoted by the Medical Research Council provided a clear description of it, and it was subsequently identified as the *encephalitis lethargica* which had been described by von Economo in Vienna in 1917.

Morley Fletcher perceived the importance of an official history of medicine in the war, and urged that this should be undertaken. He was appointed joint honorary secretary of the War Office Committee for the Medical History of the War.

He promoted the collection of pathological specimens during the war. Two thousand five hundred of these were deposited at the Royal College of Surgeons, where, unfortunately, most of them were destroyed by bombs in the Second World War.

He arranged for an artist, A. K. Maxwell, to go to France to make drawings of new types of injuries. Maxwell's coloured drawings of the effects of gas poisoning proved particularly valuable.

He had direct access to the Director-General of the Army Medical Service, and promoted researches through him. He followed his practice of giving support to independent workers, and located officers in units in France capable of making desired observations and records of various kinds of wounds, gas poisoning, and other injuries. He promoted the keeping of far more comprehensive Field Medical Cards, which provided information for subsequent treatment, and the granting of pensions. His promotion of the collection of military medical records and statistics ensured that a large body of data would be preserved, which would provide material for future investigation.

As Hopkins remarked, he saw that 'any distinction between military or other opportunist schemes of inquiry and those formed under the less urgent stimulus of peace was of little significance, and realized the permanent value which may spring from the study of problems emerging, as in war time, from unusual and temporary conditions'. Among these were the dependence of the military performance of soldiers, and the output of munition workers, on their nutrition.

The needs of war brought general recognition of the importance of these problems, and stimulated researches which were to promote far higher standards of health and physical efficiency in peace.

In an address in 1930 to medical members of the House of Commons on the work of the Medical Research Committee, he said that 'never has there been such an opportunity for medical science as in these years of war, when the bodies of men have been subjected to every extreme of physical violence, have suffered from the attacks of all kinds of disease, and from the widest variations of climate. In a literal sense the application of medical science has been one of the fundamental essentials of our victory.'

Morley Fletcher established the power of the Medical Research Committee and his own authority during the war years of 1914 to 1918. He made his personal methods the tradition of the organization. He personally sought out the young men of talent and gave them financial support without interfering with their independence. He used his own scientific judgment in assessing people and ideas. He took a great deal upon himself, and he did not spare his efforts.

This proved to be too much even for his exceptional physique. He had a severe attack of pneumonia in 1916, which left his lungs permanently impaired, and eventually became the cause of his death in 1933, at the age of fifty-nine, which was far too early for an athletic son of parents both of whom survived beyond the age of ninety.

VII

THE MEDICAL RESEARCH COUNCIL

The Medical Research Committee emerged from the First World War with the reputation of its Secretary and his methods of organization established. The question then arose of the form in which it should continue.

The experience of the war had shown that in many directions more state action was required to improve the national condition. One of the results of this concern was the founding of the Ministry of Health in 1919, with Addison as its first Minister, and Morant as Permanent Secretary. The National Insurance Commission, to which the Medical Research Committee belonged, was to merge in the new ministry.

Morley Fletcher was disturbed at the prospect of his research organization being under the new ministry. He feared that it would then become subordinate to demands for concentration of research on immediate health problems, such as epidemics, which commanded public attention and anxiety, to the neglect of fundamental research on which major improvement of health

must, in the long run, depend. His standing with Addison and
Morant secured careful consideration of his opinion, and the
original intention of placing his Research Committee under the
new ministry was reconsidered.

Lord Haldane in a report of major importance on methods of
government administration had indicated that fundamental
scientific research should not be too closely tied to ministries
directly interested in its utilization. This principle had been
followed in 1915 in the formation of the Department of Scientific
and Industrial Research, which had been placed under the Privy
Council, and not, for example, under any of the ministries of
industry and trade.

Morley Fletcher was able to appeal to this precedent, which
was perhaps even more powerful than his own good work and
argument, in securing agreement that the Medical Research
Committee should be reconstituted as the Medical Research
Council, under the Privy Council.

This reconstitution was carried out in 1920. Morley Fletcher
was able to establish his methods and principles of organizing
medical research still more firmly. He strengthened the emphasis on the scientific aspect by securing a provision that no
scientific member of the Medical Research Council should be
appointed without prior consultation with the President of the
Royal Society.

With still more independence, more emphasis on fundamental
research, and increasing finance, Morley Fletcher supported a
splendid range of work. The Medical Research Council participated in the introduction of insulin and the effective treatment
of diabetes. It assisted the research on nutrition, the discovery
of vitamins and their chemical composition. It promoted the
elucidation and treatment of deficiency diseases such as rickets.
In 1922 Morley Fletcher began to think that 'it may be true that
cod liver oil is in a real sense "bottled sunlight".' The Council
supported Lady Mellanby's extensive researches on dental caries.
Fundamental discoveries were made in the Council's laboratories on the role of particular chemical substances in disease,
such as thyroxin.

Their scientists investigated parathormone, used in tetany;
adrenalin and ephedrin in asthma, and suprarenal extracts used
in treating Addison's disease. They were concerned in research
on salvarsan and bismuth in the treatment of syphilis, and of
antimony in bilharziasis.

Important advances were made in blood transfusion for the

treatment of surgical shock, and in research on the administration of anaesthetics.

Fundamental research by Thomas Lewis on diseases of the
heart led to the recognition of the effort syndrome. The Council
set up a unit which enabled Lewis to devote himself entirely to
research. It became the model for other units, set up to enable
other talented investigators to devote themselves without distraction to their special line of investigation.

Medawar observed in 1963 that fifty years' experience had
shown the Medical Research Committee and its successor to
have been a brilliant success. 'Now that we can weigh up their
consequences its actions and intentions seem quite remarkable
in their prescience and good sense.' He thought that most of the
credit must be given to Addison for the Committee's highly
effective administrative structure, though 'we may suspect that
Walter Morley Fletcher . . . had most to do with devising the
Committee's scientific policy'. Medawar commented on the
weight of its declarations in its fifth report at the end of the First
World War, when it held that progress in medical research must
be based on science: 'the important attainments of new knowledge come from disinterested enquiry followed under the spur
of free intellectual impulse, rather than from frontal attacks made
in a utilitarian spirit upon problems of immediate practical
interest'. There was 'a real danger lest the insistent calls given
by disease and suffering for immediate relief should actually
delay progress by attracting scientific effort along the wrong
path'.

This policy naturally drew criticism from various quarters.
Many clinicians, dealing with immediate problems, felt that it was
too detached. Indeed, Medawar observed that it is a policy not
beyond all criticism, 'some yielding to social, economic and
rudely utilitarian pressures there must be'.

By 1963 the Council had about eighty research units and
groups, 'some large and world famous, but some—a kindly observer might say—merely world famous'. The Council had aimed
mainly at the support of men and ideas, many of the units formed
from time to time had been created around one person of great
ability, and dissolved after his retirement.

By this date, the Council had a staff of 2,931, of whom 788
were scientifically qualified. Of the latter, only about thirty per
cent had medical degrees. The income of the organization had
risen from £55,000 to £6 million per annum, during the first
half-century of its existence. This illustrated the range and depth

of the scientific and medical research which Morley Fletcher
had done so much to promote.

As the organization which he built up expanded and flourished
after the First World War, he devoted more time to exposition
of his views on medicine and science, and their relation to society.

VIII

MEDICINE, SCIENCE AND SOCIETY

Morley Fletcher described in 1926 how, in his first essay in
medical practice, he had sewed up the head of an injured boy.
He was feeling pride and satisfaction in being able to help him,
and he suddenly thought how intolerable it was to receive a fee
for such a service. From that time, he believed that doctors
should receive salaries and not fees.

He was invited in 1928 to advise on the organization of medical
research in India. He visited the country's medical institutions,
and was shocked by their backwardness, and by the pompous
affectations of the British government of India. One of the few
good pieces of research he saw was by McCarrison on the nutrition of rats. McCarrison had demonstrated not only that rats
became stout and well on a good diet, but they also became
handsome and well-behaved. This research with its striking
implications had, however, received little official encouragement.

Morley Fletcher delivered a notable radio lecture in 1931, on
Biology and Statecraft, in which he observed that in spite of the
discovery of the mode of transmission of malaria, by Manson and
Ross already half a century ago, the amount of malaria in India
had increased. As for Africa, 'we have now the challenge of our
responsibilities to Africa and the African peoples, to show whether
we can repair our deficiencies in time to fulfil these. If we fail
there we may become only a small insular kingdom.' He held
that scientists in state organizations should have 'equal status,
recognition, and pay with those in charge of administrative
work'.

In an address to a Public Health Congress in 1928, he referred
to the failures as well as the triumphs of science, pointing out
that in too many directions 'the help of science is not being taken,
because science has no help to give'. For instance, science was
'still silent and unhelpful' on such common ailments as measles,
whooping-cough and mumps.

After the Industrial Revolution the bodies of men, women
and children were exposed to continuously running machinery.
11*

Employers were ready to engage the best experts to keep their
machinery in order, but did not secure expert advice on keeping
the human machine in order.

In the First World War, when great and sustained production
was a matter of life and death to the country, it was discovered
that there was no coherent knowledge readily applicable to these
problems. In the emergency the Industrial Fatigue Research
Board was set up, and started much useful investigation.

He considered that nutrition was of overwhelming importance.
'I would be so bold as to say that in the teaching of modern
science, if we had to choose between housing reform and diet
reform, diet reform ought to have the preference . . .'

In 1917–18 it had been found that one out of every three men
of military age was rated C3 or unfit for most service, while one
in ten was permanently unfit. 'If any man can walk through our
crowded industrial cities and see the workers leaving the factory;
or go to a cup-tie match and see the crowd there—if he does not
have a sinking heart at the numbers of stunted figures, poor
physiques and bad teeth he sees, I think he has no eyes.'

He did not believe that it was explicable 'in terms of race and
blood' or 'by wealth and poverty', because the differences between the physiques of the Australians, Canadians, and British,
who were of the same stock, were too large to be explained in
these terms, as also were those between different members of
the same class in each of these nations.

Morley Fletcher delivered a British Science Guild Lecture, in
which he discussed the root of medical discovery. He evidently
believed that this lay in mental ability, for he expressed surprise
that the Greeks, who had a mental equipment that had never
been surpassed, nevertheless discovered no 'effective new power
to prevent or control disease'. He thought this 'one of the un-
accountable curiosities of history'.

He quoted Bacon on how to encourage science. 'If you will
have a Tree bear more fruit that it has used to do, it is not anything you can do to the boughs, but it is the stirring of the earth
and putting new mould about the roots, that must work it.' To
turn this advice to practical effect today, 'we must consider in
respect to our scientists the primary question of recruitment, of
pay and status . . .'

He said that in his experience good young scientists were very
rarely greedy for money, but the best of them wanted to do
good service in the State, and do the best for their families. They
were very sensitive to atmosphere, and were not easily drawn to

work if it was neither valued nor trusted. As for the two ancient Universities, 'the two eyes of our English mind'—in only one of them was original research work the normal avenue to recognition and promotion.

He regarded such observations as 'frightfully' boring 'old commonplaces', but their substance is still the subject of most serious discussions in the formation of the national policy for science, in 1967, nearly forty years later.

Morley Fletcher's addresses of this period showed him an assured, imaginative and happy man. His health had never fully recovered, though he made strenuous efforts to improve it, especially by deer-stalking, which was his favourite outdoor exercise. He was delighted when his son Charles followed him in 1930 to Trinity College, and he had the deepest pride and satisfaction in his success in also following him in securing a first-class in physiology, and winning a blue. He had the great joy of watching his son row in the victorious Cambridge crew of 1933.

But two days after the race, he felt that his lung was again in bad shape. He underwent an operation, but unfortunately he survived only eight days, and died on 7 June 1933.

The Medical Research Council passed a resolution in which they said that their Secretary had brought to their service 'a unique assemblage of gifts. He had had a highly distinguished career in experimental research; he was an influential teacher of science; he possessed a culture in which scientific and humane studies were well and fruitfully balanced; and he was a master of practical affairs.' Even this equipment would not have made his management of the Council's work so effective if he had not been 'one of the most vigorous spirits' of the time. 'He was always and even painfully aware of the suffering and disorder of mankind and profoundly convinced that their root lay in ignorance.' The zeal and unmistakeable honesty of these convictions were 'the foundation of his singular power'.

His deference to conscientious work and his understanding of the difficulties peculiar to original research, his eye for ability and his wide knowledge made him the perfect intermediary between the Council and the scientists it supported, and the inspiring helper of both.

His gifts and character, which were so influential in carrying out the original policy of the Council, had provided a momentum of continuing research and discovery which would be their most lasting memorial. 'The constitutional freedom, administrative effectiveness, and general good will which have been secured are in great measure the reward of his vision and the fruit of his labour.' Such was the Council's opinion of his services.

His friend and relative, the historian and Master of Trinity, G. M. Trevelyan, said that Morley Fletcher believed he had the qualities which would have made him a successful surgeon, but he chose research. He was athletic, artistic, literary and social, and had a deep interest in the public welfare, desiring to make science subserve it. Trevelyan said that in Morley Fletcher's company he often felt ashamed of his own ignorance of science, when he observed Morley Fletcher's care for humane studies. He had his faults, but never those of omission, refusal or negation. He always spoke his mind, and his opinion counted. 'It was his merit, and sometimes his difficulty, that he combined the Puritan and the Cavalier ideals.' He never ceased to say this is right, or that is wrong, sometimes with a stutter of eagerness. He was not afraid of passing moral judgments.

Trevelyan looked forward for weeks beforehand to an hour with him. Morley Fletcher talked indignantly of the waste of humanity owing to state neglect of research and science. Trevelyan thought him essentially liberal in outlook. He wished to prevent the Medical Research Council becoming a Department of State like any other in Whitehall. 'Its spirit was to be scientific, and not merely administrative. It was to keep the Government of the country in constant touch with the Royal Society, and with the best scientific minds.'

ARTHUR SCHUSTER
1851–1934

I

AN ORGANIZER OF SCIENCE

THE traditional estimation of Schuster was established before the end of the nineteenth century. In a period when scientists were valued almost entirely in terms of their particular personal discoveries, he was regarded as a good and industrious physicist, who had just missed the first rank. His studies of the spectra from electric discharge tubes had led him to investigate the electric discharge in gases at low pressure. He independently suggested that the current was carried by gaseous ions, and he made the first determination of the ratio between the charge and mass of an electrified particle by means of the magnetic deflection method. However, his method was not sufficiently precise or clearly conceived, and he failed to forestall J. J. Thomson's discovery of the electron.

It is clear now that Schuster's chief claim to fame is not in his particular discoveries, which were nevertheless considerable. It is in his organization of science, especially the Manchester school of physics, and in the international sphere. Today these contributions would be regarded as of the same weight as great particular discoveries.

Rutherford in his appreciation of Schuster after his death in 1934 described him as 'a man not only of marked ability as an investigator in physical science, but also one of signal capacity in organization and diplomacy'.

Besides his many contributions to scientific and academic organization, he had created a laboratory that was 'one of the best in England at the time', and he had himself 'had the honour of succeeding' him as its director. 'It is worthy of recall', continued Rutherford, 'that the famous researches of Bohr, Moseley and others, which in a sense laid the foundation of modern physics, were carried out there.'

After mentioning the most important organizational activities in which Schuster had engaged, Rutherford referred to his researches on the electrified particles in gaseous discharge tubes, and re-marked that 'he was the first to employ the methods which were ultimately used to determine the mass and velocity of these particles, now known as electrons. But for an overestimate of the retardation suffered by such swift particles in passing through a rarefied gas, Schuster might well have been the first discoverer of the existence of particles of mass small compared with that of the lightest atom . . .'

Rutherford also mentioned his services to meteorology, and how 'He initiated at his own personal expense a series of investigations on the physics of the upper atmosphere, using kites and light balloons. These researches at Glossop Moor . . . added materially to our knowledge of the upper atmosphere, a matter of great importance for the coming age of flying.'

Rutherford said that unobtrusive generosity was an outstanding trait in his character, and it was 'unlikely that the full extent of this help will ever be publicly known'. He was a good linguist, keenly interested in art, and 'no mean artist' himself. 'He was a man of great personal charm who gained the affection and esteem of all those who knew him well. His wisdom and experience of affairs were put to the service of all . . .'

Such was Rutherford's tribute to Schuster. Reading it thirty-three years later, it redounds more than ever to the reputation of both of them.

When Schuster first taught physics at what was then Owens College at Manchester, only ten students took the subject; when he retired from Manchester University in 1907, there were two hundred and fifty. He collected the funds and planned the design of a new physics laboratory which was opened in 1900. By 1906, £36,000 had been spent on the building and equipment, of which he had personally contributed more than one quarter; it was a large sum in those days.

He brought his most carefully designed and equipped laboratory to the most advanced state of efficiency, and then sought to place it at the disposal of the best physicist in the world by himself retiring. Through careful and persistent management, he succeeded in ensuring that Rutherford, then thirty-six and at Montreal in Canada, should be his successor. When everything had been safely arranged, Schuster resigned his chair at the age of fifty-six.

The department which Schuster bequeathed to Rutherford was furnished down to the last detail, including Hans Geiger as the professor's personal research assistant, and that 'young, energetic, and exceptionally capable' lab-boy, William Kay, who was to assist Rutherford in the original experiments on the disintegration of atoms.

Schuster arranged that Rutherford should receive the then relatively large salary of £1,600 a year. It was equal to the combined salaries of nine other graduate staff. In addition, Schuster created and endowed a special readership in theoretical physics.

These splendid facilities enabled Rutherford to organize his research on a much wider basis than before. He had many more research students, and he drew up a plan of thirty research topics. Within four years he and his students had completed the experiments which led to the establishment of the nuclear theory of the atom, and the foundation of nuclear physics.

With Geiger he developed the electrical counter. He made exact counts of the number of alpha particles emitted by a given quantity of radium in a second, and estimated the electrostatic charge on an alpha particle. His result agreed closely with the figure which Planck had deduced eight years before from his quantum theory. Rutherford had hitherto been prejudiced against the theory, but when his own experimental results agreed with it, he went round telling his friends: 'There is more in old Planck than meets the eye.'

Within six years of his arrival at Manchester, he was joined by Niels Bohr, who was enabled to work there by means of Schuster's readership in theoretical physics. The collaboration of Rutherford and Bohr brought the establishment of Bohr's quantum theory of the atom.

Rutherford and Bohr were the perfect complements of each other, and it was Schuster who created the conditions in which they could work together. Schuster represented Manchester science in its full wisdom and maturity. During his time Manchester achieved the summit of its power and wealth, and he placed Rutherford on Manchester science like a kind of crown.

After Schuster had retired from Manchester at the early age of fifty-six, he devoted more and more of his energy and administrative skill to the affairs of the Royal Society. In 1912 he succeeded Larmor as the Secretary for the physical sciences. He bought an estate near Reading, and henceforth London became the centre in which he worked. He served as Secretary until 1919, through the strenuous and disturbed period of the First World War. He applied his business ability and his personal wealth to the Society's interests. He presented it with £3,000 for the nucleus of a pension fund for the staff.

Schuster was of Jewish descent, and had been born in Germany. His early life there and his family connections had left him with a permanent interest in, and understanding of science in countries other than his own adopted one. When scientists and scholars began to discuss in the later years of the nineteenth century how the international organization of science and learning might be improved, the Royal Society nominated him as their representative. It sent him in 1899 to the preliminary meeting at Wiesbaden of the International Association of Academies. In 1905 he became the Society's representative on the Council of the Association, and he gave the Society £3,500 to assist its participation in the Association's work.

The outbreak of the First World War led to the destruction of the Association. Thereupon Schuster began to create the International Research Council. In 1919, when he was sixty-eight, he became its first Secretary. During the next nine years he succeeded in consolidating it in the difficult atmosphere of the post-war period, and then retired from the secretaryship at the age of seventy-seven. He tried hard to persuade the majority of members of the International Council to admit the German scientists, but feeling was still too high even ten years after the end of the war.

Schuster held that there were 'three types of international organizations. The first aims simply at collecting information, the second is intended to fix fundamental units or to initiate agreements on matters in which uniformity is desirable, while in the third type of organization a more direct advance of knowledge is aimed at, and research is carried out according to a combined scheme ...' He accomplished major tasks in all three types.

Schuster's efforts for the international organization of science were made still more striking by the prejudice against him during and immediately after the First World War. Like many other naturalized Britons of German birth, and especially of Jewish descent, he was subjected to scurrilous abuse and unjustifiable insinuations. These had to be brought before the law courts.

Campbell Swinton had erected a wireless set on Schuster's estate near Reading, to pick up the Paris time signal for co-ordination of observations. This was before the foundation of a broadcasting system in England. Rumours were spread that Schuster was using the set, which could receive but not transmit signals, for disloyal purposes. These were curbed by legal action, but bitter opposition was expressed against his presidency of the

British Association for the Advancement of Science, at its Manchester Meeting in 1915. No one had done more than Schuster for Manchester science, or could have been a better representative of Manchester culture. Mr H. H. Asquith, then Prime Minister, befriended him, but Schuster was very deeply hurt. At length, he mustered courage to enter the Athenaeum Club again, though in fear and trembling, and take a solitary place in the coffee-room. When he was about to leave the club, and was putting his coat on in the vestibule, he was surprised to find someone helping him on with his coat. When he turned round, he saw that it was the famous soldier Lord Roberts, whom he did not know personally, making a public gesture of social support.

Schuster did not allow the disgraceful treatment to deflect him from his admirable aims. He worked on, and lived to the age of eighty-three, long enough to see Rutherford go to Cambridge and achieve a third period of greatness, while the need for the international organization and protection of scientists became better understood, and was made plain to all persons of sense by the rise of Nazism in Germany.

Schuster was one of the greatest organizers of academic science, and yet he had characteristics which might have apparently quite disqualified him from such a work. He was shy and absent-minded. People found him difficult to get to know. He was liable to wander away from students in the middle of a conversation. In spite of these disconcerting habits he accomplished a great deal of administration in science, which was distinguished by its quality as well as its quantity.

Evidently, great achievements in the organization of science are not necessarily restricted to persons of extrovert temperament.

II

FINANCE AND HISTORY IN FRANKFORT

Arthur Schuster was born in Frankfort of an old Jewish family on 12 September 1851. His father Francis Joseph founded the very successful banking firm of Schuster Brothers, after starting life in the family firm of that name which dealt in textile goods. The Schusters' original prosperity arose in the middle of the eighteenth century, from the new textile trade of the Industrial Revolution. They traded in cotton goods, principally with England. Owing to this connection, Napoleon confiscated all the family property when he occupied Frankfort in 1808, as part of his policy of destroying British trade.

The grandfather and two of his younger brothers decided to start business in England. The younger brothers moved to England in 1811, while the eldest stayed in Frankfort, and opened a branch of the new English firm there.

One of Schuster's uncles went to Manchester to organize the textile firm. He presently moved to London, where he ultimately became the first chairman of the London and Brighton Railway. Another uncle settled in Brussels, no doubt to organize the transport of goods between Lancashire and Germany.

Schuster's father was born in 1823. He joined the family business, and travelled on its behalf. He frequently visited England, and trade fairs such as that at Leipzig. He became a skilful judge of cotton and woollen materials, but finance appealed to him more than trade. He took a brother-in-law into partnership, and started his banking firm. He soon became a leading financial and public figure in Frankfort. He served as a cavalry volunteer, recruited to suppress the revolutionary outbreaks of 1848.

Schuster's father married a Jewish lady. However, their son Arthur was converted to Christianity in his boyhood. When he was seven, his mother was afflicted with Graves's disease, or exophthalmic goitre. She became blind, and suffered from that condition for some forty years, with great fortitude. This enhanced her power of entering into mental contact with those she loved. No doubt her profound affection had a stabilizing influence on Arthur Schuster, and strengthened his tendency to quiet but tenacious persistence.

Arthur was sent to a private school at the age of six, which specialized in educating boys for commerce. He picked up arithmetic and languages quickly, but at the age of ten had an illness which caused him to be absent for some months. His parents mistakenly thought that having missed so much teaching, he should not be moved up to the next class at the end of the school year. The school authorities were prepared to promote him, but they deferred to his parents' request, and announced the decision to the whole school on speech day. Schuster was shattered by this blow to his self-esteem; he lost control of himself, and broke down. He said that until he had reached middle age, he could not recollect the event without shuddering.

His father said he could choose his profession, but naturally assumed that he would wish to join his banking firm, and the family business in Manchester, with its branches in London, Bradford and Rio de Janeiro. He engaged a private tutor for his sons, to bring them up to the standard of the Frankfort Gymnasium, and thence to the university.

Schuster had to take a small examination in Latin in order to decide on which form he should enter. The examiner passed him, not so much on the perfection of his answers, but because he had observed that he had worked independently, without troubling what the other boys were doing. Schuster felt somewhat ashamed, for he had in fact copied a sentence from one of his neighbours. Years later, he was reassured by Kelvin, who told him that in his day at Cambridge cheating in non-competitive examinations was not regarded as dishonest.

Schuster did not take kindly to the Gymnasium, which was directed by Tycho Mommsen, brother of the historian. He was a harsh and unpopular person, and Schuster spent the years under his control in discontent and rebellion, which got him into trouble both at school and home. Mommsen threatened him with expulsion, but the young Schuster obstinately and successfully worsted him. Schuster did not think the school was inefficient, but the only part of the instruction that stimulated him was the teaching of German language and literature, especially the writing of essays. Schuster has quoted one, running to about 1,200 words, on the choice of a profession, which he wrote at the age of fifteen.

In this striking effort, he says that he needed no incentive in making his choice; his mind had already been made up long ago. He would choose to be an architect. Even as a small child, he had wished to devote himself to this profession, and he had prided himself that, unlike other boys, he did not change his mind every minute. He could recollect that he had had the idea at least as early as his eighth year, for he had threatened an obstreperous teacher that he would refuse in due course to build him a beautiful house. 'It is my belief', he wrote, 'that one can get to know completely the character of a man from the games of his childhood.' He, for his part, 'considered that houses and great buildings were the greatest masterpieces of men, and I always liked best to play with building blocks'.

It had taken him only a short time to choose architecture in preference to commerce or a learned profession. He took longer to decide against learning than commerce, but it had been evident in his years at the Gymnasium that he 'never had any special inclination to study'. He thought he had been unconsciously biased against learning by an early impression that a scholar has 'no pleasure at all except from his books'.

He extended his consideration to civil and mechanical engineering. Civil engineering and architecture overlapped, but he finally chose architecture because civil engineering constructions take a long time, and he had a liking, 'when a task has been once begun, to finish it as quickly as possible'. He opted against mechanical engineering because of its variety of application. He had to subordinate himself to the demand. The mechanical engineer was unable 'to have any regard for beauty'. How different was architecture, in which taste was one of the most important elements!

The author of this essay was the father of the man who built the splendid new physical laboratory at Manchester.

The tutor who prepared Schuster for the Gymnasium was a Göttingen mathematician named Schütz, whose doctoral thesis was on the theory of numbers. Schütz remained a member of the Schuster household throughout the boy's years at school, with the duty of dealing with all educational questions that arose.

Schütz gave Schuster stimulating lessons in differential calculus, and introduced him to such subjects as Diophantine equations, and helped to open his mind to the idea of making scientific discoveries. Schuster owed much and felt grateful to Schütz, who had the faculty of making friends. Through him he became acquainted with Ernst Abbe, who later joined in the creation of the famous optical firm of Zeiss. At the time Abbe was engaged by Frankfort to regulate the city clocks.

Frankfort was the scene of important social and political events during Schuster's school-days. One quarter of the city's population was Jewish, and when Schuster was born, they still had no civil rights. Napoleon had started their emancipation under the influence of the Rothschild family, by abolishing the Ghetto. Frankfort Jews celebrated the defeat of Napoleon at Leipzig in 1813. They were not accorded civil rights until 1864, when Schuster was thirteen.

Frankfort was made the centre of the federation of German states established by the Congress of Vienna in 1815. It had a diplomatic corps, and an international outlook which drew sustenance from the Huguenot settlements in the regions, as well as the Jewish population. The Congress of Vienna had given Austria precedence in the affairs of the federation. Prussia regarded this as an affront, and Bismarck provoked the war of 1866 against Austria to transfer the precedence to Prussia, and make Berlin the centre of a German empire.

Schuster witnessed the arrival of Prussian troops, and an unpleasant Prussian doctor quartered himself on the Schuster household. However, the doctor did not reckon with the tutor Schütz, who did not like his manners, and was also a Prussian. Schütz pointed out to him that he had no proper authority, and he soon disappeared.

Schuster's school studies were not much disturbed, as the war of 1866 occurred largely during the summer vacation. His father had long intended that he should study in a French-speaking country. The conversion of Frankfort from a Free City, independent state and federal capital into a Prussian town changed his personal situation, for under Prussian law male inhabitants were liable to military service.

Schuster's father shared the strong anti-Prussian feeling, and decided to emigrate. A senior partnership in the Manchester branch of the family business became vacant. He secured temporary Swiss citizenship for his children, who became naturalized English citizens in 1875. The Prussian conquest had changed and reduced the city as a cultural centre, though it benefited its trade. The population increased under the German empire from 78,000 in 1866 to 290,000 in 1900.

Schuster left school in 1868 at the age of sixteen. Besides being coached by Schütz in mathematics, he spent some time in the laboratory of an analytical chemist, and, what he enjoyed more than anything else, instruction in water-colour drawing in a painter's studio. He described the day he left school as the happiest in his life. After he had reached the limits of the knowledge he was capable of acquiring from the 'so-called "humanitarian" teaching' of a severely classical education, he was allowed to apply himself to studies for which he had some aptitude.

On the day of his deliverance, his private tutor presented him with a copy of the German translation of Roscoe's textbook of chemistry, on the title page of which he inscribed the date: 3 April 1868. Thirty-eight years later, when Roscoe presided at the celebration of the twenty-fifth anniversary of Schuster's professorship at Manchester, Schuster reverently produced the volume. He said that his interest in spectroscopy had been aroused on that day of deliverance long ago, when his eye first fell on the beautiful coloured plates of spectra in Roscoe's book.

Roscoe said that all he claimed was that he had encouraged Schuster to become a scientist, and had secured 'his father's permission to leave the easy path of pecuniary gain which lay open to him, and to take the uphill road which alone leads to eminence in Science'.

Schuster said that his first idea of becoming a scientist was inspired by reading the obituary notices of Faraday, after his death on 25 August 1867. 'The revelation that great experimental discoveries could still be made came almost as a shock; and the idea of devoting my life to physics began to take hold of me.' Seized with this ambition, he at once tried to devise a perpetual motion, and trisect angles, disregarding his tutor's admonitions.

He was sent to Geneva in 1868, where he lodged with a pastor, to learn French. He attended lectures on mechanics, molecular physics, and comparative anatomy at the Academy founded by Calvin. He also subscribed to the course on astronomy. He found he was the only student, and the professor, Plantamour, a pupil of Bessel, said he might as well come to the Observatory for instruction. There he learned something of astronomy.

Schuster went to the new family home in Manchester for the first time in the Christmas holidays of 1869, seeing Paris and London on the way. He returned to Geneva for completion of his studies. There he had found 'attractive surroundings, effective liberty, and congenial work', which were 'all that a man should want for complete happiness'. He was very sad, and wept, when he had to leave Geneva in 1870 to settle in Manchester.

III

SETTLING IN MANCHESTER

Schuster arrived in Lancashire just before the Franco-German War. He started as an apprentice in the family firm's office in Manchester, addressing himself to the uncongenial tasks of copying letters, checking accounts, and paying weekly wages.

On 7 October 1870 he wrote in his diary that he could find happiness only in a scientific career. He ended his entry with the Latin tag *alea jacta est*, the die is cast. His aspirations passed unnoticed in the excitement of the defeat of the French, and he had to satisfy himself with reading Darwin's *Origin of Species* and Tyndall's *Heat Considered as a Mode of Motion*, and attending Roscoe's evening classes in chemistry at Owens College. He won the prize in the subsequent examination on Roscoe's course.

Meanwhile, his blind mother sensed that he was unhappy, and asked him whether this was caused by the prospect of a business life. Schuster was overwhelmed by this sudden insight, and at first denied that he was unhappy. After a few days he realized that he had made a mistake, and now told his mother what he really felt. She spoke to his father, who took a very reasonable

view of the situation. He said he could postpone entry to the
business for a year. He would seek Roscoe's advice on whether
there was any opening for a scientific career. He did not want
him to waste the hard-earned family fortune on fancy projects,
such as the construction of airships.

Schuster was pleased that his father had decided to consult
Roscoe, whose treatise on chemistry had already inspired his
interest in spectroscopy while he was still in Frankfort. He had
tried on his own initiative to discover some relation between the
wavelengths of the different lines in Roscoe's striking pictures
of spectra.

Schuster called on Roscoe at his house in Victoria Park, and
was taken for a walk in the garden, while the difficulties of earn-
ing a living by scientific research were explained to him. Roscoe
was, however, interested in his attempts to find relations between
the wavelengths of the spectral lines, and closed the discussion
with the hope that he would join the ranks of scientific men.
This marked the beginning of a lifelong friendship with Roscoe,
who advised his father that he should enter Owens College, and
study physics under Balfour Stewart. He might then proceed to
a German university and take a degree. His father accepted this
advice.

Schuster then went off for a holiday in the Welsh mountains,
where, for the only time in his life, he saw the Brocken Spectre,
the coloured halo around his own shadow, the meteorological
effect which played such an important role in C. T. R. Wilson's
career.

He started at Owens in the autumn of 1871, when the college
was still in Cobden's old house in Quay Street. He arrived when
the accommodation and equipment were very primitive, but the
creative spirit of the recently-founded college was at its height.
The youthful professoriate contained genius such as that of
Osborne Reynolds, and splendid teachers like the mathematics
professor Barker, to whom J. J. Thomson owed so much; Balfour
Stewart took a high place in this company. He had only recently
become a professor, and was neither very skilful in, nor respectful
of, academic routine. The principal of the college took to sending
him tart notes, starting very nicely, but ending with sharp criticism, which led Balfour Stewart to observe that 'every billet
has its bullet'. He had untrammelled imagination, and was willing
to consider any idea; too willing, in the opinion of some of his
contemporaries.

Like Schuster, Balfour Stewart had started life in business,

and then succeeded in moving from it into science. He became
assistant to J. D. Forbes at Edinburgh, and worked on the equilibrium of radiation in an enclosure at uniform temperature. He
discovered the fundamental relation between radiation and absorption subsequently announced by Kirchhoff, but he did not
sufficiently clinch his discovery by applications. He had a profound sense of the principles of equivalence and reciprocity
in nature.

He pondered on relative motion, and suspected that chemical
change might be accompanied by change in mass. He set his
pupil J. J. Thomson to try to detect a change in mass when mercury and iodine react. On one occasion, when the reaction was
not proceeding properly, J.J. picked up the glass flask containing
the materials to see what was the matter. The flask exploded in
his face, and many bits of glass were embedded in one of his
eyes; these were removed, but he nearly lost the sight of the
eye.

Balfour Stewart had been appointed superintendent of Kew
Observatory, where he had carried out a long series of observations on the earth's magnetism. The Observatory presently
came under the control of a Royal Society committee, with which
he disagreed, and he subsequently resigned. His work on terrestrial magnetism led him to suggest in 1882 the existence of elec-
trically-conducting layers in the upper atmosphere; what is now
known as the ionosphere. He pointed out that these conducting
layers, as they cut across the earth's lines of magnetic force owing
to convective movements of the air, would produce electric currents, in the manner of a dynamo. He thus anticipated the now
highly developed subject of cosmical electrodynamics.

Balfour Stewart's scientific intuition was greater than his
command of experimental and theoretical technique, which prevented him from establishing his profound ideas. Schuster resembled his teacher in this respect. Like him, he had the faculty
of recognizing deep and fertile lines of research, but was unable
to distil from them the fundamental laws that they implied. This
prevented him from being an individual discoverer of the first
rank, but it was not a disadvantage in an organizer of science, who
was preparing the way for the advance of others.

Roscoe suggested to Schuster as a first research that he should
try to settle the question whether an element could produce more
than one spectrum. Following this line, Schuster examined
the spectrum of nitrogen, heated in a Geissler tube with metallic
sodium. He did not obtain a satisfactory result. The spectra he

observed were peculiar. Long afterwards he saw that if he had had the insight and skill, their unravelling might have led him to the discovery of argon. But he commented that the history of science is full of 'might have been's', and he had 'always held that to come near to discovery, and not make it, only emphasizes the failure'.

Here he was too hard on himself, and discounted the contribution that such work makes to the success of others, whose major achievements depend as much on the scientific circumstances which they inherit, as on the magnitude of their own gifts. The creation of the atmosphere of discovery is more important than any particular discovery.

After Schuster had completed a year's work at Owens, he was recommended by Roscoe to go to Heidelberg, to work for a doctorate in philosophy. He accordingly went to Germany in 1872, furnished with introductions to Kirchhoff and Bunsen. He found Kirchhoff a very meticulous and precise but kind person. It was said that he had missed delivering only one lecture in his life; this was when he got married. The wedding was on Saturday, when he normally lectured. Sunday was devoted to the honeymoon, and on Monday he resumed lecturing.

His laboratory was poorly equipped. Apart from the professor's rooms, there was only one other room for research. In this single room Lippmann was devising his capillary electrometer. The only other research student was Kamerlingh Onnes, who was preparing a thesis on Foucault's pendulum, and had to be satisfied with a corner in the lecture-room. No wonder he later constructed the best-equipped research laboratory of his day, the famous low-temperature laboratory at Leiden! Lippmann, Kamerlingh Onnes and Schuster became lifelong friends.

Schuster's six months' optical research proved sterile, but he became acquainted with the literature, and learned how to use delicate optical instruments.

He now decided to take the examination for his doctorate. On the day before the examinations he had to present himself in full evening dress to the examiners. He had to take Latin as well as physics, chemistry and mathematics. The Latin examiner told him he did not see why science men should know ancient languages, and he would pass him however badly he did.

When he called on Bunsen, the stately man partly opened the door, and before Schuster could say much, told him that he knew how busy he must be, and would not detain him, and closed the door. The mathematician Königsberger was friendly, and tipped him that Kirchhoff was fond of asking questions on potential theory.

In the examination, Kirchhoff did not ask any question on potential theory, but on wave-theory of light. Both the examinee and the examiner got stuck in the equations. Kirchhoff commented that they were both rather stupid about the problem, and closed the examination.

Schuster was taken aback when Bunsen failed to appear, and he was examined by Kopp. He did not do very well in chemistry. Nevertheless, he was awarded his doctorate, though only in the second of the four classes. Schuster said that his Heidelberg examination was the only one of any importance to which he ever submitted himself.

After Heidelberg he returned to Manchester, and in 1873 was appointed the first demonstrator in the physical laboratory in Owens College, which had now been moved to Oxford Road. He spent the summer of 1874 in Weber's laboratory at Göttingen, which was also somewhat primitive. He did some research on the determination of electrical resistance, which subsequently led Maxwell to design experiments for a very accurate confirmation of Ohm's Law.

Then he went to Helmholtz's laboratory in Berlin, with an introduction from Roscoe. The laboratory contained three or four rooms, with about twelve research students. Goldstein was in the midst of his famous researches on the discharge of electricity through gases. He was convinced that the cathode rays were vibrations, but Helmholtz doubted this. Schuster said that Helmholtz was disappointed that the proof that they were particles did not come from his laboratory. He attributed the British success to Stokes, whose profound judgment, he believed, must have guided Crookes to the correct interpretation.

Helmholtz used to make daily rounds of his research students, and discuss their problems freely. His mind was as quick as Kelvin's, but he was always solemnly conscious of his dignity as an *Excellency*. His second wife was a member of the South German aristocracy, and rather fussy. When the Helmholtzes were staying with Roscoe in Manchester, she had a bad night, and in the middle of it, woke her husband, and told him she was going to die. 'That is easier said than done', observed Helmholtz, who turned on his side and fell asleep again.

Schuster said that he always considered Helmholtz's original laboratory as the ideal of what a teaching laboratory should be. All worked in the open and had the benefit of mutual criticism and inspiration. The arrangements were the very opposite of those so dear to beginners, 'that everyone should have a private room in which he could set up his apparatus without fear of outside interference'. Under such a system, the professor no longer saw the students, secrecy was encouraged, and 'the true scientific spirit in the community' was not fostered. Schuster subsequently visited Helmholtz when a big new institute on this plan had been built for him. He found the students were now working 'without a common bond and generally without scientific impulse, and mainly for the purpose of completing a dissertation . . .' All the soul and spirit of the shabby old laboratory had gone, and Helmholtz resigned soon after it was opened.

Schuster came to believe that complicated practical courses were necessary for ordinary students but not for talented men. He contended that only a small number of experimental discoveries had arisen from laboratory teaching, and he thought this was connected with the tendency to solitary work in separate rooms.

He had benefited from Balfour Stewart's methods of laboratory teaching. He left routine teaching to not very well equipped assistants. Consequently, students did not take too much notice of what they were told, and set about working things out for themselves. Balfour Stewart himself would always tackle anything difficult, and tried to find new fields of enquiry.

Schuster ultimately worked in five different laboratories, under five different leaders of science, drawing from his experience an exceptional insight into the problems of laboratory organization and inspiration.

He was about to return from Berlin to the honorary demonstratorship in physics at Owens College, when he had the fortune to be appointed Chief of the British Eclipse Expedition to Siam. This led to a long and fruitful concern with solar and geophysics.

IV

THE SUN AND MOUNTAINS

After the culture of the old Frankfort, the Schusters had found Lancashire life somewhat crude.His father never forgave a friend who recommended him to take a house at Lytham, which he had described as the Nice of England. Nor were they at once at home in the dank Lancashire climate. Schuster's father moved to Hampstead in London, and when Schuster returned from Berlin for Christmas in 1874, he went first to Hampstead. While there, he received an invitation from Norman Lockyer to join the expedition to Siam and elsewhere, being organized by the Royal Society, with Government support, to observe the eclipse of the sun in the spring of 1875.

The recent development of solar spectroscopy, in particular by Lockyer himself, had stimulated interest in this field, and Lockyer had been active in inspiring the organization of the expedition. The most important item in its programme was an attempt to photograph the solar corona. This was believed by some astronomers to be impossible. Lockyer was the obvious person to lead the expedition, but he was the secretary of the famous Royal Commission on Scientific Instruction and the Advancement of Science, presided over by the seventh Duke of Devonshire. The Commission was publishing its final reports in 1875, and it was not possible for the secretary to be spared for sufficient time to lead the expedition. A substitute for him had to be found, and the organizers turned to the young man who had published work on spectroscopy in the Proceedings of the Royal Society. So, in February 1875, Schuster received a letter from Stokes as Secretary of the Royal Society:

'I am to inform you that the Eclipse Committee of the Royal Society have appointed you to take charge of the whole expedition proceeding from England, so long as it remains united, and afterwards of that branch of it which is to go to Siam. Also that the Committee have passed a resolution that the whole observations taken by the Siam party be considered the property of the Royal Society, and be sent to that body for discussion.'

This brief letter, in characteristic Stokesian style, was a magnificent communication for a young man of twenty-three to receive. Schuster threw himself at once into mastering the programme. This was facilitated by the proximity of his father's house at Hampstead to that of Lockyer. He spent many evenings with Lockyer, discussing the arrangements, and Lockyer's instructions for the observations.

Lockyer thought that he ought to be able to re-silver optical glasses, in case any were damaged by conditions in the tropics, and sent him to Paris to learn the processes. Schuster went off, with instructions to Le Verrier, the famous director of the Paris Observatory. He learned nothing about silvering which he might not have learned equally well in London, but he had an illuminating experience with the great astronomer. Schuster first met Cornu, who exclaimed, when he was to call on Le Verrier, that he did not know whether Le Verrier was the most detestable man in Paris, but he knew he was the man he detested most.

Schuster presented himself at the Observatory, feeling very nervous. Le Verrier's assistant observed his condition, and said that he would find Le Verrier in a terrible temper; he had just returned from a funeral. Le Verrier was then sixty-four years old, and one of the autocrats of contemporary science. He fixed the nervous twenty-three-year-old Schuster with a piercing glance and asked him what he wanted. Schuster replied that Lockyer had written to him about it. So he had, said Le Verrier, but he wanted to hear Schuster's own version. Schuster explained haltingly, and Le Verrier terminated the meeting with the statement that he had already given instructions that he should receive every assistance.

After Schuster had spent a week practising silvering processes and had to return to London, he suggested that a letter of thanks to Le Verrier would be sufficient. But he was told he must see the Director again. When he was shown into Le Verrier's room, a trembling assistant was standing beside him, being cross-examined after searching for a week for a mistake in his calculations. Le Verrier presently pointed out where he had gone wrong. When the assistant had left the room, Le Verrier chuckled, and told Schuster that he had known all the time where the mistake was, but he wanted to see whether the assistant could find it out for himself.

Le Verrier's manner suddenly changed, and, to Schuster's surprise, he was invited to walk round the garden. Le Verrier talked most amiably and interestingly, and among other topics, expressed his strong disapproval of the French Government's expedition for the observation of the transit of Venus. He said all the money spent on the transit expedition of 1874 would be wasted, and nothing of value would come from it, nor from the forthcoming transit expedition of 1882, in which, as Schuster commented, he proved perfectly right.

The eclipse expedition had a staff of five scientists, including Schuster. A section of it was to break off in India to make observations. It set sail in February 1875. Schuster had a very bad time in the Bay of Biscay, and began to wonder whether the expedition would be worth it. His ship broke its propeller in the Suez Canal, and this caused a delay which threatened to prevent the Siam section from getting to Bangkok in time for the eclipse. There were angry differences of opinion, and Schuster had to exert all the authority of Stokes's letter in order to ensure that the transport connections were not missed.

Schuster had expected to find a gunboat at Singapore ready to take them to Bangkok. It was not there, so he went to see the Governor, who was very kind, but evasive. It gradually appeared that the Admiral commanding the China Squadron had been annoyed by the request for the gunboat having been transmitted through the Foreign Office and not through the Admiralty, so he had ordered the captain of the ship to sail to Hongkong. Schuster had to make other arrangements to get to Bangkok by merchant steamer.

In Siam, the members of the expedition were guests of the King. Very full arrangements were made for them, and also for a French expedition under the leadership of Lockyer's famous fellow solar-spectroscopist Janssen.

Schuster had familiarized himself with the apparatus which was to be used in the eclipse, while he was still in London. He mentioned that Colonel Alexander Strange, now famous for his views on the organization of science, had helped in explaining some of its mechanism to him.

In Siam Schuster had a good deal of work to do in assembling the instruments, and getting them into order. They were by no means ready on the day before the eclipse, and he suffered agonies of anxiety, feeling that failure would ruin his career. He sat down and wept, but was soon cheered up by one of his colleagues. He could not help almost hoping that the weather would be bad, so that he would be relieved of responsibility.

The morning of the eclipse was cloudless, and arrangements were made to protect the party from interruption, especially by the ex-Regent's elephants, which might have stampeded when the sun was eclipsed. The instrumental programme of operations proceeded without a hitch, but Schuster was startled by the appearance of the corona before the last spark of the sun had disappeared. He gave the signal for the beginning of total eclipse a little late, but fortunately not too late.

The observations made were as good as the instruments permitted. They were unable to photograph the spectrum of the corona, for the wet plates then used in photography proved insufficiently sensitive. The most important of their results was the recognition of the lines due to calcium in the chromosphere.

This discovery, which was to prove of major importance for the explanation of the constitution and mechanics of the sun, drew the young American spectroscopist G. E. Hale to visit him in Manchester. Schuster's conversation reinforced Hale's determination to pursue astrophysics. Hale went on to parallel in the United States what Schuster did in Britain, for the advance of astrophysics and the national and international organization of science. He found in Schuster 'rare and inspiring qualities'.

Returning to the Siam expedition, after the eclipse most of the members returned to their usual duties, but Schuster travelled back to England through India. He sailed to Calcutta, stayed with business friends of his father, and then travelled to Simla. There he met the private secretary of the Viceroy of India, who asked him for advice on a solar observatory in India. Their discussion led to the establishment of the Kodaikanal solar observatory in Southern India in 1899.

An acquaintance then suggested he should join a walking party, which was to climb over the Himalayas, and journey through the Vale of Kashmir. He quickly prepared for the journey, taking with him wet and dry bulb thermometers and a pocket spectroscope. Their departure was delayed by heavy rainstorms. One of Schuster's first impressions was of the enormous power of water in upheaving the surface of the earth, and cutting through mountains.

Schuster travelled four hundred miles through the Himalayas, from Kulu to Kashmir, along tracks that were higher than the Alps of Europe. The various incidents of the journey made a deep impression on him. Among these was the brutality with which his comrades beat the poor and threadbare natives in the mountains, to make them give up some of their precious milk.

The Siam expedition and the journey through the Himalayas gave Schuster experience of men and things. They brought out the psychological and physical toughness which were necessary for success in his career. Such experience at the age of twenty-four was invaluable for his future organizational life.

V

BACK IN ENGLAND

Schuster returned to Owens College at Manchester as honorary demonstrator in physics in November 1875. He gave three public lectures on the Siam expedition, and he lectured on Maxwell's theory of electricity, which had recently been expounded in Maxwell's great *Treatise on Electricity and Magnetism*, published in 1873. Schuster's was the first systematic course given anywhere on Maxwell's theory, which had put an end to the treatment of electricity as a branch of applied mathematics, and changed the conception of electrical science. Among the three students attending these lectures was J. J. Thomson, then sixteen years old.

At this time Schuster carried out an experiment suggested by Osborne Reynolds, to determine whether the rotation of the vanes of Crookes's recently invented radiometer was not due to the direct action of the light falling on them, but to internal forces. J. J. Thomson awaited the result of the experiment with intense excitement. J.J. remembered to the end of his days his relief when he heard that the rotation of the vanes was due to internal forces.

In 1876 Schuster went to Cambridge to work with Clerk Maxwell, in the recently opened Cavendish Laboratory. He was well received by Maxwell, but as he did not work for a degree his position was irregular. The university did not quite know what to do with such a person, as research students had not yet been invented in Cambridge. Maxwell's too brief life ended in 1879, so Schuster was one of the few with experience of Maxwell, besides being one of the earliest research workers in the Cavendish Laboratory.

When Rayleigh succeeded Maxwell and decided to re-determine the unit of electrical resistance, as part of this plan for promoting organized research, no one belonging to the university offered to join in, so Schuster gave up his own work to help. On the basis of their result, the Board of Trade defined the legal ohm.

While still attached to Cambridge Schuster went on the solar eclipse expedition to Colorado in 1878. In the following year he was elected a Fellow of the Royal Society, at the age of twenty-eight.

In 1881 a chair of applied mathematics was established at Owens College, to which Schuster was appointed. Among the unsuccessful candidates was the youthful J. J. Thomson, who was twenty-four, and had just completed a brilliant academic course. In the following year, 1882, Schuster went to Egypt on his third solar eclipse expedition, on which he obtained the first successful photograph of the solar corona, with very sensitive dry plates instead of the wet, comparatively insensitive ones he used in Siam.

Schuster has described how, in his early days, there was a widespread belief that the fundamental features of physical nature had already been discovered, and that there was scope only for the elucidation of detail. In general, experimental was behind theoretical research.

The discovery of spectrum analysis, and its application to the analysis of the constitution of the stars, came as one of the first major escapes from the old limited view, and experiment once

ARTHUR SCHUSTER

more overtook theory. While spectrum analysis had first been used as a means of ascertaining the chemical composition of substances, the physicists were more interested in the mechanism by which atoms emitted spectral radiation. Schuster coined the word 'spectroscopy' in 1882, to distinguish the physicist's from the chemist's approach to spectra.

His study of spectra led him on to the investigation of the physics of the electric discharge in exhausted tubes. He started from the hypothesis that the current in the discharge tube consisted of definite quantities of electricity attached to particles that acted as carriers. The idea that a separate atom of electricity might exist never occurred to him.

In 1884 and again in 1890, he was invited to give the Bakerian Lecture to the Royal Society, in which he gave accounts of the progress of his own researches and those of others in the field. He used to see Helmholtz during this period, during his summer holiday in Pontresina, and was consistently encouraged by him. Helmholtz believed that magnetic deflection of the particles in the tube would provide the key to their nature. Schuster was the first to measure the mass of the moving particles by magnetic deflections. His results were rough, as might be expected in a pioneer experiment, and he did not correctly interpret them. Consequently, the discovery of the electron remained for J. J. Thomson to make in 1897.

Like other physicists of his generation, Schuster had difficulty in abandoning old ideas, though, as will be seen presently, he had striking intuition about the science of the future. He lived to see the force of the ideas of relativity and the quantum theory, but he was never at home with them, in spite of his sense of the limitations of the traditional theories. He still wanted to see models of natural processes in his imagination. While he could never quite abandon the old ideas, he nevertheless did a great deal towards creating the conditions in which the new ideas could be brought to birth, and reared.

At Manchester he was very active in the city's cultural life. He was honorary Secretary of its famous Literary and Philosophical Society from 1885–88, and later President. In 1886 he went on his fourth solar eclipse expedition, to the West Indies. Then, in 1887, Balfour Stewart died, and he transferred from the chair of applied mathematics to the Langworthy chair of physics in the following year.

Schuster's solar studies caused him to investigate the possible effects of the sun's magnetism on periodical variations in the

12

magnetism of the earth. He raised the question whether magnetism might be a fundamental property of rotating matter. If so, the rotation of the earth might in itself be the explanation of the earth's magnetism.

His work on solar and terrestrial magnetism has been one of the stimuli of the notable research on the magnetic properties of the earth, sun and stars. Schuster's scientific achievement could not be summarized in any single startling discovery, but in the collective effect of numerous researches in many different directions. In this sense, he is a parent of astrophysics.

Hale described his contributions to this science as 'vital', mentioning in particular his theoretical researches on the law of distribution of spectral lines, the resolving power of spectroscopes, the periodicities of sunspots, the relationship between terrestrial magnetic storms and solar phenomena, and the nature of the solar atmosphere. He made the classical discovery in 1889 that the observed daily variations in the earth's magnetic field could be separated into two parts, the cause of one being above, and of the other within, the earth.

He was the first to suggest that the electrical conductivity of the upper atmosphere, or ionosphere, was produced by ultra-violet rays from the sun. Schuster's development of the Balfour Stewart theory of the electrification of the upper atmosphere was a precursor to the work of Heaviside and Kennelly, and the modern theory of the ionosphere.

Schuster had an idea that the spectroscope was an instrument that automatically found regularities in the mixture of radiations passing through space, and what it did could also be done by calculation. Consequently, he investigated methods of determining whether periodicities in collections of data of any kind were real or fortuituos. He did this by means of what he called a periodogram.

With it he showed that a periodicity in the appearance of sunspots may continue for years, and then disappear. His periodogram method has been much used for discovering periodicities in earthquakes, weather, and many other kinds of scientific data, and also in economics. Besides his personal researches, he advanced these sciences by his organizational work, as, for example, his chairmanship of the Seismological Committee of the International Association of Academies. Schuster became one of the parents of modern geophysics, and of the kind of international organization of science since typified in the International Geophysical Year.

Schuster's place in international science, and especially that part of it concerned with the physics of the sun and earth, was well put by Griffith in the twenty-fifth anniversary celebration in 1906 of his professorship: 'If it were possible to hold an Inter-planetary Conference—meeting, say, on the planet Jupiter—it is very probable that Dr Schuster would be asked to act as the earth's representative.' The force of this is still more evident today than it was half a century ago.

The great work that Schuster accomplished for international science was made possible by his personal wealth. In his day, the state had not yet learned its proper role in the support of international and national science. International action in science, in so far as it was carried out at all, depended very much on personal resources, and consequently on the rare combina-tion of scientific and international understanding, together with wealth, exemplified by Schuster.

His influence was exerted through teaching, as well as through research and organization. Among those who had been his pupils were J. J. Thomson, C. T. R. Wilson, A. S. Eddington, J. W. Nicholson, J. E. Petavel, and G. C. Simpson. The famous bio-chemist Arthur Harden worked for a time in his department, and the well-known textbook authors H. E. Hadley and D. E. Jones. Of some 120 research graduates, 38 had become teachers in technical colleges and secondary schools. Nearly a quarter of them were women who became science mistresses in notable girls' schools. This considerable contribution to women's education commands more respect today than it did in Schuster's own time.

Seven of his research men became professors, and no fewer than twenty-five went into industry. Three of his men became lawyers, and several civil servants.

Among his pupils was R. S. Hutton, who became assistant-director of the physical laboratory at Manchester, and later the first professor of metallurgy at Cambridge. As an instance of Schuster's encouragement of technology, Hutton quotes his own work in the Manchester laboratory on fused silica which was taken up and developed industrially, and led to the *Vitreosil* products. Schuster was immediately interested when he heard that the Manchester electrical engineer F. H. Royce was to col-laborate with the Hon. C. S. Rolls in making motor-cars; he purchased the first one turned out by the Derby works. Schuster also wrote several influential textbooks. These included his *Theory of Optics*, and courses on practical physics.

In 1887 Schuster married Miss Cary Loveday, a niece of Sir

Adolphus Ward, the Principal of Owens College. They had one son and four daughters, one of whom married R. S. Hutton. Schuster and his wife were active in the cultural and social life of Manchester, and they looked after the students. Mrs Schuster used to provide tea for the physics colloquium started in 1894. She organized a staff bicycle club, and the sports activities of the women students. Schuster himself had a serious accident in his garden while coaching a lady in swinging a golf club. His spectacles got smashed, and he lost an eye.

Schuster continued to live in Manchester until 1913, for several years after he had retired, and Rutherford had succeeded him. Rutherford said that 'the hospitality so freely dispensed by him and Lady Schuster made his home a happy meeting ground'. In fact, Schuster was still in Manchester when Rutherford conceived the nucleus of the atom. No doubt his influence lightened Rutherford's academic problems, and left him with the maximum energy for his epochal researches.

Schuster was knighted in 1920. He received numerous scientific honours, and was given the Royal Society's highest award, the Copley Medal, in 1931, at the age of eighty. He died on 14 October 1934. Besides having a leading part in the foundation of Manchester University, he actively supported the establishment of its Faculty of Technology.

He served on the Senate of London University, and on the Royal Commission of the Universities of Oxford and Cambridge. He was a governor of Giggleswick School. He served on the Manchester Corporation's Technical Instruction Committee, and on that of the School of Technology.

Together with his Manchester activities, he was active in government committees. He served as Chairman of the Executive Committee of the National Physical Laboratory. He had had a leading part in the organization of meteorology, as a member of the Meteorological Council, on which he served for thirty-two years. He organized the first British university department of meteorology at Manchester in 1905.

Schuster entered actively into the administration and business of the very numerous committees and organizations in which he participated, and he followed up all this work with many acts of personal generosity.

Though he was such a patient and industrious organizer, he was not afraid of using his imagination. In 1898 he published an article in *Nature* on *Potential Matter*, a speculation inspired by the vortex theory of atoms. He dreamt of atoms as 'sources through which an invisible fluid is pouring into three-dimensional space'. He asked how we can prove that matter 'is not an endless stream, constantly renewing itself and pushing forward the boundaries of our universe'? However, atoms might also be sinks through which matter is going out of our universe. If there were equal numbers of source and sink atoms, the amount of matter in our universe might remain constant.

The conception of source and sink atoms involved the notion of a fourth dimension. While this was a nightmare rather than a dream to the contemporary physicist, he, for his part, could not rid himself of it. 'Surely something is wanting in our conception of the universe. We know positive and negative electricity, north and south magnetism', why should there not be 'some extra-terrestrial matter related to terrestrial matter as the source is to the sink'?

The fact that such matter was not known did not prove its non-existence. Some day a mutual repulsion between different star groups may be discovered, which might be due to repulsion between the two kinds of matter.

In 'our glorification of the Newtonian system' we overlooked facts it failed to explain: One of these is the rotation of the galaxies, which could not be self-generated. Was this rotation initially caused by an outside body that has disappeared?

'The atom and the anti-atom may enter into chemical combination, because at small distances molecular forces would overpower gravitational repulsion.' Matter consisting of combined atoms and anti-atoms might fill a large part of space, and yet be undetectable because of its lack of gravity. It was conceivable that a meteorite flying through might upset an unstable condition of equilibruim, with the effect that the matter separated out on one side, and the anti-matter on the other; 'until two worlds are formed separating from each other, never to unite again'.

Schuster said he was not advancing these arguments as a scientific discussion. He did 'not wish to argue in favour of the existence of anti-atoms', but only to give his thoughts a free course in the contemplation of its possibilities.

Might there not be potential matter as well as potential energy? Was the axiom of the constancy of mass not an illusion based on limited experience? Whether such thoughts were inspirations or madness, or allowed to be serious possibilities for future science, they increased the interest of astronomical observation. This oldest and most juvenile of the sciences might still have surprises in store. 'May anti-matter be commended to its care!'

As Schuster did not have quite the experimental skill to discover the electron, so he had not quite the mathematical skill to work out his theoretical intuitions. But he sensed what future science might be like. This was the foundation of the judgment which enabled him to create the Manchester school of physics. It was a quality of a higher order than the routine accomplishment of ordinary investigations.

Even where he could not complete researches himself, he had a sense of what ought to be done. This is just the quality that modern mankind needs in order to make proper use of science and scientists.

Schuster's birth in one European society, and growing up in another, gave him an unusual width of social view. He paralleled in a different field Friedrich Engels, who was also born in Germany, and joined the family firm in Manchester. As Schuster brought business ability to bear on science, Engels brought it to bear on sociology. They were immigrant intellectuals, at a time when such persons were coming to England, and not going away from it.

While Schuster was a rich man compared with Engels, they were similar in giving support for their respective aims. Schuster provided the laboratory where Rutherford founded nuclear physics, and Engels the financial support that enabled Marx to write *Das Kapital*. Both of them were leaders in international organization, one in science and the other in politics. Such men as Schuster and Engels are liable to be overshadowed by the genius for whom they prepared the conditions or furnished support, but their role is worthy of more study and regard.

GEORGE BIDDELL AIRY
1801–1892

I

THE ORGANIZED LIFE

ACCORDING to modern scales of scientific value, Airy is an increasingly interesting figure. He was a scientist of great ability and energy. He published 518 papers, including 264 on scientific research, and the rest on various reports and articles. He retained an active interest in archaeology and classical studies, publishing books on the invasions of Britain by the Romans and Normans, and on the earlier Hebrew scriptures. He resembled Newton in his concrete approach to physical research, his width of scholarship, and his concern with the use of science in the national interest. But he imported into his work an organizational and inventive attitude influenced by the ideas of the Industrial Revolution. He was a transitional scientific figure between the mercantile and the industrial ages.

The most important part of his scientific publications show a masterly command of Newtonian astronomy and physics, in theory and application, but they also include a number on original subjects, some of which have become of major importance. For example, he started the mathematical theory of feed-back, in a study of the behaviour of backlash in astronomical instruments. In an entirely different direction, he suffered from severe astigmatism in one of his eyes. This disorder, as Thomas Young had demonstrated, is usually due to the refracting surfaces of the eye not being accurately spherical. Airy experimented on his eye in 1824, and showed that the astigmatism could be corrected by using a spectacle lens of cylindrical shape. He had such lenses made for him by an Ipswich optician later in the year. It was typical of Airy to make a concrete effort to solve any problem that came to his attention.

James Stuart, the first Professor of Mechanism at Cambridge, who was a man of wide experience, regarded Airy as the most outstanding man he had ever met. Stuart was the founder of the Cambridge system of extra-mural courses of lectures, by which

Cambridge professors could bring their knowledge directly to the people in the industrial districts, through 'a sort of peripatetic university', as he put it in 1866. He was a collaborator with Mrs Josephine Butler in the campaign for women's rights, and a noted Liberal Member of Parliament and of the London County Council. He worked with Gladstone and other leaders of the age. He was a founder of the *Star* newspaper, and a director of J. & J. Colman, Ltd.

When Stuart was a student at Trinity College, two of Airy's sons became his lifelong friends. After he graduated as Third Wrangler, Airy invited him to stay two months with his family at Greenwich Observatory, so he saw him intimately and sympathetically. He learned some technical astronomy while he was there, but far more important, he had 'the inestimable advantage of becoming well acquainted' with Airy. He 'was one of the most remarkable men, indeed I think I may say *the* most remarkable man, whom I ever met. In every part of his thoughts he was the most absolutely original person with whom I ever came in contact. He viewed everything from his own standpoint. He formed his opinions, reasoned out by himself. There was nothing with which he became in contact that he did not improve and illuminate. For instance, the whole Observatory was full of his inventions—doors which shut by contrivances of his own, arrangements for holding papers, for making clocks go simultaneously, for regulating pendulums, for arranging garden beds, for keeping planks from twisting, for every conceivable thing from the greatest to the smallest. On all there was the impress of an original and versatile mind, bubbling over with inventiveness. His conversation ranged over everything of human interest, historical, religious or scientific, and his ideas had the immense merit of being always couched in the most simple and intelligible language. He was a colossal-minded man, and his ideas seemed to be executed in granite.'

Stuart said that from that time until Airy's death twenty-five years later he was intimately associated with him, and his respect for him grew continually. 'He was a thoroughly Saxon man. He had all the personal habits of the Saxon yeoman. Though very abstemious he was fond of his food, drank beer in preference to any other liquor, and preserved the most marvellous digestion to the end of his life. He could sing a humorous song, generally in praise of good ale. He was very fond of the country, and had always been a great traveller.'

Stuart thought it natural that such a man should have interested him in astronomy, and he remarked that anyone who read his *Gravitation* would see how well he was 'capable of large-featured popular exposition', an art at which Stuart himself was very good.

Stuart's opinion of Airy is illuminating; it suggests that Airy was really more of an engineer than a scientist at heart. Stuart as an engineer instinctively appreciated Airy's practical, resourceful, inventive and clear competence. In fact, Airy as Lucasian professor of mathematics, had in 1827 included lectures on engineering subjects in his courses, such as the theory of bridges and trusses. Later on, he lectured on the theory of structures, taking as examples the roofs of the Sheldonian Theatre at Oxford, the Observatory at Cambridge, the Westminster Hall, and other well-known buildings. He gave the theory of the arches of London Bridge and other bridges over the Thames, and of the domes of St Paul's in London and St Peter's in Rome. He expounded the design of the suspension bridge over the Menai Strait, and of the vaulting in King's College Chapel.

Airy was awarded the Telford Medal of the Institution of Civil Engineers in 1867, for a paper 'On the use of the Suspension Bridge with stiffened Roadway for Railway and other Bridges of Great Span'. His readiness to attack any problem would have been advantageous in engineering, but in science it caused him to make mistakes through undertaking too much, often with dogmatic confidence.

His organizational gift was manifested very early. When he was a student, he began systematically classifying the knowledge he acquired. This helped him to defeat all other candidates in the Cambridge Mathematical Tripos and other examinations. He became Senior Wrangler, and won virtually every prize within reach. His systematic management of knowledge enabled him throughout life to deal with an extraordinary range of matters with exceptional speed and orderliness. After he became Astronomer Royal he introduced a punched hole system for filing Greenwich Observatory papers, which anticipated one of the modern business filing systems.

His passion for orderliness so grew on him that, by the end of his life, he became more concerned about the classification than the contents of his papers. This was regarded as a foible in his own day, but today, when information has become so copious that the principles of handling it are now often more important than most of the information, it may be assessed differently.

Airy pursued his own advancement with a modern pertinacity.

12*

No scientist of today has surpassed him in the diligent cultivation of his career. Sheepshanks's explanation of why he was so acceptable to authority has already been quoted in the chapter on Babbage. He deferred to the wishes of his superiors, though he did not disguise his own opinions. Even when these were flatly against official desires he expressed them, but swallowed their rejection without a murmur. Consequently, he became very popular in the higher reaches of Whitehall.

When Airy retired in 1881, after forty-five years as Astronomer Royal, the Admiralty, to which he was responsible, communicated the Report of the Board of Visitors, in which his services to Astronomy, Navigation, and the allied sciences were summarized, in a resolution proposed by J. C. Adams and seconded by Stokes. They considered that Airy had not only maintained, but greatly extended the ancient reputation of the Royal Observatory. The astronomical and other work would form an enduring monument to his 'Scientific insight and his powers of organization'.

They mentioned especially, among his many services to science, the complete reorganization of the Observatory's equipment; the designing of exceptionally stable and delicate instruments for the increased accuracy of observation, which the advance of astronomy demanded; the extension of the means of making observations of the Moon; the investigation of the effect of the iron of ships upon compasses and the correction of the errors arising from this source; and the establishment at the Observatory and in other centres of a system of time signals, since extensively developed by the Government. He had devoted himself in the most unsparing manner to the Observatory, and had watched over its interests with 'an assiduity inspired by the strongest personal attachment to the Institution'. Besides adopting every scientific discovery and invention which in his judgment appeared to be useful, he had shown sound judgment on the need for changes, and the best moment for introducing them.

He had not only maintained the most remarkable punctuality in the working out and publication of the observations carried out under his own direction, but had had worked out, and made available, his predecessors' observations of the moon and planets.

On his contributions to science not directly connected with the Observatory, they referred particularly to his researches on the theory of the tides, and to the wave-theory of light.

This resolution was all the more impressive, in that it was moved by such eminent scientists. More particularly, it was proposed by J. C. Adams, who, in view of Airy's failure to appreciate, and act as promptly as he should have done, with regard to Adams's discovery of *Neptune*, might have been expected to be at least not prejudiced in Airy's favour.

E. J. Routh, the most famous of Cambridge teachers of mathematics, married Airy's daughter Hilda. He was well qualified to understand Airy, and he wrote the obituary notice of him for the Royal Society. He remarked that from the beginning, Airy's mind was turned to practical applications. When he introduced Continental mathematical methods, he immediately applied them to current problems, and expounded them in textbooks, which were much used. Routh thought that his discovery of a new inequality in the motions of Venus and the Earth was one of his more notable astronomical achievements. It was the first specific improvement in the solar tables made by an Englishman since the time of Halley.

While Newton and Bernoulli had founded the theory of tides and Laplace had applied it to the oceans, Airy had worked it out for rivers. He explained why the tide came in faster than it went out; the movement of the broken water on the edge of a shoal; the solitary wave, and breaking waves. He investigated the effect of the wind, tidal waves, the effect of friction, and the form of the wave in broad channels with shallow sides.

Delaunay had suggested in 1866 that the apparent acceleration in the motion of the moon is due to the retardation of the rotation of the earth, owing to the friction of the tides. Airy worked this out in detail. He applied his knowledge of the tides to determine the place where Caesar landed in his invasion of England. Halley had suggested that he had landed at Deal. Airy showed that Caesar's description of the tides at the landing place were more like those at Pevensey. His interest in such historical questions led him to work out the probable dates for the famous eclipses associated with Agathocles, Thales and Xerxes. In the course of these researches, he pointed out the accuracy of early Chinese eclipse observations.

Another example of Airy's versatile practical mind was his investigation of magnetization in iron bridges. The iron becomes particularly susceptible to magnetization when a train passes over it. The magnetic behaviour of one bridge was found to be anomalous. Enquiry showed that when it was being built a quarter of a century before, a section had fallen while being raised. The magnetic effect of this on the section was detectable experimentally long afterwards. Today, events which affected the earth's strata millions of years ago are being inferred from the state of magnetization now observed in these strata.

Airy's systematic methods of working and of handling information enabled him to deal with many queries that would not appear to have been in the province of the Astronomer Royal. The Government acquired the habit of consulting him on scientific and technical problems, many of which were not, or only remotely connected with astronomy, because he was a government servant, knew his place, and was efficient and businesslike, as Sheepshanks had so well described.

He was appointed a member of many commissions, including those set up to advise on whether the railways should adopt the broad or the narrow gauge. George Stephenson was in favour of the narrow gauge, and Airy, a fellow-Northumbrian, supported his view. The Commission decided in favour of the narrow gauge, in spite of opposition in Parliament, backed especially by scientific evidence collected with the important new instruments, invented by Babbage, for observing the running behaviour of railway locomotives and vehicles. This contribution by Babbage helped to put the design of the running characteristics of vehicles and permanent way on a more scientific basis.

A small but able body of expert opinion considered that the Commission had made a mistake, for the broad gauge was demonstrably superior, especially for smooth running at high speed. The broad gauge suited the rich passenger, while the narrow suited the freight merchant. Stephenson was more impressed by the immediate economic argument in favour of the narrow gauge, which would be cheaper to construct, and would involve less expense in the amalgamation of existing systems. Today, with the contraction of the railway network, some may argue that broad gauge lines between the main cities would have been the better decision. So, perhaps, even in this case also, Airy was wrong and Babbage right.

The Government sought Airy's advice on the problem of magnetic compass navigation with iron ships. He showed how this could be done theoretically, but was hindered in practice by the sluggishness of existing compasses when used in iron ships. William Thomson overcame this difficulty by substituting a number of small for one large magnet. He patented the device, which was highly profitable. Airy received nothing for his advice, but he regarded himself as the father of the modern marine made of iron ships.

Besides being mechanically minded, Airy had a taste for computing, which indeed was a fundamental part of practical astronomy. He prided himself on the completeness and punctuality of the Observatory's computing. He had at times seventeen persons engaged as computers, and his chief personal research in his later years was on the elaboration of Numerical Lunar Theory. He persevered with it even after his powers had declined. In the end he recognized that it was vitiated by numerical errors. The vast programme of computation ought to have been done by a mechanical computer, but he had failed during more than sixty years to promote computer development.

In his early days, in 1823, he had made sketches of machines for computing and the solution of equations. This had been done under the influence of Babbage's activities on calculating machines. In spite of this interest, he did not succeed in carrying the design of computers forward. Then, many years later, he advised the government of the day that Babbage's computer was 'worthless'. Intellectually, he was to suffer for his mistake by the collapse of his lunar theory, on which he had set so much value.

Airy was consulted in 1873 by the engineers W. H. Barlow and T. Bouch on the problem of wind pressure on their projected suspension bridge over the Firth of Forth. The bridge built by Bouch over the River Tay was blown down in the notorious disaster of 1879, and in the subsequent enquiries, Airy's views on the wind pressure on bridges were severely criticized. Bouch had already started the preliminary construction for the suspension across the Forth. It was immediately stopped, and a far stronger bridge of cantilever type was designed by Benjamin Baker, and adopted. Bouch's design was shown to be faulty. Baker's cantilever bridge is still standing, and one of the wonders of the world. He made it much stronger than was necessary, which is not in keeping with commercial principles, but, like the Great Pyramid, satisfying to the human spirit.

Nearly everything came into Airy's administrative net. In 1860 he was busy on the bells of the Westminster clock, and on the smoky chimneys of the Palace.

Airy fiercely criticized what he described as the faulty principles of construction of the famous iron and glass building erected for the Great Exhibition of 1851. The building proved to be one of the most original and important of modern times, and the foundation of modern steel and glass architecture.

Airy could equally be on the wrong side in abstract science. He ridiculed Faraday's idea of lines of force, which contained the notion of the electromagnetic field. He said he could 'hardly imagine any one who knows the agreement between observation and calculation based on action at a distance to hesitate an instant between this simple and precise action on the one hand and anything so vague and varying as lines of force on the other'.

Like others of his generation, he believed that the temperature of the earth depended entirely on external causes, and come 'in no discoverable degree from the interior'. He commented that this had important implications for solar action and for geology. He was, however, progressive on applied mathematics. He sharply criticized the Cambridge Tripos Examination, saying in 1859 that he thought it very bad. It was 'utterly perverted by the insane love of Problems, and by the foolish importance given to wholly useless parts of Algebraical Geometry. For the sake of these, every Physical Subject and every useful application of pure mathematics are cut down or not mentioned.'

He suggested in 1866 that more applied mathematics should be introduced. In Mechanics, he emphasized 'that part in which the abstract ideas of *power* and *duty* occur'. While including Magnetism, he was prepared to omit 'Mineralogy and Mathematical Electricity'.

Airy wrote to the great pure mathematician Cayley that he measured the value of pure mathematics by 'the utility of the power which it gives'. For this reason, partial differential equations stood very high, though only as far as equations of the second order. Up to that point they are the mathematical apparatus for dealing with 'the great problems of nature concerning *time*, and *infinite division of matter*, and *space*'. But beyond the second order they apply to nothing. He thought that the study of pure mathematics might be of use to a few very able men, not to the majority. Their time could be far more profitably devoted to carefully selected physical subjects, bearing on the natural phenomena before them, so that every student could perceive their value.

He considered that pure mathematics made 'no step towards natural science or utilitarian science, the two subjects which the world specially desires'. The Cambridge Examiners were not directing young men towards those subjects desired by the nation, and were therefore failing in their duty as educators.

Cayley replied that in a university everything should not be subordinated to education, it was a place for the cultivation of all science. He suggested that even the solution of practical problems would not always be made by searching for it with the available mathematical resources, but that it would be necessary to 'prospect' for new mathematics, which would be found to furnish the methods for dealing with problems that were not amenable to existing methods.

Airy expressed surprise that Cayley questioned the dominance of education in the activities of a university. He did not doubt that students who had passed their examinations should be allowed to pursue such mathematical novelties as appealed to them, but he objected to the Examiner using his position to force students to study those subjects that happened to be to his taste. He conceived that 'the obligation to the nation and the duty to follow the national sense on education (as far as it can be gathered from its best representatives) to be undoubted; and to be, in the intensity of the obligation and duty, most serious'.

Airy had a modern sense of the national importance of training in applied science and technology, and treated them as at least on a level with pure science. The fact was that the views of Airy and Cayley were of equal weight, but at the time nearly everyone assumed that pure took precedence over applied science. The lack of balance between pure and applied science was one of the weaknesses of the British social structure in its intellectual and educational aspects.

Airy was not assisted by an impressive physique, though he was wiry and could withstand fatigue. His figure was slight, and he presently acquired a pronounced stoop. While he worked extremely regularly, and kept strictly to a routine, he did not work excessively long hours.

E. J. Routh, who in his own field had a similar authoritarian spirit, described how he had listened to him lecturing to an audience of 3,000 in the Free Trade Hall at Manchester. Notwithstanding his weak voice, he retained their attention to the very end. 'The charm of Airy's lectures lay in the clearness of his explanations. The subjects of his lectures were generally those to which his attention had been turned by other causes, so that he had much that was new to tell. His manner was slightly hesitating, and he used frequent repetitions, which perhaps were necessary from the newness of the ideas. As the lecturer proceeded, his hearers forgot these imperfections and found their whole attention rivetted to the subject matter.'

In most discussions of Airy's behaviour, the existing condition of science has usually been taken as given. He has been judged by how far he fitted in with contemporary scientific traditions, and how far he did not. His mistakes, especially in the *Neptune* affair, have been intensively studied, and have been interpreted largely in psychological terms.

Here, another question is asked. What was wrong with the British scientific situation, which caused Airy's mistakes to have such significance? Why did the British scientific situation not possess self-correcting features that would have prevented or mitigated them?

Why was Airy cast in a role where the effects of his limitations were magnified rather than reduced? Looking at him as a problem in personnel management, what were the mistakes of those who chose to put him in a position to which he was not very well suited?

One may assert that the chief culprit in the *Neptune* and computer affairs was not Airy, but the contemporary system of British science. It was the system rather than any person or group of persons which was most at fault. If Airy's immense talents had been more appropriately utilized, he might have performed a very great service for British applied science and technology, and have done much to keep it in the position it held in the first half of the nineteenth century.

II

TAKING CHAIRS BY STORM

George Biddell Airy was born at Alnwick in Northumberland on 27 July 1801. He was the eldest son of William Airy, an Excise officer for the county. William Airy had started life as a farm worker in Lincolnshire, but his great physical strength, intelligence and determined character had enabled him to save some money, buy books, and educate himself during the winters. When he went to Northumberland, smuggling there was very active. William Airy attacked the smugglers boldly, and seized much contraband goods, not without danger to himself. He was presently moved to Hereford, where the education of his eldest son George was started in local elementary schools.

Airy, like Adam Smith, was the son of an excise officer, and like him was influenced by his father's ideas; he probably owed his realistic attitude to economic and practical affairs to him. He grew up with a set of moral and financial principles more suited for dealing with smugglers than academics.

He acquired a good deal of information from his father's books when he was a boy. Like Thomas Young and other scientists in their boyhood, he found a Dictionary of the Arts and Sciences particularly fascinating. He learned about ship-building, navigation and other subjects from this work. Airy's strong interest in technology and the application of science continued throughout his life.

In 1810 his father was moved to Essex, and settled at Colchester. This brought George in contact with his uncle, Arthur Biddell, a prosperous farmer and land valuer at Playford near Ipswich. Arthur Biddell had an excellent library, and George found in him an understanding friend, keenly interested in engineering and science, and in history and antiquities. He spent a winter holiday with him when he was about twelve, and contrived to spend more and more time at Playford, until he regularly lived with his uncle for about a third of a year. Airy, again like Thomas Young, was largely brought up not in his father's house but in that of a relative. Through Arthur Biddell, Airy became acquainted with the noted engineer Cubitt, and Thomas Clarkson, the slave-trade abolitionist.

In 1813 he was sent to Colchester Grammar School. His father gave him a celestial globe, from which he first learned about stars. He regarded these as the 'birth-stars' of his astronomical knowledge. He made paper models of geometrical solids, and such constructions as batteries and fortresses. He learned about the construction of the steam engine from the Dictionary of Arts and Sciences, and inspected an engine of the latest type in the local brewery with 'extreme felicity', when it was open for repairs. He made a plan of a threshing machine at Playford.

Then he became interested in optics through experiments with the object-glass of an opera glass. He wrote that the acquisition of an accurate knowledge of optical constructions was 'one of the most charming attainments' he ever reached. He had a wave of chemical enthusiasm, which led to the suggestion (again like Thomas Young) that he should be apprenticed to a chemist. He surveyed and made a map of his uncle's farm.

At school he exhibited an extraordinary memory. He could learn hundreds of lines of Latin or Greek verse. In 1816 he repeated 2,394 lines, 'probably without missing a word'. His headmaster entertained a high opinion of his powers, but did not like him.

His father, who had in the meantime lost his position in the Excise, thought that he might go to Cambridge, but dropped the idea because of the expense. His uncle asked Clarkson, who had rented the neighbouring farm, to receive the youth and form an opinion of his knowledge and abilities. The result was that his uncle persuaded his father to permit him to compete for a scholarship at Cambridge.

He began to read appropriate mathematics textbooks, learnt fluxions, and was coached by the Grammar School's mathematics master, who had formerly been a fellow of Sidney Sussex College, but was 'an indifferent mathematician of the Cambridge school'. George found his instruction extremely valuable, not on account of his knowledge of mathematics, for George already knew more than he did, but for guidance on the Cambridge attitude to mathematics; he indicated which branches were particularly studied, and the accurate Cambridge methods of treating them. By the age of sixteen he had read and thoroughly understood Newton's *Principia*, and could write out any proposition. At length, his teacher terminated the coaching engagement, because George had become too much for him.

During the same period, Airy concentrated in school hours on classics, reading through the whole of Sophocles very carefully. He became a competent classical scholar, and left school in the summer of 1819.

Mr Clarkson had been considering which college Airy ought to go to, and at first thought of Peterhouse. But his friend Mr J. D. Hustler, a tutor and mathematician at Trinity, told him that Airy was just the sort of person who ought to go to Trinity. Airy was subjected to various examinations on behalf of the college, in which his answers made a deep impression. He was admitted as a sizar under Hustler.

He left for Cambridge in October 1819, knowing no one except Hustler, but with introductions to several fellows of the college, including George Peacock. He called on Peacock as soon as possible, who told him not to hesitate to consult him on any matter on which he desired advice. Airy did this for several years, and always received from him all the assistance he could give. Peacock was a Durham man, and Airy was born in Northumberland.

Airy's mathematical ability was immediately recognized, but he became generally prominent from the circumstance that he was about the last undergraduate to give up wearing 'drab knee breeches' in favour of the 'trowsers' which were coming in.

Peacock gave Airy a copy of the translation of Lacroix's *Differential Calculus* by Babbage, Herschel and himself, with a copy of their Examples, based on the book. He worked at it very industriously, and became one of the few men in Cambridge to know the new methods well. He began to learn French, for he saw that it was absolutely necessary in order to learn modern mathematics. Airy said later that he thought the old books were more useful for students who intended to enter practical life, but for those who aimed at more difficult and intellectually more important work, they were quite insufficient.

Airy saw Peacock nearly every day, who set special problems for him. Peacock gave him the run of his personal library, which was very important, as Peacock was the only man in Cambridge with the latest continental works on mathematics and physics. When an undergraduate, he was already given special facilities in the libraries of the University and Trinity College. He came out first in the Freshman's Year in 1820. Undergraduates, some of them his seniors, asked him to coach them. He declined, but he noted that in this year he came to understand how he 'stood among men'.

He presently moved onto Peacock's staircase in Trinity, and Peacock sent a young man from Newcastle, one of his personal friends, to him as a pupil. He devoted much of his effort to theoretical astronomy and allied parts of physics. In 1821 his friend Mr Cubitt called on him; Cubitt 'was engaged in erecting a treadmill at Cambridge Gaol, and had some thoughts of sending plans for the Cambridge Observatory, the erection of which was then proposed'. Airy was also working on the classical subjects required in his examinations. In every kind of examination he always came out first, sometimes doubling the next man's marks.

At this time his father became an invalid, afflicted with pains in the legs which prevented him from going to bed for weeks together.

Airy made research essays in many directions, especially in astronomy and optics. In 1819, and before he came to Cambridge, he had devised a plan for constructing reflecting telescopes with silvered glass mirrors. He showed it to Peacock, who was much impressed. It became the subject of his first published research, which appeared in 1822. Peacock brought it to the notice of John Herschel, who invited Airy to meet him at breakfast.

Peacock offered to bear the expense of having the instrument made. Airy found, however, that there were practical difficulties, and he dropped the project before he had solved them. In the following year, 1823, he took the Mathematical Tripos examination, and came out Senior Wrangler. This was followed by his winning the First Smith's Prize.

Airy was now able to take pupils more systematically. Peacock advised him not to have more than four; all became men of some note. The teaching was very thorough. In the Long Vacation, he and his friend, the mathematician Drinkwater, engaged a house and servants in Swansea, and took pupils. They started work at six in the morning, and after strenuous intellectual efforts went rowing and sailing off Swansea. On one occasion, two were washed overboard in a rough sea, but being strong swimmers, were rescued. Airy wondered whether this combination of severe intellectual labour and physical exercise was a good thing, for all of them suffered from painful boils.

He now had a little spare money, made from the coaching. He used it for a tour to Northern England and Scotland, seeing for the first time rocks on the landscape, and clouds on mountains, so little had he travelled till then.

At the end of 1823 he stayed in London for a week with James South, the amateur astronomer. Airy had apparently written to him about the difficulty with his telescope. South allowed him to use his astronomical instruments. Airy said that this was his first experience of practical astronomy. South took him to one of Humphry Davy's evening parties, to enquire from Davy and Young about a vacancy at the Royal Observatory. Airy ascertained that the post would not automatically lead to the position of Astronomer Royal, so he did not pursue it.

In the summer of 1824 Airy went on a walking tour with his brother in Derbyshire. Like other scientists in the previous half-century, he made a point of visiting mines, factories, canals and other works of the Industrial Revolution, besides exploring the landscape.

He had an introduction to the Reverend Richard Smith, the Private Chaplain to the Duke of Devonshire, who had formerly been a fellow of Trinity College. He had two sons and seven daughters, noted for their attractiveness and accomplishments. The Duke of Devonshire was reported to have said that Mr Smith had a daughter who was the most beautiful girl he ever saw. This young lady, Richarda, was nineteen. Airy fell in love with her at first sight, and proposed to her two days later. He had no means and no clear prospects, so Richarda's father would not hear of an engagement.

Airy had to wait nearly six years before the marriage, which proved a very successful one. Richarda did much to smooth Airy's relations with the world, though she was unable to save him completely from himself.

Airy was elected a fellow of Trinity in 1824, at the same time as Thomas Babington Macaulay, who was one year his senior. The Athenaeum Club was founded at about this time by Davy and others. Airy was nominated for it, but declined. He became active as a college mathematical tutor, and pursued researches especially in mathematical astronomy and optics. He also engaged in several big numerical computations, for which he had a taste and aptitude.

He sought advice from Clarkson and Peacock on a profession, no doubt in order to enable him to marry sooner, but his friends, though kind, had nothing constructive to suggest.

In 1825 he made another walking tour, seeing aqueducts and suspension bridges. Then he took a party of pupils to Keswick. Clarkson gave him an introduction to Southey and Wordsworth. He saw a good deal of Southey, who lent him many books, including, apparently, Machiavelli. Wordsworth he saw only occasionally, but he thoroughly explored the mountains, taking with him a geological hammer and a mountain barometer, which he found 'very interesting companions'.

Back in Cambridge he prepared his first book: *Mathematical Tracts on Physical Astronomy*. It included treatments of lunar theory, the figure of the earth, and precession and nutation, together with a tract on the calculus of variations. It was published in 1826, and contributed much to the modernization of Cambridge mathematical physics. He added a tract on the Undulating Theory of Optics in the second edition, published in 1831. This performed a similar service for the wave-theory of light.

Meanwhile, Peacock advised him to raise his rate for coaching from 60 to 100 guineas for three terms. Not all of his old pupils were prepared to pay so much, but the rise saved him from 'engrossment by pupils . . . the worst of all things that can happen to a man who hopes to distinguish himself'.

His studies of gravitational theory led him to consider the possibility of carrying out an experiment, suggested long before by Francis Bacon, to observe the strength of gravity in a deep mine. He told Whewell of his idea, who was interested, and wanted to join in it. Airy thought first of taking a clock down a mine in Derbyshire, about which he enquired through his future father-in-law, but Whewell had in the meantime made enquiries and learned that the Dolcoath mine in Cornwall would be more suitable.

Airy corresponded with Paris, Davy and Herschel, and with Young as Secretary of the Board of Longitude, about the loan of instruments and pendulums. He practised pendulum observations at Cambridge, went to London and was lent four chronometers from the Royal Observatory. He and Whewell made a complicated series of pendulum observations at the bottom of the mine. But the experiments were brought to an end by an inexplicable occurrence. The most important instruments had been packed in a basket to be brought to the surface. When it arrived, with Airy standing by, it was on fire, and the instruments damaged. Airy wrote that 'whether a superstitious miner had intentionally fired it, or whether the snuff of a candle had been thrown into it, is not known'. Airy repeated the experiments that had failed in 1826 and 1828, at Harton Colliery in Lancashire, in 1855. He found that gravity had increased by one part in 900 at a depth of 1,260 feet.

In 1826 Airy coached his Long Vacation pupils in Orleans. He visited Paris, and with introductions from Peacock, South, Herschel and Young, met Laplace and Arago. He subsequently attended the Institut, and heard one of Ampère's lectures. Among his manifold activities, he found time to take lessons in Italian, and write an encyclopaedia article on steam engines.

In the autumn of 1826 the Lucasian professorship, Newton's chair, became vacant. Whewell advised Airy to apply. Airy received £150 as a college tutor, whereas the Lucasian professor's salary was only about £90, so he decided to withdraw. But once more, Peacock rendered him 'a very important service'. He explained to him the advantages of the position, so Airy changed his mind, and remained a candidate. There were two other candidates, Babbage and the head of one of the colleges. The latter candidature was against the rules of the University, and Babbage threatened legal proceedings if this candidature continued. It was in consequence withdrawn, and the election lay between Airy and Babbage.

Airy was unanimously elected, and immediately prepared to revive the delivery of professorial lectures. For these there was no official place, time or term. He had to start in a private room in the old Botanic Garden. His resumption of the delivery of professorial lectures was much approved, and strengthened his position in university politics. It belonged to his middle-class attitude of not taking money without making a tangible return.

His personal affairs were nevertheless in a trying state. His father was in financial difficulties, and suffering from hallucinations. His fiancée Richarda, with most of the Smith family in Derbyshire, were attacked by a dangerous fever. As Lucasian professor his income had gone down, and he had a great aversion to entering the Church as a means of increasing it. His fellowship of Trinity as a layman would end in seven years' time.

Airy was now twenty-six years old. As Lucasian professor he was an Examiner for the Smith's Prizes. He determined to make the examination public, by introducing the printing of the papers, which had not been done previously. Also, by virtue of this position, Airy became a member of the Board of Longitude. He joined Herschel in leading the group which wished to reform the Board, which had become inefficient. The Secretary, Young, resisted change as much as possible.

At this time, in 1827, Herschel suggested that he should apply for the vacant chair of astronomy at Trinity College in Dublin. Airy applied, but he found that the electors preferred to offer it to their brilliant student, William Rowan Hamilton, who was twenty-two, had not yet graduated, and had not applied for the job. Airy accordingly withdrew. On the return journey he had to pass through Birmingham. While waiting in a coffee-room there, he solved a geometrical problem which enabled him to write an important paper on spherical aberration in the eyepieces of optical instruments. He was very active in optical research, and was consulted on bridges and other engineering works.

His researches on the sun's motion led him to discover a new irregularity in it. He reported this to the Board of Longitude, adding this to the other corrections that the reformers desired in the Nautical Almanac, but Young objected.

Towards the end of 1827, Peacock informed him that the Plumian professor was dying. Airy instantly thought of succeeding him, for the salary of the chair was much better than that of the Lucasian. The Plumian chair carried with it direction of the Observatory, and a house.

This would give him a larger permanent income, a home, and further scope. He knew that the majority of the electors, of whom he was himself one as Lucasian professor, wanted him to take it, and he let it be known that he would do so, if the present salary of £300 a year should be increased to £500. He drafted a manifesto to the University, requesting that the salary should be increased. At the electoral meeting he told the other electors that he could not undertake the responsibility of conducting the Observatory without the increase. They agreed, and the salary was raised to £500 a year.

Referring to his operations to secure the Plumian chair, Airy wrote that 'the University had never before been taken by storm in such a manner, and there was some commotion about it. I believe that very few persons would have taken the same step.' Airy's activities were more like those of an excise officer boarding a ship and seizing goods, than of a country gentleman with scientific tastes securing his objects, without overt conflict, by social dexterity.

Airy started the Observatory Journal, and settled into the house in the spring of 1828. His father had died in the previous year, and his mother and sister came to live with him. Two more years were to pass before it was felt that the appropriate conditions for his marriage to Richarda Smith had been achieved.

III

ACHIEVING AN AMBITION

Airy had moved into the University Observatory, and had almost achieved one of the great objects of his life, 'but not quite'. He was determined not to regard the addition to his salary as absolutely certain until a payment had actually been made to him. Until this was done, he carefully refrained from taking any irrevocable steps.

He organized the astronomical observing according to an orderly system. This was 'quite a novelty'. His system was presently adopted in some other European observatories. This introduced more organization into the general prosecution of astronomy, and made astronomical information easier to find and to use. He toured Europe, met Quetelet, Plana and other leading astronomers, and established many valuable connections.

He pursued numerous researches in physical astronomy, and returned to Cambridge, where, at last, he received the cheque making up his salary to the agreed figure. On the first available day afterwards, he left for Derbyshire to propose to Richarda Smith, and was accepted. However, before they were married by her father, he was able to slip away for a few days, during which he met George and Robert Stephenson, busy on the Manchester and Liverpool Railway. He married Richarda in March 1830, and in April she was already drawing pictures of interference effects for illustrations at her husband's university lectures.

In this year, Airy was asked to name the moderator for the degree examination. He named Challis, who was to succeed him as Plumian professor and participate in the affairs of the discovery of Neptune. Challis had originally been introduced to him by Charles Musgrave, who had been Airy's own introducer to Peacock. From the beginning of his Cambridge life Challis was indebted to Airy, and presently became one of his virtual lieutenants.

In 1831 the Royal Society presented its chief award, the Copley Medal, to Airy for his researches in optics; he was then thirty years old. Airy was equally active in physical astronomy. As in optics, he was inspired by the French school, especially by the treatise of Biot on this subject. His report on the condition of astronomy, which he wrote for the British Association after its foundation meeting in 1831, was held to be unduly critical of British astronomers, but Airy refused to alter a word of it.

Meanwhile, his friend Richard Sheepshanks thought that 'something might be done to advance the interests' of Airy at the Cambridge Observatory, by writing an article on *Gravitation* for the *Penny Cyclopaedia*, associated with the Society for the Diffusion of Useful Knowledge, in which Brougham, then Lord Chancellor, was keenly interested. Airy wrote the article, which was published as a book, and remains a masterpiece of exposition for the general reader.

Sheepshanks sent a copy to Brougham. A few days later the President of the Royal Society, the Duke of Sussex, invited Airy to breakfast, and then spoke to him, on the part of the Government, about his becoming Astronomer Royal. Airy also wrote an article on *Greenwich* for the *Penny Cyclopaedia*. Later in 1834 he was provisionally offered the position of Astronomer Royal, but the Government had changed, and the negotiations were held up.

Robert Peel had become Prime Minister, and Lyndhurst Lord Chancellor. Lyndhurst had formerly been appreciative of Airy, so Airy wrote to him in 1835, asking him for a Suffolk church living for his brother William. Lyndhurst declined this request, but shortly afterwards Airy received a letter from Peel, whom he had met at dinner with the Duke of Sussex, offering a government pension of £300 a year without terms, for himself or his wife. Airy replied on the next day, accepting it on behalf of his wife. Mrs Airy was twenty-six when she received this government pension for life.

Peel in his letter said that the House of Commons had expressed the opinion that pensions on the Civil List should be granted only for certain public services, in which scientific or literary eminence were especially mentioned. He said that his first address with regard to science had been made to him, without previous communication with any other person. He considered Airy had the first claim on the Royal Favour because of his scientific eminence, and the inadequacy of his emoluments as Plumian professor at Cambridge.

Peel's help for Airy, then still only thirty-three, was paralleled in 1842 by a comparable intervention on behalf of Lyon Playfair, then only twenty-four, promising his support in obtaining a satisfactory scientific post in Britain, if he would refrain from going to Canada. Peel's direct intervention as Prime Minister in scientific matters did not, unfortunately for Britain, become established practice until more than a century later.

However, Peel's ministry was short-lived, and the Whigs returned to power. Lord Auckland again became First Lord of the Admiralty, and Airy was again approached on becoming Astronomer Royal. He accepted the position on certain conditions. One was that the First Assistant should be removed, so that he could appoint another. He wished to obtain a man with a good Cambridge degree, and consulted William Hopkins, the famous mathematical teacher who subsequently coached W. Thomson, Stokes, and Clerk Maxwell. He secured a satisfactory man, and when one of the other assistants, disappointed at not being promoted, resigned, Airy appointed James Glaisher to this vacancy.

Airy continued to reside at Cambridge until various alterations had been made at Greenwich. He reformed the running of the Cambridge Observatory. He devised a system of thirty printed skeleton forms, to simplify and routinize the computing of results from observations. He completed the reduction of all outstanding observations, so that not a single figure was left to be worked out by his successor.

At the end of 1835 Lord John Russell offered him a knighthood, as a mark of esteem to the scientific world in general, as well as to him. It was to indicate to foreign countries the consideration felt for him personally, as well as for the position he held among his learned contemporaries. Airy declined the honour, on the ground that he already occupied 'a position of great comfort' through the liberality of the King and State. This caused him to consider himself a devoted servant of the country, and to debar him from increasing his fortune in other ways. Nevertheless, his income was not sufficient to support the kind of establishment expected of a man of title. He said that his services would always be at the command of the Government on any scientific subject on which they might be of the slightest use.

Airy said that he introduced the exposition of the undulatory theory of light in his optics lectures at Cambridge in 1828. Each lecture lasted nominally an hour, but he encouraged students to stop and talk with him. This went on for about another hour. He enjoyed the lectures, but presently found that, as additions to his other work, they were taxing his strength, so he wanted to drop them. While Plumian professor, he secured more adequate equipment for the Cambridge Observatory, and improved its programme of observations.

Near the end of each year he procured a diary for the following year, and put down in it observations to be made on each day of the new year. 'This system gave wonderful steadiness to the plan of observations for the next year.' He introduced and extended the same system at Greenwich. Airy was an innovator in the planning of astronomical observation and research.

His chief friends in Cambridge were Whewell, Sedgwick, Peacock and Sheepshanks, the *Northern Lights*. He was closest to Whewell in spirit. They both came from the lower middle class, and had been poor boys who owed a great deal to Cambridge, and Trinity College in particular. They were both obstinate men of great mental power and industry, but circumscribed in imagination.

Adam Sedgwick was a North Yorkshireman who was widely admired and loved. He was the most popular man of the Cambridge of his day, and he could speak effectively to a crowd of four thousand miners on a North Sea shore.

Peacock was Airy's earliest and staunchest friend in his student days. When he died in 1858, Airy wrote to his widow, describing how, as a student, he had come to look to him in all respects 'as to a parent'. All his debts to his other friends in the University added together were not comparable with what he felt he owed to him.

Sheepshanks, who came of a well-to-do family, had won a fellowship at Trinity, and devoted himself to astronomy. He had the means to choose and pursue his interests. He and his sister had a London house, where Airy frequently stayed on his London visits during his Cambridge professorship. Sheepshanks supported Airy in his astronomical disputes, especially those with the amateur astronomer Sir James South, and, as had already been mentioned, with Babbage. Sheepshanks's sister founded the exhibition for astronomy, named after him, on the advice of Airy.

These four closest friends were from seven to fifteen years older than Airy, who seemed to step straight from studentship into mature middle age, without passing through a young man's characteristic phases. He was a slight figure of medium height, with a heavy forehead. He never took the least interest in athletics and sports, though he was a good walker, and could endure much fatigue. Nor was he upset by physical danger.

In 1845 he descended to a depth of 1,900 feet in the Tresavean Mine in Cornwall. He went down by the 'man-engine', a kind of elevator that took the passenger up or down a step at a time. All he had to do was to move sideways, no other effort being required. The elevator was unprotected, and the passenger was exposed to the danger of slipping into the abyss. At the bottom, Airy was prostrated by the heat and bad air, and had to be helped by the miners in the ascent, until he reached a level where the air was fresher.

In debate Airy was very self-reliant and absolutely fearless, if not aggressive.

His son Wilfrid, who edited his *Autobiography*, and was a civil engineer by profession, said that his father's life 'was essentially that of a hard-working, business man, and differed from that of other hard-working people only in the quality and variety of his work. It was not an exciting life, but it was full of interest, and his work brought him into close relations with many scientific men, and with many men high in the State. His real business life commenced after he became Astronomer Royal, and from that time forward, during the 45 years that he remained in office, he was so entirely wrapped up in the duties of his post that the history of the Observatory is the history of his life.'

These views were published in 1896, and exhibited a then unusual conception of the scientific life. As a civil engineer, Wilfrid Airy was no doubt influenced by the civil engineer's attitude to his profession in his conception of his father's life. To some extent, he interpreted his father's career in terms of a civil engineer's principles, who, though a technical man, has to pay so much attention to the business aspect of his work. Nevertheless, Wilfrid Airy was helped by his background to interpret his father's life in terms which, if only partly acceptable, are more modern than those customarily adopted at the end of the nineteenth century, in interpreting the lives of scientists.

Airy himself was elected an Honorary Member of the Institution of Civil Engineers in 1842; he had much of the scientific engineer in him. As scientific engineering had not permeated practice sufficiently in his day to provide scope for his particular talents, he had to seek another profession. One of the few paths then open to intellectually able youths without social advantages was the Cambridge school of mathematics. He succeeded in rising through it, because he was very able, but he was not fundamentally suited to abstract science. He lacked the imagination necessary for creative theorizing, and his practical business sense, which would have been so valuable in engineering, could not find appropriate scope in the science of his day. In fact, his business methods were somewhat incongruous in the field in which he was working, and they caused irritation. For example, he introduced clocking-in at Greenwich. He refused to start his system of 'incessant eye-observations' in 1840, until he had secured 'a "Watchman's Clock" for mechanical verification of the regular attendance of the Assistants'.

Airy foresaw the business effects of technological advance. After seeing the work in progress on the large new docks at Southampton in 1842, he remarked that people were saying that when it was finished it would attract a good deal of London commerce, and he would not be surprised at it. 'For it is very much easier for ships to get to Southampton than into London, and the railway carriage will make them almost one.'

His friend the instrument-maker Ransome noticed the punched-hole system Airy had introduced for classifying papers. Airy originally made the holes with a hand-punch. Ransome said he could provide him with something better, and supplied him with a punching machine, which became the prototype of all used in the Observatory.

With his particular bent and position, it was natural that Airy was appointed Chairman of the Commission for restoring the Standards of Measurement, which had been destroyed when the Houses of Parliament were burnt in 1834.

IV

THE ASTRONOMER ROYAL FAILS TO RECOGNIZE THE DISCOVERY OF A NEW PLANET

After the British Association was founded in 1831, Airy was asked by that body to make a report on the state of Astronomy. In it he dealt with the perturbations in the movement of the planet *Uranus*. These perturbations led to the suspicion that *Uranus* was being affected by an undiscovered planet. Mathematical astronomers began to investigate the problem. The Senior Wrangler of 1843, John Couch Adams, stimulated by Airy's report, decided to devote himself to it. He deduced from the perturbations the place in the sky where the unknown planet might be found.

John Couch Adams, like Airy, was a man of modest social origin, who owed his scientific career to his own ability. But unlike Airy, he came from a more stable environment. His father and his ancestors were tenant farmers. His parents were devoted, and his home was happy and comfortable. As soon as their eldest son's talent became evident, they made every effort, though they had no spare resources, to secure an appropriate education for him.

In this encouraging environment, John virtually educated himself. At about the age of twelve, he discovered scientific and mathematical books in the library of the Devonport Mechanics' Institute, and in the course of the next few years, worked by himself through Vince's treatise on *Fluxions*. Thus Adams found his opportunity through the movement for the democratization of science, of which Brougham was the head.

At the age of fifteen he was given John Herschel's *Astronomy* as a school prize. This directed his interest into astronomy. The Adams's were assisted in finding the means to send John to Cambridge by a small legacy received in 1836, and by his own efforts as a tutor to the sons of local gentlemen.

At Cambridge Adams had a sweeping academic success like that of Airy. He duly became Senior Wrangler, more than doubling the next man's marks. Before this, in 1841, he had picked up in a bookshop a copy of Airy's British Association report of 1832 on astronomy. He had scanned the pages and noted his comments on the perturbation of Uranus.

Adams wrote a note on 3 July 1841, that he had 'Formed a design, this week, of investigating, as soon as possible after taking my degree, the irregularities in the motion of Uranus, which are yet unaccounted for; in order to find whether they may be attributed to the action of an undiscovered planet beyond it; and if possible thence to determine the elements of its orbit, &c., approximately, which would probably lead to its discovery . . .'

Adams was further stimulated by Mary Somerville's comments on the possiblity of a new planet in the revised edition of her *Connexion of the Physical Sciences*, one of the works of scientific exposition inspired by Brougham.

As soon as Adams's position was settled by his election to a fellowship at St John's College in 1843, he explained his project to Challis, who gave him encouragement, and promised all help within his power. After six months' work, mostly at his Cornish home, Adams obtained an approximate solution of the problem. He asked Challis for assistance in securing further data from

Greenwich, and in February 1844 Challis wrote to Airy for them. Airy sent the additional material by return of post.

However, Adams did not make immediate use of it, because of the pressure of college duties, and of other astronomical work in which Challis had requested his aid. At the Cambridge Meeting of the British Association in 1845 he saw for the first time Herschel, Airy, Hamilton and other great men, which inspired him to further efforts. By September he had obtained an improved solution, and Challis suggested he should send his figures to Airy. Adams suggested he should deliver them in person, as he was passing through London on his way to Cornwall for the vacation. Challis gave him an excellent letter of introduction.

Adams left figures with Challis, to enable him to make a search for the planet with the powerful Cambridge telescope, which would easily reveal its disc, if it was there. Adams did not specifically ask Challis to make a search, and Challis did not act on the hint in Adams's figures.

Meanwhile, Adams did not act on the advice of one of his scientific friends to send his figures for publication, but decided to call on Airy. When he called, he found Airy was away in France, attending a meeting of the Institut. He left Challis's letter, and went on to Cornwall. Airy, on his return, found the letter, and politely wrote to Challis, saying he was very much interested in Adams's researches, and would like to hear of them from Adams by letter.

Adams did not write, but called again, on his way back to Cambridge. This was in the afternoon, and Airy was out. Adams left a paper with his results, and said he would call again later in the day. Mrs Airy was given the paper, but not told that Adams would return later. When Adams returned, the butler told him Airy was at dinner, and could not be disturbed. The butler did not inform Airy that Adams had made a second call.

Airy read the paper which Adams had left, but he was not impressed. He had long before come to the conclusion that it would not be possible to deduce the position of the planet until the data were vastly more complete. He thought that it would be necessary to observe Uranus for several centuries before sufficient data would be collected.

Departing from his usual habit, Airy did not reply promptly to Adams on his paper. When he did, he was polite, but raised a technical query. This seemed to Adams a triviality, and he did not reply to it. Challis also thought Airy's query trivial, and told him so. Airy explained that his query had to do with the law of gravitation. Airy was concerned with the question of whether the inverse-square law obtained at the distance of the hypothetical new planet. If it did not, Adams's calculations might be correct, but his theory of a new planet would be false.

Whether or not this was the full explanation of Airy's doubts, he seemed to have some deep feeling of uncertainty about Adams's whole conception. As Adams had not replied to Airy's letter, Airy took the view that it would be out of place for him to write to Adams again.

Seven days after Airy's letter to Adams, Le Verrier presented his first memoir on the theory of *Uranus* to the French Academy of Sciences, in which he gave a new and thorough analysis of the perturbations. He said he would deal with the cause of these in a second memoir. Airy was greatly impressed by the memoir which, in his opinion, placed the theory of *Uranus* on a satisfactory basis for the first time.

Le Verrier continued work on his second memoir, which he presented to the French Academy of Sciences at the beginning of June 1846. Airy received a copy later in the month, and immediately sent most enthusiastic approval of it to Le Verrier.

Airy said that he had hitherto doubted the accuracy of Adams's results, but Le Verrier's paper had removed these doubts. Now that their results substantially agreed, he considered that the resources of one observatory should be devoted to looking for the new planet.

These events caused Challis to lose confidence in Adams's results. He behaved as if the reliable evidence for the new planet had come from Le Verrier. He adopted Airy's view, and followed his lead. Challis was deeply indebted to Airy for his scientific career, besides being an amenable man. He regarded himself as, to some extent, Airy's pupil and follower, and tied to him by bonds of loyalty.

Le Verrier replied to Airy's appreciation by offering to send him figures to help in the search for the new planet. Airy was no more willing to do this for Le Verrier than for Adams. He excused himself by saying that he was going abroad, though he did not leave until six weeks later. In the meantime, he met the astronomer Hansen on a visit to Cambridge. They went for a walk together, and on the bridge over the river in St John's College, they happened to meet Adams. It would have seemed to have been a most fortunate opportunity for a quick exchange of views, and a removal of misunderstandings, but they had only a perfunctory conversation lasting about two minutes. Airy,

GEORGE BIDDELL AIRY

whose memory was normally very retentive, could not recollect what had transpired.

Four days later he went to Ely to visit his old tutor, George Peacock, now Dean of Ely, while still holding the Lowndean Chair of Geometry and Astronomy in Cambridge. Peacock questioned his old pupil in his characteristically forthright and penetrating way about the new planet, and what he was doing about it. Airy deferred to Peacock as he would not to anyone else. Three days later he wrote to Challis, asking him to search for the new planet. He followed this with a second more urgent request.

Challis decided to undertake the search, and Adams supplied him with data. After four nights of observation Challis paused for a check, to see whether the stars observed in the later were the same as those in the earlier observations.

At the end of August 1846 Le Verrier produced a third memoir giving his calculation of the actual position of the new planet. It was received by the French observational astronomers with as much indifference as that with which Adams's research had been treated in England.

Three days after the publication of Le Verrier's third memoir, Adams sent his sixth revision of figures to Airy, but Airy was at Wiesbaden, and it was not forwarded to him. At the same time, Challis wrote directly to Wiesbaden, saying that he found that many more observations would be required than he could make during the remainder of the year.

Le Verrier was met with just as discouraging frustration from his French colleagues, but he was tougher. He had received a copy of a dissertation from a young German astronomer, J. G. Galle, which he had not bothered to acknowledge. It occurred to him that he might be made use of, so he wrote him a most flattering letter on the dissertation, and then asked him to search for the new planet.

Galle had difficulty in persuading his chief, J. F. Encke, the Director of the Berlin Observatory, to permit him to use the instruments for this purpose, but he succeeded. On 23 September 1846 he and a colleague directed the telescope at the region indicated by Le Verrier, and within a few hours had recognized the new planet.

Challis did not immediately hear of Galle's discovery. He continued his search, spurred by Le Verrier's third memoir. On 29 September he thought he saw a planetary disc, and decided to check in on the following night. On the next day a friend called,

13

and Challis told him of the observation. His friend suggested that he should look at the region again with a higher telescopic power. After dinner they set off to the Observatory to do this. The sky was clear when they arrived, but Mrs Challis insisted that they must have tea before making the observation. When they got to the telescope the sky had clouded.

Shortly afterwards, Challis learned of Galle's discovery. He continued the check of his observations, and he found that one of the stars he had observed on 12 August was not there on 30 July. He had seen the new planet, but failed to recognize it.

Galle's discovery was followed by angry controversy, in which the events just summarized were analysed in detail, publicly and privately. Airy defended himself with the dogged determination and skill of a senior civil servant. Critics of the British organization of science, and of astronomy in particular, discussed the affairs at length, and the national prestige of Britain and France became involved.

The details of the affair were highly interesting in themselves, but they were more important as manifestations of deeper causes, of which the majority of disputants were scarcely conscious.

Adams and Le Verrier first met at the British Association Meeting of 1847. Very fortunately, they took to each other, and became firm friends. As the years went by, the details of the affair faded, and they were universally recognized as the co-discoverers of *Neptune*. Adams lived to lead the appreciation of Airy's contributions to astronomy and science. By the centenary of the great discovery, it seemed that Adams and Le Verrier were lucky as well as gifted men. Factors that they had not recognized had, by chance, not vitiated their predictions. It is not inconceivable that Airy's doubts were better founded than he has long been given credit for.

V

WERE AIRY'S DOUBTS WHOLLY UNFOUNDED?

The centenary of the discovery of *Neptune* occurred in 1946, and became the occasion for re-examination of the events which led to the discovery. Since then, it has become clear that the calculations of both Adams and Le Verrier (of which Le Verrier's were the more accurate) were based on an incomplete theoretical solution of the problem.

Both of them had aimed at calculating the orbit and mass of the new planet. From its complete description, its position at any time could easily be deduced, and all that would be necessary to discover it would be to point the telescope in the appropriate direction.

Actually, the orbits that they marked out for *Neptune* were not even approximately correct. Both of them had assumed that *Neptune* would obey Bode's law, which indicates that the distance of the planets from the sun follow a regular mathematical progression. Neptune, however, does not obey this law. In fact, what Adams and Le Verrier did was to find out where the planet was at the time when they were making their calculations. Fortunately for them, it happened that the position of the planet could be calculated approximately, without previously making a correct evaluation of the orbit.

J. E. Littlewood and R. A. Lyttleton have shown that Adams and Le Verrier might have secured their effective result by very much simpler calculations, in which the extensive computing calculations for evaluating the orbit in detail is eliminated.

Airy's actions in the discovery of *Neptune* have often been regarded as those of a habit-ridden reactionary scientific civil servant. He was indeed a master of the civil servant's technique of never giving anything away in controversy. He wrote his *Autobiography* as if his ministry might be asked questions about it at any moment in Parliament. He had the same attitude in his exchanges over the *Neptune* discovery.

Besides his intuition that Adams's calculations were open to doubt, his attitude was influenced by social and psychological factors, as may be seen from the following considerations.

Thirty-five years after the *Neptune* affair, J. C. Adams was the leader in recognizing Airy's contribution to science; how was this possible? It is scarcely to be explained as merely generosity on Adams's part.

First of all, Airy's contribution was so large that when all his mistakes were allowed for, the positive remainder was immense. Secondly, Airy was a courageous man. His deference to persons in social authority belonged to the principles of the son of an excise official; he really believed in them.

Airy was counted as progressive in education and politics. He was the first outstanding product of the reform of Cambridge mathematics by John Herschel, Babbage and Peacock, but unlike them he did not adopt the eighteenth-century gentlemanly social tradition. He was brought up on the continental mathematics and science, and when a young man he became its most effective propagator in Cambridge. He was inspired by Biot's *Elementary*

Treatise on Physical Astronomy, the publication of which began in 1810. But he practised the new science, as a hard-working, self-made member of the new nineteenth-century professional middle class.

He published a work on mathematical astronomy and the calculus of variations in 1826, in the modern notation. This work had an important influence on the development of the Cambridge school of mathematical physics. When he was appointed to the Lucasian chair in 1826 he dealt with mechanics, hydrostatics and optics by the modern mathematical methods, and he taught the French development of the wave-theory of light. His course was a sign of the end of the old university régime, and the beginning of the more professional training of scientists, who had hitherto regarded themselves as gentlemen amateurs. Now they were becoming the scientific section of the middle class.

Airy was against the religious tests at Cambridge and Oxford in awards for degrees, and was in favour of higher education for women, though he would not go so far as to give them university degrees. He feared that the publicity which accompanied the announcement of their names in the results of the examinations for degrees might impair their feminine delicacy.

His middle line of opinion and behaviour extended in other directions. Airy proposed to Gladstone in 1853 that he should take advantage of the occasion of making a new copper currency to introduce the decimal system, but he was careful to add, like successors more than a century later, that he 'was always strenuous about preserving the Pound Sterling'.

He was a strong nineteenth-century Liberal in politics. He was appointed Astronomer Royal in 1836 by a Liberal Government, and retained that position until 1881, right through the heart of the century. He declined a knighthood three times before accepting it. The reason that he always gave was that his income was not large enough to support the social position of a knight.

Airy manifested the characteristics of the social class to which he belonged, and which was becoming far more important. His life spanned the nineteenth century almost exactly. He was born in the Industrial North, which was so influential in the first half of that century. He and his friends, the *Northern Lights*, had revived Cambridge in the second quarter of that century.

Airy's preoccupation with money and income, and his hard-headed attitude to affairs, so characteristic of the contemporary middle class, was illustrated by his management of the change from the Lucasian to the Plumian professorship at Cambridge.

Since his student days Airy had organized his life in detail. He had kept meticulous accounts of his meagre finances by the double entry system. He had regular hours of work, and did not allow his régime to be interrupted. His systematic orderliness enabled him to do a great deal of work, yet it also was a factor in preventing him from receiving Adams, and thus losing for Adams and for Britain the honour of having exclusively discovered the new planet.

Today, Airy's devotion to order and organization in the scientific life does not appear as unattractive as it used to do. Airy's type of scientific activity, with its strengths and its limitations, has a new interest for a generation that cannot afford not to make the best use of talent. Airy should not merely be blamed for his mistakes, if they were mistakes, but should be studied, in order to see how society could have made still better use of his exceptional powers, and could have reduced the impact of his limitations, where this appears to have been unfortunate.

Airy was hindered in the highest regions of science not so much by his devotion to organization, as to his attempt to utilize organization to do everything himself. It was his difficulty in working easily with scientific colleagues which led to his remembered mistakes, while his numerous and varied contributions, and his versatility, have become undervalued. His recording and classifying of information has provided a valuable source of material for understanding the relations between science and society in the nineteenth century.

Airy's prejudice in favour of the French astronomer increased the anger of the British, who felt that he had let British science and Britain down. Yet this prejudice was not without its justification. Airy had helped to reform Cambridge science by importing French ideas. He properly esteemed French science, and no doubt aspired to be elected to the Institut, as he was, in due course. Le Verrier was a French scientist, eight years older than Adams, and had published more. He appeared to Airy more senior and mature, and also, perhaps, a potential supporter for French scientific honours. It was not surprising that Airy was inclined to trust his results more than those of the young Cambridge man.

VI

BRITISH ASTRONOMER

In 1842 Airy wrote in his report to the Board of Visitors of the

Royal Observatory: 'I trust that I am doing well in rendering Greenwich, even more distinctly than it has been heretofore, the place of reference to all the world for important observations, and results of observations, on which the system of the universe is founded. As regards myself, I have been accustomed, in these matters, to lay aside private considerations; to consider myself not as mere Director of Greenwich Observatory, but (however unworthy personally) as British Astronomer, required some-times by my office to interfere (when no personal offence is given) in the concerns of other establishments of the State.'

Airy's talent was administrative rather than statesmanlike, and the existing organization of science could not provide it with appropriate scope. He had more individual initiative than was good for his particular talent. As the right-hand man and administrative executive of a statesman of science, he might have accomplished very great things. If he had been incorporated in a larger and more differentiated organization, he might have been saved from many of his mistakes.

Airy's view of himself and his position, like Lord Cherwell's view of himself and his position in the Second World War, caused him to make mistakes. He was prepared to lay down the scientific law even in directions where he was not very well in-formed or endowed, and there was no other scientist in official circles with sufficient status to correct him. His intentions were good. He said that he believed in the principle of the division of labour in astronomy. But in practice, he claimed the right to make the division, so that sole authority tended to remain with himself. It did not count for nothing that he was an admirer of Cromwell.

He emphasized the role of science, and of astronomy in parti-cular, as the servant of the State. He observed in his report of 1858 that 'Viewing the close dependence of Nautical Astronomy upon accurate knowledge of time, there is perhaps no department of the Observatory which answers more completely to the origi-nal utilitarian intentions of the Founder of the Royal Obser-vatory.' Among other things, he improved Admiralty telescopes, and lighthouses.

He prepared in 1849 for the 'extensive dissemination through-out the kingdom of accurate time signals' by electrical methods. He presently expressed satisfaction that 'the Royal Observatory is thus quietly contributing to the punctuality of business through a large portion of this busy country'.

He adopted American electrical techniques for observing

transits of stars. He developed photographic self-registering techniques, and claimed a large share in the introduction of self-registering systems for magnetic and meteorological observations. Airy was widely consulted on the founding of observatories in Britain and British territories. John Quincy Adams consulted him on observatories in the United States. Airy proposed the method for determining the frontier between the United States and Canada, as marked by the boundary of the state of Maine.

Airy's conception of himself as *British Astronomer*, if not as *World Astronomer*, leading the astronomy of all mankind, was a striking expression, in the field of science, of the British conception of itself and its role in the world, at the height of British imperial power. He was born within memory of the mercantile and outward-looking society of the age of exploration and navigation, which had given birth to the Royal Society, the Royal Observatory, Newton, and modern science. He was educated after the Industrial Revolution but before the invention of the railways. His mind began to unfold at the end of the Newtonian age; it received a Newtonian impress, but acquired the post-Newtonian mathematical technique, which had been developed mainly in revolutionary France. He belonged partly to the world of Newton, and partly to that of nineteenth-century industrialism, but not wholly to either. This was one of the causes of his remarkable mixture of notable achievements and sterile failures. While this damaged his fame within any narrow conception of science, it made his career specially interesting and significant.

Airy appears to have had a happy family life, within the confines of the nineteenth-century conception of paternal authority. He took for granted his precedence in all things, but fought with his characteristic determination for all who were close to him.

He had nine children, of whom six survived him. He was stricken in 1839, when two of his sons died of fever within a week. One daughter died of consumption in 1852, and the other, Hilda, as has been mentioned, married E. J. Routh. His three sons, Hubert, Osmund and Wilfrid, had scientific or technical interests. Hubert, who became a government inspector, made researches on the mechanism of the movements of the branches of trees, showing why they have circular and wavy motions which contrast with the swaying of a field of corn. It is due to the elasticity of the wood in different directions. Osmund graduated in medicine.

Airy owned a cottage at Playford near Ispwich, where he had lived with his uncle in his youth. Routh described how he often retired to it for rest and recreation. 'Here he had spent his boyhood, and here at last he was laid in the grave by the side of his wife. Visiting the village every year, he could remember five generations of more than one family, and could give the early history of most of the others. The last scene of his life may be said to have begun and ended here.' He had a fall from which he never properly rallied. He went to his house at Greenwich, but he gradually sank, and passed away on 2 January 1892. His funeral at Playford 'was quiet and simple, fitting the noble simplicity of his life'.

Airy retired from the Royal Observatory when he was eighty. He published his new lunar theory in 1886, when he was eighty-five. He was President of the Royal Society in 1871, and in 1873 was elected one of the eight Foreign Associates of the French Institut. He received many other honours, but he said that, of all, he esteemed most his Honorary Freedom of the City of London. He particularly appreciated the regard of what was then the most powerful centre of world industry and trade.

REFERENCES

INTRODUCTION

1 *English Men of Science:* Their Nature and Nurture, by Francis Galton. London, 1874.
2 *Scientists: Their Pyschological World,* by Bernice T. Eiduson. New York, 1962.
3 *The Making of a Scientist,* by Anne Roe. New York, 1953.
4 *Characteristics of Engineers and Scientists,* by Lee E. Danielson. Ann Arbor, 1960.

WILSON

1 'Charles Thomson Rees Wilson', by P. M. S. Blackett. *Biographical Memoirs* of Fellows of the Royal Society, Vol. 6, pp. 269–95, 1960.
2 'Reminiscences of my Early Years', by C. T. R. Wilson. *Notes and Records of the Royal Society,* Vol. 14, No. 2, pp. 163–73. November 1959.
3 'Inventor of the Cloud Chamber', by James Paton. *The Scotsman,* 14 February 1959.
4 *The Scotsman,* 16 November 1959.
5 'Ben Nevis sixty years ago', by C. T. R. Wilson. *Weather,* Vol. IX, No. 10, October 1954.
6 *Address* by Sir E. V. Appleton, at lunch on 17 February 1959, in honour of C. T. R. Wilson's 90th birthday.
7 'Inspiration among the Clouds' *Glasgow Herald,* 14 February 1959.
8 'C. T. R. Wilson': Obituary by N. Feather. *Nature,* pp. 1842–1843, Vol. 184, 12 December 1959.
9 'C. T. R. Wilson': Obituary by T.W.W. *Quarterly Journal of the Royal Meteorological Society,* p. 293, Vol. 86, 1960.
10 'On the Cloud Method of Making Visible Ions and the tracks of Ionizing Particles'. Nobel Lecture by C. T. R. Wilson, Stockholm, 12 December 1927. *Les Prix Nobel,* 1927.
11 'The Rutherford Memorial Lecture, 1965', by P. I. Dee, F.R.S. *Proc. Roy. Soc.,* A, Vol. 298, pp. 103–22, 1967.
12 'An Index to C. T. R. Wilson's Laboratory Records and

13*

Notebooks in the Library of the Royal Society', by P. I. Dee and T. W. Wormell. *Notes and Records of the Royal Society*, Vol. 18, No. 1, June 1963.

RAYLEIGH

1 *John William Strutt, Third Baron Rayleigh*, by Robert John Strutt, Fourth Baron Rayleigh. London, 1924.
2 'An Appraisal of Rayleigh', by John N. Howard. *Applied Optics*, Vol. 3, No. 10, October 1964.
3 'Rayleigh Day Ceremony' on the Dedication of the Rayleigh Archives, U.S. Air Force Cambridge Research Laboratories, Bedford, Mass. 30 March 1966.
4 *Scientific Papers*, by Lord Rayleigh. 6 vols., 1869–1919. Cambridge, 1899–1920.

YOUNG

1 *Life of Thomas Young*, by George Peacock. London, 1855.
2 *Thomas Young*, by Alexander Wood and Frank Oldham. Cambridge, 1954.
3 *A Course of Lectures on Natural Philosophy and the Mechanical Arts*, by Thomas Young. 2 vols. London, 1807.
4 *The Miscellaneous Works of Dr Thomas Young*, edited by George Peacock and John Leitch. 3 vols. London, 1855.
5 *Encyclopaedia Britannica*, 6th Edition and Supplement (contributions by Young). 1823–24.
6 *New Fragments*, by J. Tyndall. London, 1892.
7 *Popular Lectures*, by H. H. Helmholtz. London, 1873.
8 *Scientific Papers*, by James Clerk Maxwell. 2 vols. Cambridge, 1890.
9 *Collected Papers*, by Lord Rayleigh, Vol. III. Cambridge.
10 *The Scientific Papers of the Honourable Henry Cavendish*, Vols. I & II. Cambridge, 1921.
11 'General Theorems chiefly Porisms in the Higher Geometry', by Henry Brougham. *Phil. Trans. Roy. Soc.*, Vol. 88, pp. 378–96. London, 1798.
12 *British Magazine*, London, 1800.
13 'Outline of Experiments and Enquiries respecting Sound and Light', by Thomas Young. *Phil. Trans. Roy. Soc.*, 1801.
14 'The Mechanism of the Eye', by Thomas Young. *Phil. Trans. Roy. Soc.*, 1801.

15 'Theory of Light and Colour', by Thomas Young. Bakerian Lecture, *Phil. Trans. Roy. Soc.*, London, 1802.
16 *The Edinburgh Review*, Vol. II, etc. Edinburgh, 1802 onwards.
17 'Men of Vision'. *British Medical Journal*, 24 October 1967.

HUXLEY

1 *Life and Letters of Thomas Henry Huxley*, by Leonard Huxley. 2 vols. London, 1900.
2 *Lectures and Essays*, by T. H. Huxley. The Thinkers' Library, No. 17. London, 1931.
3 *T. H. Huxley's Diary on the Voyage of H.M.S.* Rattlesnake, edited by Julian Huxley. London, 1935.
4 'Thomas Henry Huxley', by Leslie Stephen. *Nineteenth Century*, Vol. XLVIII, pp. 905–18. London, 1900.
5 'Professor Tyndall', by T. H. Huxley. *Nineteenth Century*, Vol. XXXV, pp. 1–11. London, 1894.
6 *T. H. Huxley*, Scientist, Humanist and Educator, by Cyril Bibby. London, 1959.
7 *Collected Essays*, by T. H. Huxley. 9 vols. London, 1893 etc.
8 *Huxley Memorial Lectures*, 1925–1932. London, 1932.
9 *Lay Sermons, Addresses and Reviews*, by T. H. Huxley. London, 1870.
10 *Thomas Henry Huxley*, a Sketch of his Life and Work, by P. Chalmers Mitchell. London, 1900.
11 'Thomas Henry Huxley'. *D.N.B.*
12 *A Diary of the Voyage of H.M.S.* Beagle, by Charles Darwin, Edited by Nora Barlow. Cambridge, 1933.

TYNDALL

1 *Life and Work of John Tyndall*, by A. S. Eve and C. H. Creasy. London, 1945.
2 *Fragments of Science*, by John Tyndall, Vols. 1 and II. 8th edition. London, 1892.
3 *New Fragments*, by John Tyndall. New York, 1892.
4 'John Tyndall'. *Encyclopaedia Britannica*. 11th edition. 1911.
5 *Nature*, 18 August 1945.

DE MORGAN

1 *Memoirs of Augustus de Morgan*, by Sophia Elizabeth de Morgan. London, 1882.

2 *A Budget of Paradoxes*, by Augustus de Morgan. London, 1872.
3 Obituary: *Monthly Notices of the Royal Astronomical Society*, Vol. XXXII, p. 112. February 1872.
4 *University College, London, 1826–1926*, by H. Hale Bellot. London, 1929.
5 *Ten British Mathematicians*, by Alex. Macfarlane. London, 1916.
6 *Ten British Physicists*, by Alex Macfarlane. London, 1919.
7 *Men of Mathematics*, by E. T. Bell. London, 1937.
8 *The North British Review*, No. XLVI. Edinburgh, August 1855.
9 *The Quarterly Journal of Education*. London, 1831–35.
10 *The Penny Cyclopaedia*. London, 1831–59.
11 'A Mathematical Centenary', by Sir Edward Collingwood. *New Scientist*, Vol. 25, No. 426, 14 January 1965.

DEWAR

1 *James Dewar*, by H. E. Armstrong, F.R.S., London, 1924.
2 'Dewar at the Royal Institution', by K. Mendelssohn, F.R.S. *Proc. Roy. Inst.*, Vol. 41, Part II, No. 189, pp. 212–33. London, 1966.
3 *Engineering at Cambridge University, 1783–1965*, by T. J. N. Hilken. Cambridge, 1967.
4 *Recollections of a Technologist*, by R. S. Hutton. London, 1964.
5 'James Dewar'. *D.N.B.*

REYNOLDS

1 *Osborne Reynolds*, by A. H. Gibson. London, 1946.
2 'Osborne Reynolds, 1842–1912'. *Proc. Roy. Soc.*, Series A, Vol. 88, pp. XV–XXI, 1913.
3 *Biographical Fragments*, by Sir Arthur Schuster. London, 1932.
4 *Recollections and Reflections*, by Sir J. J. Thomson. London, 1936.
5 *A History of Technology*, edited by Charles Singer et al., Vol. V, Chap. 22, pp. 547–50. Oxford, 1954.
6 *The Mastery of the Air*, by Sir Graham Hutton. London, 1965.

7 *Engineering at Cambridge University, 1783–1965*, by T. J. N. Hilken. Cambridge, 1967.

8 'Osborne Reynolds'. *D.N.B.*

BABBAGE

1 *Passages from the Life of a Philosopher*, by Charles Babbage. London, 1864.

2 *On the Economy of Machinery and Manufactures*, by Charles Babbage. 4th edition. London, 1835.

3 *Reflections on the Decline of Science in England*, by Charles Babbage. London, 1830.

4 *The Exposition of 1851*, or Views of the Industry, the Science and the Government of England, by Charles Babbage. 2nd edition. London, 1851.

5 *Faster than Thought*, A Symposium on Digital Computer Machines, edited by B. V. Bowden. London, 1953.

6 *Monthly Notices of the Royal Astronomical Society*, Vol. XXXI, 9 February. London, 1872.

7 'Charles Babbage'. *D.N.B.*

8 *Letter to the Board of Visitors of the Greenwich Royal Observatory in reply to the calumnies of Mr Babbage* at their meeting in June 1853 and in his book entitled: The Exposition of 1851, by R. Sheepshanks. London, 1854.

9 *A Word to the Wise* (on Life Peers), by Charles Babbage. London, 1833.

10 *An Elementary Treatise on the Differential and Integral Calculus*, by S. F. Lacroix, Translated by C. Babbage, G. Peacock and J. F. W. Herschel. Cambridge, 1816.

11 *Babbage's Calculating Engines*, by Henry Prevost Babbage. London, 1889.

12 *The Ninth Bridgewater Treatise*, by Charles Babbage. London, 1837.

13 *The History of Mathematics in Cambridge*, by W. W. Rouse Ball. Cambridge, 1889.

14 'R. Sheepshanks'. *D.N.B.*

15 *The Life and Letters of Anna Isabella, Lady Noel Byron*, by Ethel Colburn Mayne. With an Introduction and Epilogue by Mary, Countess of Lovelace. London, 1929.

16 'Memoir of Charles Babbage'. MSS in the Museum of the History of Science, Oxford.

17 'Charles Babbage and his Difference Engines', by L. H.

Dudley Buxton. *Trans. Newcomen Society*, Vol. XIV. London, 1933–34.

18 *Charles Babbage and his Calculating Engines*, edited by E. and P. Morrison. London, 1961.

19 *Irascible Genius*. A Life of Charles Babbage, by Maboth Moseley. London, 1964.

20 'Invention', Presidential Address by J. Fletcher Moulton, K.C., F.R.S., M.P., Junior Institution of Engineers, 1903–4. *Record of Trans. J. Inst. of Eng.*, Vol. XIV, pp. 83–104. London, 1905.

21 *Recollections of a Technologist*, by R. S. Hutton. London, 1965.

22 *Engineering at Cambridge University, 1783–1965*, by T. J. N. Hilken. Cambridge, 1967.

MORLEY FLETCHER

1 *The Bright Countenance*, by Maisie Fletcher, London, 1957.

2 'Memorial to the late Sir Walter Morley Fletcher'. Oxford, 1937.

3 Articles on the 50th Anniversary of the Medical Research Council. *Nature*, Vol. 200, pp. 1039–42, 1963. *British Medical Journal*, Vol. 2, pp. 1279–1281 and 1287–1294, 1963.

4 *History of the Cambridge University Pitt Club*, by W. M. and C. M. Fletcher, Cambridge, 1935.

5 *Obituary Notices of Fellows of the Royal Society*, No. 2. December 1933, London.

6 *Nature*, July 1st, 1933.

7 *British Medical Journal*, Vol. I, pp. 1085–6, 1933.

8 *Lancet*, Vol. I, pp. 1319–21, 1933.

9 *D.N.B.*

SCHUSTER

1 *Biographical Fragments*, by Sir Arthur Schuster, F.R.S. London, 1932.

2 *The Progress of Physics* during 33 years (1875–1910), by Sir Arthur Schuster, F.R.S. Cambridge, 1911.

3 *The Physical Laboratories of the University of Manchester*, prepared in commemoration of the 25th anniversary of the election of Dr A. Schuster, F.R.S., to a professorship in Owens College. Manchester, 1906.

4 'Sir Arthur Schuster 1815–1934'. *Obituary Notices of Fellows of the Royal Society*, I., 1932–35, pp. 4, 9–23.
5 *The Times*, 15 and 17 October, 1934.
6 'The History of Science in Manchester', by J. G. Crowther. *Bulletin of the Institute of Physics*, pp. 294–8, November, 1960.
7 *Recollections of a Technologist*, by R. S. Hutton. London, 1964.
8 'Sir Arthur Schuster', by G. E. Hale. *Astrophysical Journal*, Vol. 81, pp. 97–106, 1935.
9 'Arthur Schuster'. *D.N.B.*

AIRY

1 *Autobiography of Sir George Biddell Airy*, edited by Wilfrid Airy. Cambridge, 1896.
2 *The Discovery of Neptune*, by Morton Grosser. Cambridge, Mass., 1962.
3 'The Rediscovery of *Neptune*', by R. A. Lyttleton. *Vistas in Astronomy*, Vol. III, pp. 25–46. London, 1960.
4 *Ten British Physicists*, by Alexander Macfarlane. London, 1919.
5 'George Biddell Airy', by E. J. R. *Proc. Roy. Soc.*, Vol. LI, pp. I–XXI. London, 1892.
6 *Engineering at Cambridge, 1783–1965*, by T. J. N. Hilken. Cambridge, 1967.

INDEX